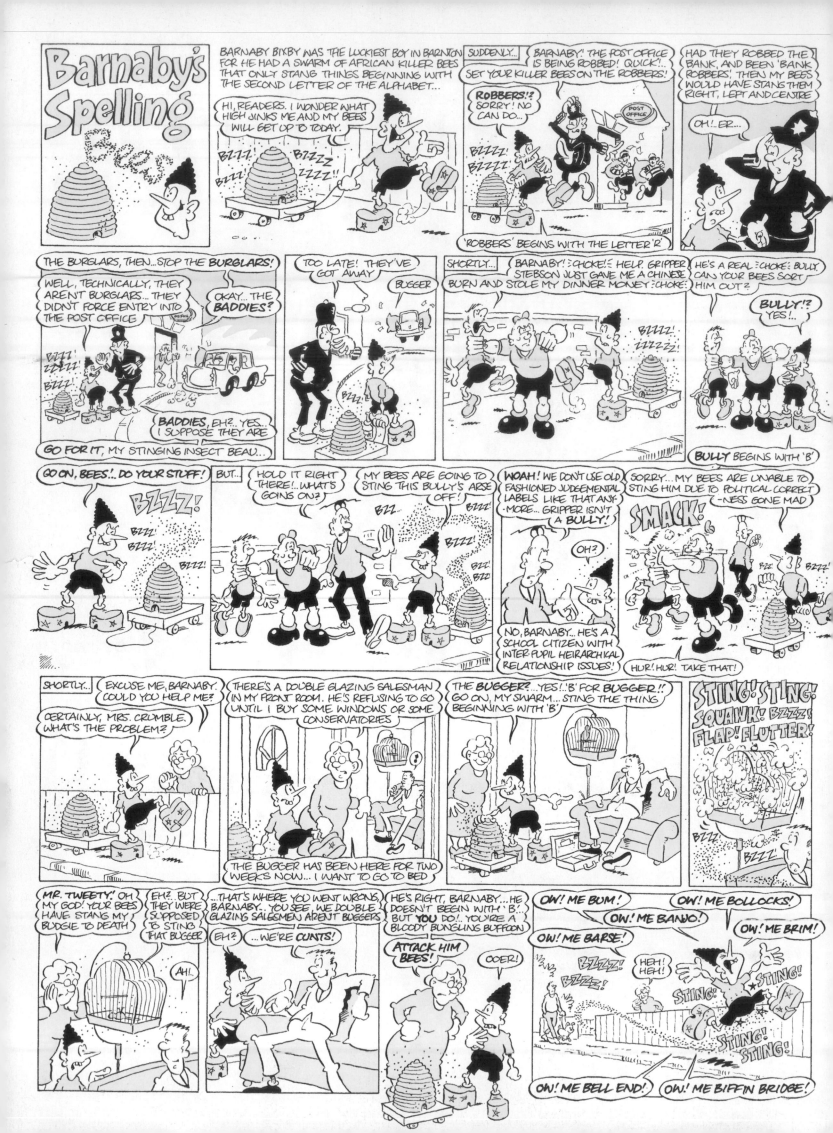

OH, LORDY...IT'S

FAT SLAGS

'ERE, DID Y' SEE RUSSELL BRAND ON TELLY LAST NIGHT, TRAY?...IS HE GORGEOUS OR WOT?

HE'S NOT MY CUP OF TEA...

FUCKED 2000 WOMEN HE HAS- 2001 IF I'D GOT OWT T' DO WI' IT

EEH, SAN. HE LOOKS LIKE HE'S BEEN DRAGGED THROUGH A HEDGE BACK-WARDS...SCRUFFY SOD... LOOKS AS THOUGH HE COULD DO WI' A GOOD WASH IF T'ASK ME

THAT'S HIS APPEAL, TRAY... IT'S THE BIT O' ROUGH LOOK... I'D GIVE OWT TO 'AVE A MAN LIKE HIM, I WOULD

WELL THERE'S A MAN EXACTLY LIKE HIM GOES THROUGH THE BINS BEHIND NETTO

WOT... THAT SCOTCH TRAMP?

AYE!

HE'S NOWT LIKE RUSSELL BRAND... HE GOBS OFF AFTER TWO PUSHES FOR A START

OOWACK! OOWACK!

GOOD MORNING!

OOH!... YOU'VE GORRA CUSTOMER, SAN.

I'D LIKE THIS DRESS DRY CLEANED PLEASE...BUT I MUST HAVE IT DONE BY MONDAY

MONDAY?. AYE, NO PROBS.

I'M MEETING THE LORD MAYOR TO COLLECT AN AWARD, YOU SEE

OOH, IT'S A NICE LITTLE COCKTAIL DRESS, INNIT, SAN

AYE!...IT'S LUSH!

I WISH I HAD ONE O' THESE...

BAZ'S TAKIN' ME T' THE DARTS SOCIAL AT THE DOG AN' HAMMER ON SATURDAY... THERE'S A PROMOTION ON VODKA SHOTS.

I'D KNOCK 'EM DEAD IN ONE OF THESE

WELL WHY DON'T YOU BORROW IT, SAN?

EH?

YOU HEARD HER...

SHE'S NOT PICKING IT UP UNTIL MONDAY...

YOU COULD TAKE IT HOME TONIGHT, WEAR IT AT THE DO ON SATURDAY, AN' BRING IT BACK MONDAY MORNING

D'Y' RECKON?

AYE!...

STICK IT IN YER BAG, SAN. DON'T SPILL OWT ON IT AN' SHE'LL BE NONE THE WISER...

MONDAY...

AND IT GIVES ME GREAT PLEASURE TO...ER...PRESENT... SNIFF!.. YOU WITH THE... SNIFF!... AWARD FOR ...SNIFF! SNIFF!...

CAN ANYBODY SMELL SICK?

MEDDLESOME RATBAG

THE ATMOSPHERE HERE AT THE RIO CARNIVAL IS INCREDIBLE ~ REVELLERS IN BRIGHTLY-COLOURED COSTUMES THRONG THE STREETS, SINGING AND DANCING THROUGHOUT THE NIGHT

THE WHOLE CITY IS UNITED IN THIS HUGE CELEBRATION OF LIFE

SLAM!

RIO

ROAR!

BRAZIL AIRLINES

FULCHESTER AIRPORT

AIROPORTO DE RIO DE JANEIRO

WELCOME TO RIO

HOTEL DOS CENTRE DE RIO

A ROOM WITH A WINDOW FACING THE MAIN STREET? CERTAINLY MADAM, HERE'S YOUR KEY...

SNATCH

WILL YOU KINDLY KEEP THE NOISE DOWN OUT THERE, PLEASE?

HOTEL CENTRE DE RIO

THERE'S PEOPLE TRYING TO SLEEP, YOU KNOW

Letterbocks

Letterbocks, Viz Comic,
PO Box 656, North Shields, NE30 4XX.
Email: letters@viz.co.uk

I DON'T understand my wife. Like most men, I often mis-aim when going to the toilet. But if, as she says, it's no bother for me to wipe the seat after I've had a piss, then surely it's just as little bother for her to do it before she has one.

J Tupwell, Barnsley

THE government tells us that we are eating too many pies and dying of heart disease, then in the next breath they're telling us we are living too long and there'll be no more pension money left for us. I wish they'd make their minds up.

John Swearsbadly, e-mail

MY girlfriend spent the first 27 years of her life believing that a lamb was a cross between a sheep and a goat. Thankfully she didn't become a teacher until she was 28.

Stuart Sheppard, e-mail

THE other day I was walking down the street when I lost my footing on some wet leaves. I struggled to keep my balance for several seconds with my legs going all over the place before I finally fell and hit the pavement. It would not have been so embarrassing, only there was a man in his garden nearby with a drum kit practising a little drum roll that ended in a cymbal clash.

T Crumbhorn Birmingham

Trees, the Law & YOU
with Tree Lawyer **Quercus Pubescens QC.**

A HORSE CHESTNUT tree in my garden overhangs the street and drops its conkers onto the pavement. On their way to school, children pick the conkers up to play with them. However, as the tree is rooted in my garden I believe that the conkers belong to me. I don't want them, it's just that I cannot abide theft. Am I correct and how can I stop them being stolen?

T Barnstaple, Looe

★ Yes, Mr Barnstaple, the conkers are yours, regardless of where they fall and taking them from the pavement is theft. However, in the same way that you wouldn't leave your wallet on the street, leaving the conkers there is asking for trouble. Try gathering them up before the children set out for school, or if you don't want them, simply run over them with a garden roller.

MY NEIGHBOUR has an apple tree which overhangs my greenhouse. In the summer, it drops its apples through the glass. We have known him for twenty years and he is a lovely, reasonable man. I am sure he would happily cut of the offending branches if I asked him, but I would like to instigate really costly and acrimonious legal proceedings. Have I got a case and how would I go about it?

Mr L Ridley, Carlton

★ Indeed you have got a case, Mr Ridley. Your neighbour is being negligent in allowing the apples to overhang your greenhouse. Get your solicitor to issue a writ, suing for the cost of repairs. If he tries to come around to discuss it, take out a restraining order forbidding from coming within 50 yards of you.

The man next door to me recently planted a forsythea in his garden. Over the years it has grown quite high and is cutting out a lot of light to my kitchen. Can I force him to prune it back?

Ron Hubbard, London

★ Forsythea is a shrub, and as my area is tree law, I am unable to advise.

MY husband worked down the pit all his life and didn't retire until he was 65. Now I hear that Dame Kelly Holmes is set to pick up her pension and free bus pass after retiring at the age of 32. It doesn't seem fair.

Edna Carstairs Essex

ON A recent visit to London, I was amazed to see the Queen riding by in a horse-drawn cart. I would have thought that someone in her position could afford a car.

Alan Heath e-mail

I'VE always thought that my arsehole was brown, but my girlfriend insists that it is pink. I don't know whether or not to believe her.

Mark Smith, e-mail

I SEE in the news recently that a young man in South Dakota has been placed on the sex offenders register after being caught *in flagrante* with a shop dummy. In stark contrast, when Andrew McCarthy's character in the movie *Mannequin* forms a close relationship with a shop dummy, his on-screen antics are dubbed a delightful romantic comedy. Once again it's one rule for Andrew McCarthy playing a character in a movie and... you know the rest. Give me £5.

Christina Martin e-mail

RADIO 2's Steve Wright only reads out letters from people who say how much they love him and his show.

I know this because me and my mates write to him regularly to tell him we think he's a cunt and he never reads our letters out.

Mark Edwards Leek

AM I the only one who has noticed that Peter jackson's latest blockbuster *King Kong* is a blatant rip-off of the classic 1930s film *King Kong?* I hope Mr Jackson has some good lawyers.

Anthony Witheyman e-mail

HATS OFF to the England cricketers for their achievements in the Ashes this summer, which rightly earned Andrew 'Freddie' Flintoff BBC Sports personality of the Year. Winning a two-team tournament against a nation with a much smaller population once in every ten attempts, then never shutting up about it, makes me proud to be British.

Ben Hunt e-mail

I BELIEVE that Her Majesty the Queen should be publicly beheaded and replaced as head of state by Pliers out of Chaka Demus and Pliers. It may not be a popular opinion, but this was a free country last time I checked.

Pliers out of Chaka Demus and Pliers e-mail

THERE'S a sign up at my workplace which reads 'You don't have to be mad to work here - but it helps'. Surely this is yet another case of positive discrimination going too far.

James MacDougall e-mail

I WAS walking through Woking town centre the other day when I stopped to consult a map I saw standing outside the shopping centre. Imagine my shock when I spotted the words 'You Are Here' with a large arrow pointing at the exact location I was standing. Is anyone else uncomfortable with all this new technology the nanny state is using to monitor our every move?

Andy Council e-mail

RECENTLY Australian television has started to broadcast a British programme called *Coronation Street*. However, they appear to have started in the middle of the series. I was wondering if any of your readers have heard of this programme, and if so, could they please give me a quick synopsis of the plot to date?

Lisa e-mail

* Are there any readers out there willing to give it a go? Outline the entire plot of Coronation Street, including all the murders, wedding dramas and fires at Mike Baldwin's factory. There's a crisp £20 note for the person who sums the plot up in the fewest words.

WHILE THE nation despairs at the sad demise of George Best, at least we can take some solace in the knowledge that he lived long enough to see his son Callum finish a creditable 4th in *Celebrity Love Island*.

Tony Trehane e-mail

I WOULD like to invite any of my games teachers to come and practise their rugby tackles on me again now that I'm a Hell's Angel and no longer a 12 year-old boy.

Colin B e-mail

THEY SAY that wisdom comes with age. Well, last week during a particularly cold spell, an old woman got on the bus and taking her gloves off said "I always take my gloves off because it makes your hands warm up

MILD OUTSIDE?

NO. IT'S BITTER.

quicker". And all these years I've been putting my gloves ON in cold weather. What a fool I am.

T Harcross
London

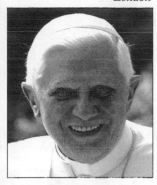

THE POPE recently announced that he is going to drop the Catholic idea of Limbo because 'It has always been only a theological hypothesis'. What, a bit like God?

Christina Martin
e-mail

IT IS heartening to know that in these so-called troubled times, the only problems that people seek an Agony Aunt's advice on are illicit sex sessions with workmen and lesbian love romps. Perhaps the world isn't such a bad place after all.

Jonathan Woodhouse
e-mail

I'M A projectionist at my local cinema and I am baffled as to why people, usually the hairy single people, sit and watch the credits at the end. Does it matter who the animal trainer was in Narnia? Go, for fuck's sake, I'm waiting to turn the lamp off so I can go home that little bit earlier for a spliff.

Tugger
e-mail

I COULD never understand why Brian McFadden dumped his huge-breasted wife Kerry Katona. But those Iceland adverts over Christmas really opened my eyes. Wise move.

Martin Mannion
e-mail

THE OTHER day I was walking to work on a very frosty morning. I wasn't looking where I was going and I stepped on a patch of ice and ended up doing the splits. I was in utter agony, but what made it worse was that a man nearby was practising his swanee whistle.

T Crumbhorn
Birmingham

TOP TIPS

CONVINCE bar staff that your pint is off by sticking your finger up your arse before holding the glass close to their nose.
Gordano, e-mail

BEFORE brushing your teeth, eat something sweet, such as a piece of chocolate. That way you can be sure of getting good value for the toothpaste that you use.
John Twomey, Kilburn

PUBLIC toilet users. When you realise the person in the next cubicle is holding fire until you leave, simply open and close the toilet door without leaving. Their first plop can then be greeted with a huge cheer.
Sam, e-mail

WEIGHT watchers. After reaching your ideal weight, maintain it by weighing yourself before and after a dump. The weight difference is the amount of food you can eat before having another dump.
Nick Brook, e-mail

SUPERMARKETS Help promote healthy living by putting your cakes, ice creams, pies etc. in aisles that are too narrow row for fatties to fit through.
Serena Keough, e-mail

SAT'S SAT!

Day Trip was Out of this World

EXCLUSIVE!

NOTTINGHAMSHIRE couple drove their car all the way to Mars's largest moon Phobos after following the instructions given by their car's sat-nav computer.

Brian and Maureen Bromide from Ragnall, near Worksop, programmed the £200 device to tell them the best way to get to Alton Towers. However, due to an error at the manufacturers, a journey that should have only taken ninety minutes took over 2 years.

Machine

Brian, 58, told reporters: "I thought there was something funny going on when the machine told me not to take the A38 but stay on the M1. I've been to Alton Towers many a time and I know the way quite well, but I thought it must know a quicker route."

bowl

Even when the onboard set told Mr Bromide to accelerate his Toyota Yaris in order to escape the gravitational pull of the Earth he carried on despite the complaints coming from his passenger seat. "My wife kept telling me we were lost but I just turned the radio up," said Brian.

"Looking back, perhaps I should have listened to her!" he added.

Despite the lack of white knuckle rides, over-priced food and oxygen, the Bromides said they didn't mind their 100 million mile diversion to the red planet. "We had plenty of sandwiches and the weather was dry so it wasn't a total wash out," they told us in unison.

Have Your Say...

AUSTRALIAN happy shopper polymath Rolf Harris has sparked controversy with his recent portrait of Her Majesty the Queen on her 80th birthday. Consensus in the art establishment is that the painting attempted a bold juxtaposition of form against content and succeeded in establishing an internal humanist rhetorical diaolgue which subverts its function whilst wittily transgressing the aegis of its own moral framework. Meanwhile public opinion seems to be that he's got the mouth wrong. We went onto the streets to see what YOU thought of of the bearded didgerydoo player's Royal portrait.

...I DON'T know why everyone is criticising it. Picasso was hailed as a genius for his portraits and they're rubbish. At least Harris got the Queen's ears on the side of her head and her nose roughly between her eyes.
T Petty, Birmingham

...I WAS very excited when I heard that Harris was going to paint the Queen, but I feel very let down by the result. He hasn't signed it with a 'Rolferoo' which I think are the best bits of his paintings.
Gladys Whalebone, Corsett

...IT'S ALL very well to criticise, but how do we know that everyone else who has ever painted or photographed Her Majesty hasn't got the mouth wrong and Rolf is the only one who has got it right?
B Rix, Whitehall

...WHAT was the BBC thinking of, getting an artistic lightweight such has Harris to paint Her Majesty's birthday portrait? The job should have gone to a serious artist like Tracey Emin who could have shit in the Queen's bed for her birthday.
Edna Carstairs, Purfleet

...IT'S NOT a bad painting, but a friend of my dad's could have done better. He does these dead good oil paintings of fantasy sword and sorcery scenes. He could have done a dead good one of the Queen dressed like Xena, Warrior Princess standing on an orange planet with three moons fighting a massive alien snake. And he only charges twenty quid.
Mrs Trellis, North Wales

...I AGREE with most critics when they say that the mouth is wrong, but on the plus side the hair and eyes are very good. Perhaps Harris should have painted Her Majesty reading a newspaper so as you could just see the good bits poking above it.
Mr Onion, Onionbury

...I WAS disgusted by the painting. When I first saw it on breakfast television on December 19th, I was so enraged on the Queen's behalf that I put my foot through the television and sent Rolf the bill. He paid up and I bought a brand new 48 inch plasma screen.
R Watiss, Sykes

...I THINK that the portrait is insulting, not only to Her Majesty, buit also to the British people. I think the Antipodean wobble board player should be put on the sex offenders register and transported in chains back to Australia where he came from. And further.
Dave Clark, Fife

...THE portrait is absolute rubbish and shows that Harris cannot paint for toffee. He should stick to what he is good at. Although what that is, I haven't got a clue.
J Geiles, Band

...LIKENESSES are always tricky, especially when the subject is iconic, like the Queen. As chief editorial cartoonist for the *Sun* newspaper, I am required to do likenesses on a daily basis, and have learned a few tricks of the trade. Harris could have painted the Queen wearing a T-shirt with 'HM the Queen' written on it in big black letters, or perhaps painted a newspaper with the headline 'Rolf Harris Paints the Queen' in the corner of the portrait.
B Caldwell, Wapping

...I DON'T know much about art, but I know what I like. I think he should have done her tits bigger. Surely she must have bigger tits than that.
Jim Pansie, Yeovil

...A LOT has been said about how Harris hasn't done the tits big enough. But it must have been very tricky for him, as staring at the Queen's knockers could be construed as treason, punishable by death. What he should have done was pencilled them in roughly, and then consulted someone who has actually seen them, such as the Duke of Edinburgh, or that bloke who broke into the palace and sat on her bed.
Rose Royce, Carwash

Mountains of TERROR

BRITAIN'S climbers were facing huge delays yesterday after security measures were stepped up at the country's highest peaks.

Government minister for Vertiginous Geographical Features Dr Kim Howells put all mainland mountains on a state of scarlet alert after intelligence services received information from a credible source that a terrorist strike was imminent. It is thought that a network of Al Qaeda cells were plotting to simultaneously blow the tops off ten British peaks including *Snowdon, Ben Nevis* and *Scafell Pike.*

In a coordinated nationwide sting, codenamed 'Operation Absolutely Certain This Time', police arrested 20,000 men with beards, before shooting them in the arm and releasing them without charge.

Miss Howells told a press conference yesterday: "I fully understand that the new security measures we are implementing will cause a certain amount of inconvenience to mountaineers, but in the light of this not at all imaginary threat, we feel we have no option but to put them in place."

Under the temporary restrictions climbers will not be allowed to take rucksacks, ropes, woolly hats or food and drink onto any British slope. Kendal mint cake will be allowed, but mountaineers will be required to take a bite out of each bar in front of a government official in order to prove that it is not made out of Semtex plastic explosive painted white.

"The danger that our mountains will get their pointy tops blown off by Islamic extremists is real and imminent," Miss Howells continued. "A bomb hidden inside a ham sandwich and wrapped in foil could be detonated in seconds using a fuse made with threads teased from the bobble off a woolly hat. In the circumstances, these farcical security

Bin Laden Peak Plot Foiled

precautions are fully justified."

"Innocent climbers have nothing to fear," she added. "Unless of course they look foreign, in which case it may be necessary for police to shoot them a little bit."

Meanwhile, there was chaos at the feet of Britain's mountains yesterday as the new measures came into force. In Llanberis at the base of Snowdon, the queue of climbers waiting to take to the slopes snaked through the gift shop, twice round the mountain railway cafe and out into the car park. It was estimated that mountaineers were having to wait up to more than 4 hours before setting out on their climbs, and frustrations were beginning to boil over.

"My wife and I have been climbing Snowdon every summer for more than thirty years," fumed hillwalker Halford Topman. "And this is the first time we've had our flasks of soup confiscated and been given internal rectal examinations by machine gun-toting policemen."

"We won't be coming back next year, and that's for sure," he added.

HILLWALKERS! Here it is, your handy cut out and keep MOUN

ALERT COLOUR: Beige
ATROCITY STATUS: Highly unlikely
SCAREDNESS PERCENTAGE: 0%
ACTION: None. Food and drink may be taken onto mountain. No restriction on rucksacks, kagouls and bobble hats.

ALERT COLOUR: Taupe
ATROCITY STATUS: Unlikely
SCAREDNESS PERCENTAGE: 2%
ACTION: Little. All items allowed on mountain, but could be subject to random spot checks.

ALERT COLOUR: Fawn
ATROCITY STATUS: Slightly less unlikely than taupe, but still fairly unlikely.
SCAREDNESS PERCENTAGE: 3%
ACTION: As taupe, with unlimited access to lower slopes. However, security personnel may be stationed on crags near the summits.

ALERT COLOUR: Eau de Nil
ATROCITY STATUS: Possible
SCAREDNESS PERCENTAGE: 11%
ACTION: As fawn, plus CCTV cameras installed on summits. All mountaineers subjected to intrusive body cavity searches.

ALERT COLOUR: A
ATROCITY STATUS
SCAREDNESS PER
ACTION: As eau de kagoul hood drawst wiches tasted in fr stationed behind o search checks on m

We're all going on...

Osama Holiday

MORAG: ***Clocked Bin Laden in gift shop***

EVIL Al Qaeda boss Osama Bin Laden has spent the summer scaling Britain's tallest mountains to scout ut locations for his terrorist outrages. That's according Fortwilliam woman Morag Drambuie, who spotted the ave-dwelling Tora Bora tyrant buying souvenirs in the en Nevis giftshop where she works.

"It was definitely him," recalls the 2-year-old grandmother of thirty. He'd tried to disguise himself y wearing glasses, talking with Lancashire accent and making mself about a foot shorter than e is in the paper, but he wasn't ooling me."

And chillingly, the 9-11 master-ind was not alone. For Morag ecognised his companion as one other than extradited hook-anded cleric Abu Hamza.

"I spotted him immediately," he remembers. "He was trying pass himself off as Bin Laden's ife. He'd shaved his beard off, st about ten stone and was earing false breasts and mittens ver his hooks."

Morag's suspicion was aroused hen she spotted the sinister ouple studying a map of Ben evis and the surrounding area n a teatowel. "The map is very etailed," she continues. "It hows all the major peaks in the rampians, such as Ben Lawers, en Vorlich, Ben Lomond and Ben

Eagle-eyed Morag Spots Bin up Ben

Cruachan. It was clear to me that Bin Laden and Hamza were plotting which peaks to take out in a bomb outrage."

Morag immediately tried to call the SAS, but by the time she had got their number from Directory Enquiries the pair had already made their escape. She recalls sadly: "They came up to the till and bought a tin of shortbread, a Scottish piper doll in a plastic tube and several humorous postcards depicting the Loch Ness monster with a tartan hat and ginger hair. Then they asked me for directions to Mallaig before driving off in a blue car."

A police spokesman confirmed that Morag's sighting was being taken seriously. Sgt Tam O'Shanter of the Glen Scaddle Anti-Terrorist Squad told us: "If anyone sees an elderly couple in a blue car, we would urge them to get in touch with the SAS immediately."

BOMB EVERY MOUNTAIN

REVEALED! **Bin Laden's Plans for Britain's Summits**

BEN NEVIS
Al Quaeda cell plotted to take out highest UK peak with stick of dynamite hidden in sausage roll, detonated using heat from flask of tea.

SNOWDON
In echo of 9-11 attacks, suicide train driver planned to hijack mountain railway engine 'Hywel Dda' and crash it at 4mph into toilets next to cafe at summit.

SCAFELL PIKE
Disguised as hillwalker, Mullah Umar plotted to scale slope and blow off summit with dirty bomb hidden inside Scotch egg.

BEN MACDUI
Bombers intended to drill out Kit-Kats and Penguins then fill them with nitro-glycerine to blow top of mountain to smithereens.

CRIB Y DDYSOL
Tupperware box of processed cheese sandwiches made with plastic explosives instead of cheese was planned to explode peak.

DUNKERY BEACON
Terrorists intended to use massive nail bomb hidden in hollowed out Soreen malt-loaf to level popular Somerset landmark.

HELVELLYN
Extremists conspired to fit 4 empty Pringles tubes together to make 'Super-Bazooka' to destroy cairn on Lake District mountain top.

CAMEDD LLEWELYN
Hook-handed Finsbury Park cleric Abu Hamza planned to lob hand-grenades painted to look like small pineapples at 3491ft Welsh summit.

PEN Y GHENT
Suicide hiker aimed to fill climbing boots with TNT and jump up and down on top of Yorkshire mountain until they went off.

SHINING TOR
Tinfoil from round sandwiches fashioned into solar dish was to focus rays of sun onto pac-a-mac impregnated with gunpowder.

TERROR ALERT LEVEL GUIDE

BRITAIN'S mountains are subject to constantly changing alert levels which indicate the likelihood of a terrorist attack. The different statuses range from Beige to Maroon. But what do those colours actually mean?

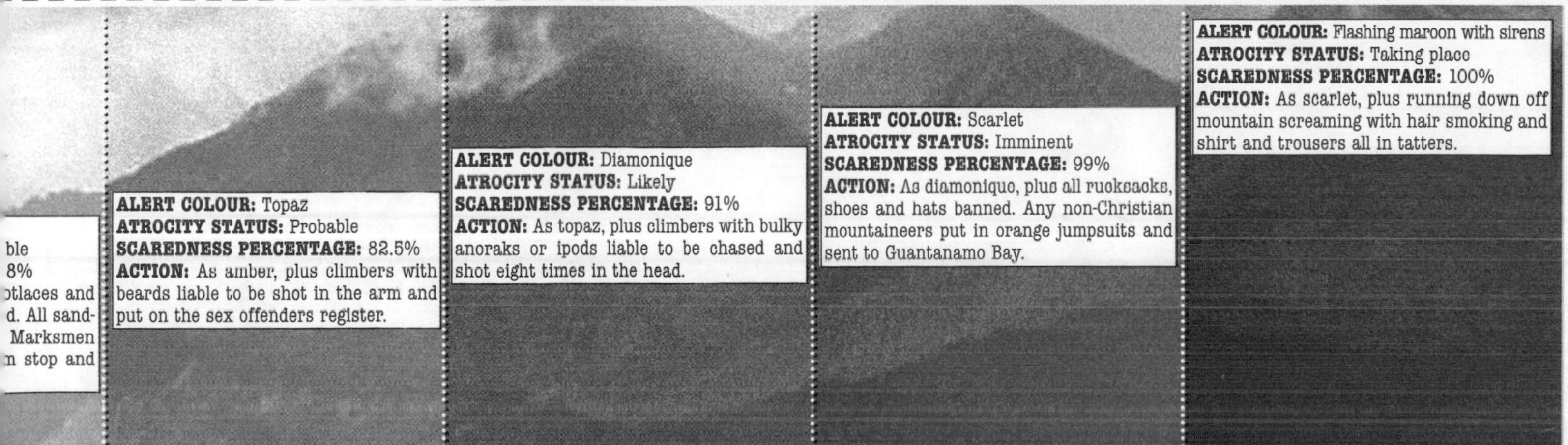

ble
8%
otlaces and
d. All sand-
Marksmen
n stop and

ALERT COLOUR: Topaz
ATROCITY STATUS: Probable
SCAREDNESS PERCENTAGE: 82.5%
ACTION: As amber, plus climbers with beards liable to be shot in the arm and put on the sex offenders register.

ALERT COLOUR: Diamonique
ATROCITY STATUS: Likely
SCAREDNESS PERCENTAGE: 91%
ACTION: As topaz, plus climbers with bulky anoraks or ipods liable to be chased and shot eight times in the head.

ALERT COLOUR: Scarlet
ATROCITY STATUS: Imminent
SCAREDNESS PERCENTAGE: 99%
ACTION: As diamonique, plus all rucksacks, shoes and hats banned. Any non-Christian mountaineers put in orange jumpsuits and sent to Guantanamo Bay.

ALERT COLOUR: Flashing maroon with sirens
ATROCITY STATUS: Taking place
SCAREDNESS PERCENTAGE: 100%
ACTION: As scarlet, plus running down off mountain screaming with hair smoking and shirt and trousers all in tatters.

FROM JUNGLE TO PETE DOHERTY...

THE STORY OF CRACK

EVERYONE loves to see Pete Doherty up to his hilarious, headline-grabbing antics. Whether he's embarrassing himself on stage at Live8 or frantically flushing the toilet every time he hears a police siren, chances are the Babyshambles frontman is ripped to his pale, sweating tits on his favourite drug. But what is it? Where does it come from? And how does it reach Pete? Find out by reading this fascinating tale...

DOHERTY'S crack begins its life 8000 miles across the ocean in Colombia on the mountainous slopes of the Andes where the seeds are sown in the early spring. Suitable areas for cultivation are carefully selected by the growers, and existing food crops such as wheat or corn are cleared to ready the soil for the coca plant.

SIX months later the plants have grown up strong and healthy and are ready for harvesting. The whole family joins in gathering the leaves from the bushes and loading them onto the backs of llamas. These sturdy pack animals are the lorries of the Andes and can carry their own body weight in unprocessed drugs.

BACK at the farm, the coca leaves are trodden in the same way that a French farmer treads grapes to make wine. Once again, all the family join in. The process is well underway, but it will still be many weeks before this green paste is in a form that can get former Libertines singer Pete off his face.

THE farming is over, and now begins a more technical phase. In a secret laboratory hidden deep in the jungle and safe from prying eyes, a scientist has set up a giant chemistry set. He alone understands the magical process whereby the sticky, green paste is refined into the sparkling, white crystals to which Doherty is a hopeless slave.

IT IS time for the rocks of crack to bid farewell to the land of their birth. In an airport hotel room, a man known as a 'mule' collects his precious cargo. The drugs are carefully wrapped in special balloons and packed safely inside him before he begins an exciting aeroplane journey to London.

DURING his 12-hour flight, the mule can sit back, relax and enjoy the view. However, at lunchtime, he must politely refuse the stewardess's temping offer of a meal. With fifty ping-pong ball sized parcels of Doherty's crack packed in his rectum, he dare not risk a visit to the toilet.

ON arrival, the 'Nothing to Declare' channel must be negotiated. The experienced mule will choose his moment carefully. He knows that he is less likely to be stopped if he follows a pretty lady, whose suitcase containing bras and skimpy knickers acts as an irresistible lure for the red-blooded customs officers.

ONCE safely in his hotel, the mule can finally begin unpacking his precious cargo. It is taken off his hands by a London contact, a man known only as the importer. Although it is now in the same city as Pete, there are still several more links in the chain before the drug finds its way into the Babyshambles vocalist's glass crack pipe.

IN A hotel room on the other side of London, the importer meets with another business contact known as the distributor, to whom he plans to sell the crack. In the drug business as in many others, there is a lot of dishonesty, and the distributor has to be very careful to check that the drugs are of good quality before handing over his hard earned money.

SATISFIED with the quality of the crack, the distributor hands over the cash. The two men shake hands and the drugs deal is done. All that remains now is for the importer to be shot in the back of the head by the distributor's business associates, a process known as whacking, and his money returned.

THE DISTRIBUTOR is a canny businessman and knows that he can maximise his profits if the crack is mixed or 'cut' with cheap substances that look similar. Just like your butcher mixes sawdust and phlegm into his sausage meat, a drugs dealer will mix the crack with rock salt, drain cleaner or crumbled up firelighters.

NOW that the crack has been cut and wrapped into convenient pipe-sized packages, it is finally time for it to hit the streets. A Babyshambles roadie is sent out of the stage door up a back alley to buy Doherty's crack. This is known as 'scoring'. A score of crack will cost Pete's roadie between £10 and £30, depending on how 'dry' the streets are.

AT last. After a year long 8000-mile journey from the jungles of South America, Doherty finally has his crack. Eagerly, he pops it into his straight-shooter pipe and has himself a few puffs before going on stage. Producing a brief feeling of euphoria as well as hallucinations, paranoid delusions, erratic heartbeats, itching and delusional parasitosis, it weaves its magic on the talented pop star.

THE following day, the world wakes up to the familiar story that Doherty has made a complete arse of himself once more. Meanwhile, on the other side of the world, a field of golden corn is being torched in readiness for the next crop of young coca plants. And so the wonderful crack cycle continues.

SID the SEX

TITS OOT!

TYNESIDE'S SILVER-TONGUED CAVALIER

ONE NIGHT...

MEET YUZ AALL AT HALF PAST THREE THE MORRA MORNIN' DOON THE QUAYSIDE, THEN LADS, EH?

HALF THREE DOON THE QUAYSIDE? WHAT FAWA, SID?

I'M JUST GANNIN' T' BED AT THAT TIME, MAN.

THIS ARTIST...HE'S ASKED FOR LURDS O' GEORDIES T'GAN DOON THERE THE MORRA AN' STRIP OFF BOLLACK NAIRKED SUR AS HE CAN TEK PICKCHAS.

OH AYE, I'VE SEEN 'IM ON THE TELLY. HE'S A YANK, AN' HE GANS AALL AWA THE WORLD GETTIN' THOOSANDS OF PEOPLE T' TEK THEIR CLURS OFF FORRIM.

SOONDS LIKE A FUCKIN' DORTY PORVORT T'ME.

NAH, MAN. HE'S DEEIN' IT FOR ART! HE GETS GEET BIG CROODS T' STAND IN THE RICK WHILE HE TEKS ARTY PHURTURS. IT'S CAALLED AN INSTALLATION OR SUMMAT. HE'S EXPECTIN' TWO THOOSAND THE MORRA.

TWO THOOSAND!?!

AYE...AN HALF OF 'EM WILL BE BORDS, MAN!

...WELL, I DIVEN'T KNAA ABOOT ART, BUT I KNAA WHAT I LIKE...AN' I LIKE TWO THOOSAND TITS AN' A THOOSAND FANNIES.

WELL I WOULDN'T GET TOO EXCITED, SID. YUZ'LL NOT GET NEE TOPS AN' FINGNI AN' THAT.

WHY, I KNAA THAT, BAZ, MAN. BUT YER CAN 'TRY BEFORE YER BUY', LIKE JAMIE OLIVER SEZ IN THAT SAINSBURYS ADVORT.

HOO! WHAT D'YUZ MEAN, SID?

THINK ABOOT IT, MAN. YUZ CAN CHECK OOT THE GOODS...

...HOO MANY TIMES HAVE YUZ BROUGHT A BORD HURME, AN' WHEN YUZ'VE GOT HER BRA OFF, HER KNOCKAZ HAVE BIN A BIT OF A LET DOON? I MEAN, I'VE LOST COONT, ME'SEL.

GOOD POINT, SID.

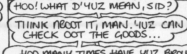

WELL, THER'LL BE NAIRN OF THAT THE MORRA, LADS. WHAT YUZ SEE IS WHAT YUZ'LL GET.

AYE, HE'S REET. AN' THEY'LL AALL BE YER ARTY-TYPE BORDS AN' AALL. AN' THEMS ARE AALL GAGGIN' FORRIT.

AYE. WELL KNURN FACT, THAT. ARTY BORDS ARE GAGGIN' FORRIT.

C'MON, LADS. WHAT D' YUZ SAY WE GAN FORRIT?

AYE!

MIND YEE, SID. WHAT'S GOOD FO' THE GOOSE IS GOOD FO' THE GANDAH...

...AALL THE BORDS'LL BE CHECKIN' OOT THE FELLAS' BAIT TINS. SO YUZ'D BETTER BE LOOKIN' YER BEST.

GOOD POINT, BAZ. I'LL HAVE A BIT OF A STRUM ON THE BUS DOON, GET ME'SEL HALF A TEACAKE ON.

3.45 NEXT MORNING...

HERE HE COMES NOO.

WHAT KEPT YER, SID? WE THOUGHT YUZ HAD CHICKENED OOT.

NAH! I GOT HOYED OFF THE FUCKIN' BUS. I HAD TO WAALK FROM THE FUCKIN' HAYMARKET.

PP VI206

ANY DECENT TUSSAGE ABOOT, LADS?

BITS AN' BOBS, SID. THERE'S A CANNY FEW COFFIN DODGERS, BUT THERE'S PLENTY OF QUALITY BLAART BOONCIN' ABOOT.

AYE. I THINK WUZ'LL STAND A BETTER CHANCE OF COPAN' OFF IF WE SPLIT UP.

GOOD IDEA, BOB. ANYRURD, PEOPLE MIGHT THINK WUZ'RE FOUR SHORT LIFTAZ IF WE STICK TOGETHER.

REET, LADS. SEE YUZ BACK AT THE PUB.

AYE. GOOD HUNTIN', LADS.

SHORTLY...

RIGHT EVERYBODY. SAY **CHEESE!**...

CLICK!

CHEESE!

HOO, PET. MY NAME'S SID. DO YOU LIKE ART?

DO I LIKE ART?... WELL, IT DEPENDS ON WHAT YOU MEAN BY ART...

...I MEAN, I'M FASCINATED BY **THIS** ARTIST, THE MISMATCH BETWEEN THE QUESTIONS HE IS ASKING ABOUT THE NOTION OF SPACE, BEING AND OTHERNESS, AND THE MEDIUM IN WHICH HE HAS CHOSEN TO ANSWER THEM. IT'S THE JUXTAPOSITION HE CREATES BETWEEN THE URBAN AND THE ORGANIC, IF YOU WILL. IT SEEMS TO ME THAT...

SO... YOU **DO** LIKE ART, THEN?

WELL, IN THE BROAD SENSE IN WHICH YOU ASK, YES. YES, I DO LIKE ART.

WELL GET A LURD OF ME COCK, LOVE. IT'S A **MASTERPIECE!**

THRUST!

14

WELL, REALLY!

SLAP!

OW!

SHORTLY...

RIGHT, EVERBODY! WE'RE READY FOR THE LAST PICTURE. EVERYONE STAND ON THE MILLENNIUM BRIDGE.

SHUFFLE! SHUFFLE!

WATCH THE BIRDIE!... YOU AT THE END, JUST MOVE IN A LITTLE BIT... THAT'S LOVELY...

CLICK!

OKAY! THANK YOU, EVERYBODY! YOU CAN ALL PUT YOUR CLOTHES ON AND GO HOME.

WELL THAT WAS QUITE AN EXPERIENCE, WASN'T IT?

AYE, PET! THEY'RE SMASHIN! I MEAN, IT WAS SMASHIN!

IT'S MARVELLOUS THAT SO MANY PEOPLE HAVE TURNED OUT TO SUPPORT A COMMUNITY-BASED ART PROJECT SUCH AS THIS, DON'T YOU THINK?

CAR PARK →

ERM, AYE, PET! IT'S CANNY!

I MEAN, I THINK IT IS SO IMPORTANT THAT ART BREAKS DOWN OUR SOCIETY'S TABOOS SURROUNDING NAKEDNESS, DON'T YOU?

OH, AYE, PET. I DO. AYE.

I THINK THE ARTIST IS REALLY CHALLENGING OUR CONCEPTS OF THE NAKED FORM AND ASKING US TO RE-EVALUATE OUR SENSE OF NAKEDNESS, DRAWING A DISTINCTION BETWEEN NAKEDNESS AND NUDITY, DON'T YOU THINK?

ERM... AYE!

LISTEN, WOULD YOU LIKE TO COME BACK TO MY FLAT? WE CAN DISCUSS SOME OF THE CONTEMPORARY ARTISTIC ISSUES SURROUNDING THE QUESTIONS THE ARTIST RAISED OVER A COFFEE.

AYE, PET! CHAMPION.

TEN MINUTES LATER...

... I MEAN, I'M VERY COMFORTABLE WITH MY BODY, AND I DON'T FIND OTHER PEOPLE'S NUDITY AT ALL REMARKABLE.

ERM... AYE, PET!

RUB! RUB!

...THAT'S WHY I FOUND POSING JUST NOW SUCH A LIBERATING EXPERIENCE, TO HAVE SHARED MY NUDITY WITH A GROUP OF PEOPLE FOR WHOM THE FACT WE HAD NO CLOTHES ON WAS NOT AN ISSUE.

AYE.

YOU MAKE YOURSELF COMFORTABLE, I'LL PUT THE KETTLE ON.

I FEEL THAT THE ARTIST HAS DONE SO MUCH TO MAKE NAKEDNESS ACCEPTABLE, TO BREAK DOWN SOCIETY'S HANG-UPS AND PREJUDICES.

ERM... AYE!

THIS IS IT! THIS IS IT!

I MEAN, I'M NOT ASHAMED OF MY BODY AND NEITHER WAS ANYONE ELSE AT THE INSTALLATION...

LOB!

ER.... THAT'S REET, PET!

... BUT SOCIETY SEEMS TO THINK THAT PUBLIC NAKEDNESS IS A CAUSE FOR...

SCREAM!

CRASH!

HELP! POLICE! THERE'S A NAKED MAN IN MY FLAT!

THREE MONTHS LATER...

SEZ HERE..." A NEWCASTLE MAN WAS TODAY CONVICTED OF INDECENT EXPOSURE WHEN HE STRIPPED NAKED IN FRONT OF A WOMAN IN HER TYNESIDE FLAT..."

HEH! HEH!

"SIDNEY SMUTT, 30, OF BYKER PLEADED NOT GUILTY BUT HIS CLAIM THAT HE TOOK HIS CLORTHES OFF IN ORDER TO "ASK QUESTIONS ABOOT SOCIETY'S CONCEPTS OF THE NAKED FORM AND RE-EVALUATE OUR SENSE OF NAKEDNESS" WERE DISMISSED BY MAGISTRATES AND HE WAS FINED 300 POONDS AN' PUT ON THE SEX OFFENDER'S REGISTER FOR TWO YEARS."

HEH! HEH! FAME AT LAST, EH, SID?

FUCK OFF, THE LOT O'YUZ.

ROGER MELLIE
THE MAN ON THE TELLY

HI, TOM!...YOU WANTED TO SEE ME?

ER...YES...IT'S A LITTLE...ER DELICATE, ROGER, SO I'LL JUST OUT WITH IT...

I KNOW YOU'VE BEEN HAVING A FEW FINANCIAL TROUBLES OF LATE...AND I JUST WONDERED...WELL, HOW DESPERATE THINGS ARE

TO TELL YOU THE TRUTH, TOM, I'M IN FUCKING SHIT STREET...

I'VE GOT THREE EX-WIVES BLEEDING ME DRY. I'VE GOT A BOOKIE'S SLATE AS LONG AS A GRANNY'S TIT, AND THE TAX MAN'S ON MY BACK FOR FUCK KNOWS HOW MUCH

RIGHT...SO PRETTY DESPERATE THEN

LISTEN, ROGER...HAVE YOU THOUGHT ABOUT...VERMIN LOANS?

VERMIN LOANS!?! ARE YOU TAKING THE PISS OR WHAT, TOM?

I MIGHT BE HARD UP, BUT I'M NOT FUCKING STUPID. HAVE YOU SEEN THE RE-PAYMENT RATES? FUCKING ASTRONOMICAL, THEY ARE

BLOKE I KNOW TOOK A LOAN OUT WITH 'EM, MISSED ONE PAYMENT...NEXT THING HE KNOWS, THERE'S SOME BIG UGLY FUCKER WITH A DOG BANGING ON HIS FRONT DOOR.

FUCKING PIRATES, TOM. THE LOT OF 'EM. CROOKS. I'D RATHER SELL ONE OF MY KIDNEYS THAN BORROW ANY MONEY OFF THEM ROBDOGS

BORROW!?!...NO, I WASN'T SUGGESTING YOU BORROW FROM THEM...I MEANT HAVE YOU THOUGHT ABOUT DOING THEIR ADVERT?

THEY CALLED ME AND ASKED IF I THOUGHT YOU'D BE UP FOR IT

UP FOR IT?...DOES A BEAR SHIT IN THE WOODS, TOM? HOW MUCH?

FIFTY GRAND?

FIFTY!? FUCK ME, TOM...I CAN SEE WHAT PHIL TUFFNALL WAS UP TO NOW...IT'S BEING FILMED IN A CALL CENTRE TOMORROW. HERE'S THE ADDRESS AND THE SCRIPT...TEN O'CLOCK. DON'T BE LATE

FOR FIFTY GRAND!? THAT'S ME AT THE DOOR, TOM

11.48 NEXT MORNING...

WHERE THE HELL'S ROGER!?

SORRY I'M LATE, TOM...I WAS OUT TILL ALL HOURS CELEBRATING THIS GIG...GOT A BIT CARRIED AWAY.

JESUS CHRIST, ROGER. FIFTY GRAND FOR AN HOUR'S WORK AND YOU CAN'T EVEN TURN UP ON TIME...AND WHO'S THIS?

THIS IS KRISTY

IT'S KIRSTY, ROGER

PICKED HER UP LAST NIGHT, TOM. FUCKING CRACKER, ISN'T SHE?...SIZE OF THEM TITS, EH?...I PROMISED HER A PART IN THE AD...THOUGHT SHE COULD BE THE BIRD WHO ANSWERS THE PHONE

LOOK, ROGER...THE DIRECTOR OF THIS AD IS FARTING FIRE...YOU'RE TWO HOURS LATE, YOU LOOK LIKE YOU'VE SLEPT IN A GUTTER AND NOW YOU'RE TRYING TO RE-CAST THE AD

YOU'RE GOING TO LOSE THIS ONE IF YOU'RE NOT CAREFUL, ROGER...FIFTY BIG ONES! NOW JUST GET ON WITH IT.

KEEP YOUR HAIR ON, TOM

SO...OKAY...QUIET ON SET...THREE!...TWO!...ONE!...ACTION!

HI! I'M TV'S ROGER MELLIE...

YOU KNOW, WE ALL HAVE FINANCIAL DIFFICULTIES FROM TIME TO TIME...AND WHEN WE DO, IT'S GOOD TO KNOW HELP IS AT HAND

...AND THAT'S WHERE THOSE NICE PEOPLE AT VERMIN LOANS COME IN......YOU'RE WELCOME, SIR...GOODBYE.

16

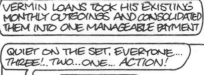

19

Some Broadcasters Do Face Legal Action

AN ACCIDENT-PRONE PENSIONER has described his shock at discovering that he was the unwitting star of a 1970s television series.

Mr. Frank Spencer, a retired 68-year-old with learning difficulties, says he had no idea he was being followed by a camera crew and only realised when the series was repeated six or seven times on BBC2 last year.

"I was having a lot of harassments at the time," he admits. "The BBC was taking advantage of my bad luck. I'm very upset. It wasn't a very nice thing to do. Hmmm."

SECRETLY

Mr. Spencer was secretly filmed from 1973 to 1978 as he suffered a series of mishaps and continually failed to hold down a series of low-wage jobs. During the course of the series, made as Spencer was attempting to get over the death of his mother, millions saw him:

✳ Desperately trying to hold on to the rear bumper of a Morris Minor hanging off the edge of a cliff, an event which caused him trauma-induced flashbacks for decades

✳ Falling through a ceiling into the bed of his violent next-door-neighbour, a bar manager who had previously threatened to murder Mr. Spencer

✳ Clinging to a church steeple while dressed up as a frightening Christmas elf.

SQUIRRELY

Spencer's wife Elizabeth and daughter Jessica were also filmed with Elizabeth's full co-operation, according to Frank. "I didn't know anything

about it. Betty did. She let them film me and kept all the money. She let them make me look like a fool but I'm not a fool. I'm just a little bit clumsy.

"I think that's why she left me. And why I lost touch with her and my daughter," Frank laughs nervously. "That's why I'm living in a home now. I've got nothing. I don't even have my beret any more. The cat did a whoopsee in it and I had to throw it out."

SCROTUM NEWS
............Roundup............

The Isle of Man Gazette

The Isle of Man has passed a new law limiting scrotum size. Douglas town councillor Frank O'Dougal explained: "If the Mayor can get your scrotum in his mouth, you'll be allowed to stay on the island. If he can't fit it in, you'll be pushed into the sea. It's as simple as that."

Corriera della Serra

Bosses at Florence's Prado art gallery have been under fire after putting the scrotum from Michelangelo's sculpture **David** up for sale on internet auction site eBay. The carved marble scrotum, which dates from 1543 and weighs in at a hefty thirty-two tons, has yet to attract any bids, but is available as a Buy It Now for £100.

Ohio Telegraph & Argus

American scientists have discovered a solution to obesity - tickling your scrotum with a feather! Boffins at Massachussetts Institute of Technology recently announced that an overweight Baltimore man had lost over 30 stones after just ten minutes of tickling his scrotum with a feather. "We don't know how or why it works, we only know it does!" said a delighted spokesman.

The Daily Express

Noel Edmonds is set to invest some of the many millions he has made from his hit show **Deal or No Deal** in a theme park modelled on his own scrotum. The tidy-bearded telly host is intending to build the park on the site of a disused cokeworks in Ferry Fryston, West Yorkshire. If all goes according to plan, **Noel's ScrotumWorld** will be the world's second largest scrotum-based tourist attraction, after **Catchphrase** presenter Roy Walker's 300 acre **Roy's ScrotumLand** which is just outside Bellshill, Glasgow.

Letterbocks

Letterbocks,
Viz Comic,
PO Box 656,
North Shields,
NE30 4XX

letters@viz.co.uk

❖ **I RECENTLY** got a letter from the *Viz* subscriptions manager saying that I was one of their most valued readers. It doesn't say much for the rest of you, does it?

Alan Heath
e-mail

❖ **I AM** contantly reading about valuable antiques being put under the hammer. Wouldn't it be a better idea simply to sell these items, rather than smashing them to smithereens?

R Warskyj
Dundee

❖ **ALAN SHEARER**'s goal against Portsmouth took him above the 200 scored by Jackie Milburn and made him Newcastle United's highest ever scorer. However, 'Wor Jackie' scored 238 goals for the Toon, 38 of which were not counted as they were scored during the war. Well if wartime goals don't count, Shearer should have 106 goals deducted, as we have been fighting a 'War on Terror' since 11th September 2001, at which point he had only scored 95.

Gladstone Gamble
Newcastle

❖ **I FEEL** very sorry for Ruth Kelly after she was hit by an egg thrown by a Fathers For Justice campaigner. But spare

Ruth Kelly (above) and (inset) the egg that hit her head.

a thought for the late Charlie Cairoli. He had eggs smashed on his head week after week, and they were often thrown by his colleagues. If it happens again, Ms Kelly should take a leaf out of Charlie's book, snipping the thrower's braces with a pair of scissors and filling his hat with a load of shaving foam.

R Hemple
Wales

❖ **YOU KNOW** what I love about Clover? It's the way that it's churned.

Captain Henry
e-mail

❖ **IT SADDENED** me greatly that the American govern-

❖ **DOG** owners. Don't waste money on a lead. Simply walk your dog backwards holding its tail.

Shauny Boy, e-mail

❖ **BRITISH** army. Ensure confusion amongst your troops by charging them 30p for a bottle of Becks In Hohne Garrison, Germany, then make them sit through a 30 minute lecture on the dangers of alcohol the day after a heavy session.

Rye, e-mail

❖ **TEENAGERS.** Make sure your dad doesn't find out you've been watching his porn films by not whistling the theme tune to Emmanuelle at the dinner table.

Richard Bowen, e-mail

PHILANTHROPISTS. Be careful when giving street alcoholics money for 'a cup of tea', as some of the less scrupulous ones may be tempted to spend it on strong liquor.

Mark Jordan, e-mail

FATTIES. Take a tip from smokers and stop your cravings for chips by Sellotaping a crisp to the top of your arm each morning.

L Zebra, Chessington

LADY drivers. Draw a little diagram on a Post-it showing the position of the hand brake and gearstick, and stick it to your dashboard. This will save you having to look for them when the lights go green.

Barno, London

I WAS interested to see that Richard Branson is offering trips into space with his new venture Virgin Galactic. Passengers will be taken to the edge of space for twenty minutes before being returned to the Earth. This is from the man who can't get a train into Manchester Victoria. The big twat.

T Thorne, Hexham

ment chose to execute a 76-year-old, wheelchair-bound man who was also deaf and blind. Still, at least they executed somebody white for a change.

T Hennesey
London

IN RESPONSE to the letter (above) from T Hennesey, the 76-year-old blind, deaf, executee in question, Clarence Ray Allen, wasn't black, admittedly, but he was a native American Indian known as Running Bear. So they're still adhering to their policy of not executing anybody white wherever possible.

H Bucket
Wallsall

IT'S ALL very well the two previous writers knocking the Americans for their over-zealous use of the death penalty, but one thing is for sure - that 76-year-old deaf, blind, partially paralysed man will not kill anyone again.

T Bovil
Texas

I FOUND this picture in the sports page of the *Daily Telegraph*. It shows a fourth official at a football match apparently with his cock in his hand. What's going on there?

Dick Spotter
Poulton-Le-Fylde

IT WAS with much surprise that I actually laughed at a

strip in the latest issue of *Viz*, namely Sid the Sexist. Unfortunately, as I am suffering from a back injury, this had something of a downside. In future, could you please let your readers know on the cover whether or not the contents are going to be funny.

Yokie Boy Steve D
e-mail

I DON'T know how the picture editor of the *Guernsey Press* slipped this one past his editor, but it certainly brightened my Christmas. The pearl necklace was a lovely touch.

Paul Killick
Guernsey

CHARLES and Eddy are leaving it fashionably late to capitalise on the sucess of their 1992 smash 'Would I Lie to You?' If they are not careful they are in danger of being labelled 'one hit wonders.'

Steven Mayne
e-mail

WHY DO celebrities who voiceover the Tesco's advert always refer to the chain as 'we'? I for one have never seen Cilla Black holding a tenner suspiciously up to the light, or Jimmy Nail pushing four trolleys through the car park in the pissing rain for three pound peanut an hour.

Bradbury Thrashnut
e-mail

I THOUGHT of you the moment I saw this fantas-

tic photo of John Redwood pleasuring a cardboard sheep outside the Houses of Parliament. Does this man's depravity know no limits?

Jamie
Cumbria

THEY SAY that slow and steady wins the race. Bollocks! I am an athletics coach specialising in the 100 metre sprint, and I find the best tactic by far is to go as quickly as possible.

Ashley Smith
e-mail

OVER 40,000 black bears are killed by hunters each year in America. Do these people not understand that bears are part of a delicate ecocycle, and that by killing them they are upsetting the food chain? If they are going to shoot bears, they should be responsible and smash 30 wasps' nests for each one shot.

Derek Dougan
Fulchester

MY BROTHER once told me that if you did a cartwheel and farted at the same time you would shit yourself. I just wonder if any gymnasts had ever done this and could confirm or deny it.

Shaggy
e-mail

LAST WEEK my wife walked in on me whilst I was lying stark naked, masturbating over a copy of *Razzle*. She said she was disgusted and what

UP THE RSC CORNER

I was doing undermined our relationship. If I had walked in on her and found her masturbating stark naked, perhaps playing with a vibrator, rather than undermine it, I think it would strengthen our relationship no end. Honestly, I'll never understand women.

NA Fouracres
Lutterworth

B&Q should think about opening a couple of shops in Venice. I have just returned from there and the place is falling apart. The Italians might know a bit about history and art, but they clearly know fuck all about DIY.

Don Bloor
e-mail

WHY DON'T NHS bosses start hiring obsessive compulsives as nurses? Their attention to hygiene and constant hand washing would see an end to MRSA outbreaks in no time.

Stu Bray
e-mail

I DON'T like Prince Philip because he says some very racist things. But I also don't like him because he's Greek, so I don't know quite where this leaves me.

Barry Lionsegg
London

Lettersocks
Britain's Most Socksually Explicit
SOCK FORUM

I OFTEN have trouble telling my right from my left, which results in all sorts of embarrassing mishaps. In order to help me out a friend bought me a pair of socks with 'R' on the right one and 'L' on the left. However I put them on the wrong feet, and consequently took a wrong turn into the ladies' public lavatories and was arrested.

T Harpic, Tooting

I ALWAYS lose a sock in the wash so now I wash them in threes.

J Domestos, Liverpool

SOCK FACT
Many people think that socks were invented by the inventor Sir Edward Sock, but they're wrong. In fact, Sir Edward invented 'Soccer' - a game similar to Football - and he took the name from the big long socks that players wear, which he also happened to invent!

SOCK FACT
A sock is technically a shoe, without a sole or laces. A sock made out of rubber is called a 'Wellington Boot', or 'Welly'. A sock appendaged with fingers that you put on your hand is called a glove. And one you put on your head is a hat.

EVERY year at Christmas I always ask for something good, like a drill, but always end up being given socks. Over the years I have found myself becoming attached to my collection of socks, so much so that last year, I asked for socks. And what did I get? Well, socks, actually, so it was alright.

P Toilet-Duck, Hastings

I USED to get my husband socks every year at Christmas, until he got really cross and told me he was sick of being given socks! I thought he was being very ungrateful until he pointed out that he was Arthur Askey, the no-footed dead entertainer and, as such, had no use for socks!

Mrs A Askey, Liverpool

I THINK that the cast of ITV's *Cold Feet* simply aren't wearing thick enough socks. If I was them I'd try a pair of hiking socks, like Thorlos from Millets.

J Vim, Hackney

Sock Puzzle Time

SOCK WORD

Down
1. Something you put on your feet, not socks (5).

Across
2. Something you put on your feet, not shoes (5).

ODD SOCK OUT
Which is the odd sock out of these three socks?

A
B
C

Answers: Sockword: 1D. Shoes, 2A. Socks, Odd Sock Out, Sock C.

SOCK FACT
Despite being called Socrates, Socrates didn't actually wear socks! He wore sandals, a strappy, leather type of sock, worn on the feet. However, Socrates the Brazilian footballer DID wear socks, invented by Sir Edward Sock, who also invented the game Soccer.

Soap Update!

WE'VE got all the gossip about what's been going on this week in your fave soaps, you stupid idiots!

EastEnders
THE ARGUMENT between *Pat* and *Ian* over which type of sausage is the best rages on and culminates in a heated confrontation in The Vic. Will this create a permanent rift in their relationship?

Meanwhile, *Phil* is none too pleased to find a goat in his bedroom, chewing up his duvet. He is convinced that *Peggy* is behind it and vows to hide one of her shoes by way of revenge.

And there's excitement for *Billy* when he eats a pie and finds that it is quite delicious. *Sonia* is still ugly.

Emmerdale
THERE'S drama in store for *Matthew* as he drops a cup. Will it break?

Outside the Woolpack *Tom* avoids embarrassment when he trips over but then runs for a bit so that it looked deliberate.

There's occasional, mild confusion for *Scott* when he keeps thinking that it's Thursday.

And *Bob* finally loses it when *Jean*, once again, fails to put the biscuit tin back in its usual place. He beats her to death with a clown's shoe.

Coronation St.
IT'S DECISION time for *Danny* who can't settle on which trousers to wear. Will he choose the black or the brown pair?

Charlie drops a hammer whilst fixing a gutter at the Rover's, but luckily it doesn't hit anyone.

Frankie thinks that she might have a yoghurt, but doesn't.

And *Norris* discovers an unexpected penchant for bukkake...with messy results for *Rita* and *Emily*!

ROAD RAGE
POST BAG

• To the woman in Sheffield town centre last night who wanted ME to mount a foothigh curb because SHE drove down a one-way street. Your husband's face said it all.

E Bigtime, e-mail

• To the driver of the black BMW M3 who cut me up on the way to work this morning and then gave me the V-sign when I blew my horn at him.

If you are reading this and would like your wing mirror back, it's in the bushes at the junction of College Road and Harrow Road.

Oz, London

★ *Are you a faultless driver who doesn't know how some arseholes passed their test? Then don't get road rage, get Page Rage. Write to:* **Road Rage Post Bag, Viz Comic, PO Box 656, North Shields, NE30 4XX.**

I THINK THAT ELEPHANT IS GOING TO CHARGE US

GAME RESERVE ENTRY £5

ROGER MELLIE — THE MAN ON THE TELLY

IT SAYS HERE THAT HE... "CARRIED OUT A SEX ACT TOO SHOCKING TO DESCRIBE IN A FAMILY NEWSPAPER...."

WELL, YOU KNOW WHAT THAT WAS, DON'T YOU?

MATE OF MINE WORKS ON NEWS AT TEN... HE SAYS HE WAS GETTIN' THEM TO SHIT THEIR TROLLEYS, THEN HE WAS TAKING THEIR SHITTED PANTS HOME IN HIS BRIEF-CASE...

FUCK KNOWS WHAT HE DID WITH 'EM... THE MIND BOGGLES

FULL OF STORIES LIKE THAT, MY MATE... TOLD ME THIS DEAD GOOD ONE ABOUT WHAT JEFFREY ARCHER GOT CAUGHT DOING IN THE BOGS AT THE HOUSE OF LORDS...

...YOU'RE NOT GOING TO FUCKIN' BELIEVE THIS, BUT APPARENTLY...

YOU KNOW... I DON'T THINK IT WAS SUCH A GOOD IDEA GETTING ROGER TO REVIEW THE PAPERS ON 'NEWSROUND'

I'm a I'm a Celebrity Get Me Out of Here
Celebrity, Get Me Out of Here!

BALL'S UP: *Tommy* (right) *hauled Bobby* (left) *out of well* (inset).

PINT-SIZED funnyman Bobby Ball has managed to escape death yet again, thanks to the quick-thinking of the man he shouted at on stage and on television during the mid-1980s.

Former welder Ball, real name Robert Bullet, had to be rescued by former welder comedy partner Tommy Cannon, real name Tom Gun, after spending 14 hours trapped down a well. Ball, 60, had thrown a 2p coin into the well in order to make a wish, but climbed down the shaft to retrieve it when the wish failed to come true.

The Oldham-born born again Christian, famous for his catch-phrases like 'Rock on, Tommy', was only reported missing when he failed to turn up for his 2am shift driving the minicab he co-owns with his straightman sidekick Cannon. The pair's next-door neighbour Eric Burgess explained that Cannon instinctively realized that the bubble-permed Ball, famous for his catch-phrases

By Our LWT Correspondent
METAL MICHAEL

like 'You little liar', was in trouble.

"Bobby's only ever late for a shift when he's in peril, and it's always Tommy that has to rescue him," Burgess told reporters. "When Bobby didn't show for work, Tom remembered something he'd said earlier that day about going to the well to make a wish. He drove straight to the well and wound his red-bracesed pal back to the surface."

death

Cannon has saved Ball, famous for his catch-phrases like 'What do you mean, axed due to poor piggin' viewing figures?', from

certain death on two previous occasions. Ball almost suffocated last year when he was playing in an abandoned freezer and the door shut on him. And in 2004 he half-drowned in the local duck pond while trying to catch tadpoles in a jam jar.

The double act have vowed to be back on the road within a matter of days when they

have sufficiently recovered from their ordeal.

"They never like disappointing their punters," said Eric. "Old Mrs Greening always uses their cab to visit her husband in the hospice because of the pensioners' discount. Although if she doesn't get there by Thursday then the nurse says it'll probably be too late."

ROGER MELLIE THE MAN ON THE TELLY

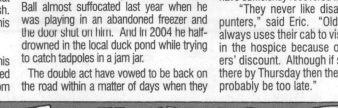

GILBERT RATCHET

OLD DEAR INTEREST

25

IT'S THE BACONS

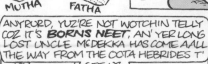

26

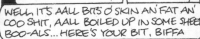

The adventures of DAZ SAMPSON

NEXT WEEK — DAZ RAPS AN END TO RACIAL INTOLERANCE.

27

WOO-OOO-OOO-OOO-OOO-OOO-OOO!

Ghost Box

Britain's Most Pant Shittingest Letters Page

WARNING! This page contains explicit accounts of supernatural activity and should not be read by persons of a nervous disposition.

HALLOWEEN is upon us once more, and in the last issue, we didn't ask you to tell us your spooky tales, those little inexplicable events that send a shiver down your spine. But they came flooding in anyway. Here's a selection of the hairest raising stories we received...

It was a normal enough day. I had just got back from doing the school run and I was sitting down having a nice cuppa before making a start on the housework. All of a sudden I heard a noise. It was probably a ghost.

Ethel Breakdown, Truro

My husband John took this snap at a family wedding and it came out all blurred. The man at the chemist said the blurring was probably caused by psychic energy off a ghost.

Carol Mediocrity, Beeston

I don't usually pick up hitchhikers but on a rainy night last year I saw a young girl by the side of the road and stopped to offer her a lift. We chatted away and she seemed perfectly normal. When I dropped her off at her destination she said 'thanks' and off she went. I couldn't help thinking that maybe she was one of those ghost hitchhikers. I have no reason for thinking this other than it makes my otherwise dull life more interesting.

Brian Liar, Glasgow

My husband Dave, 42, and I were sitting in our lounge one night when all the lights mysteriously went out. The electricity board later informed us that it was a power cut but we still believe it was something more sinister, like a ghost.

Carol Idiotic, Chertsey

My house has always smelled of cigar smoke and our neighbour recently let slip that the old man who owned the house before us and passed away there, smoked cigars! Admittedly my husband smokes them too and is definitely the source of the odour, but it is still spooky.

Janice Nobody, Orpington

Every time I put something down in my house it gets mysteriously moved. For instance, the other day I put the post on the sideboard and when I got home it had been moved to the kitchen table - and opened too! My husband keeps telling me that it was him but I think he is just trying to protect me from the dreadful knowledge of the evil ghost that roams our house.

Susan Cakemixture, Dudley

My husband and I are both big Elvis Presley fans and we recently made a pilgrimage to Graceland, where I took this photograph of my husband looking at Elvis's grave. When we got the photos back, our blood ran cold. There, standing on the tombstone, was the ghost of Elvis Presley himself, in full Las Vegas gear. We were very disappointed, as we always thought he was best in his '68 Comeback Special era.

Doreen Bileduct, Hastings

Our house is built on the site of an old Roman fort. One night last year, I was watching the telly when suddenly the lights started flickering and the room went freezing cold. To my horror, an entire cohort of transparent Roman soldiers marched through the wall, across the room and out through the other wall. This went on for half an hour and was accompanied by the sound of horses' hooves and the clanking of armour. I was frozen with fear. When my husband came in from the pub I told him of my ghostly experience. You can imagine my relief when he explained it was probably a trick of the light.

Marjorie Steel, Chelmsford

I didn't believe in ghosts at all, until one night last month when the spookiest thing happened. Needless to say, I believe in them now.

Doris Pancreas, Hull

I visited Althrop House where Lady Di is buried and I saw her ghost in the toilets. Luckily, I had my camera handy and I took this photograph *(above)*. Strangely, I did not feel at all scared as, just as when she was alive, her spectre radiated goodness and did a lot for charity.

Mavis Gallbladder, Rhyll

The other night I was awoken by a loud thump from downstairs. I have always been terrified of ghosts, so you can imagine my state of mind as I crept downstairs to confront the supernatural horror I was certain lay in wait for me. I was so relieved when I opened the front room door to discover it wasn't a ghost at all, merely an knife-wielding maniac who had stabbed his way out of a local hospital for the criminally insane.

Ethyl Bromide, Leeds

I was working late the other night when I saw a skeleton. I nearly jumped out of my skin, and ran screaming to find the security guard, where I breathlessly explained what I'd seen. How foolish I felt when he explained that I am the chief radiographer at North Tyneside Hospital, and I had been looking at an X-Ray.

Dr Edward Canning, Luton

During a recent visit to Hampton Court. I took this picture of my husband standing by a grave. When I got the film developed, my blood ran cold. Beside my husband, who is an HenryVIII impersonator, can be seen the ghostly figure of a man in combat fatigues and a red fleece.

Ethyl Plywood, Hove

My husband and I moved into an old house last summer and I was disturbed when a neighbour told me it was known locally as the House of Death. She explained that in Victorian times the family who lived there had been murdered in their beds by an escaped lunatic who then dismembered and ate them. Last week on the anniversary of the killings I was woken in the night by loud screaming. My bed flew into the air and started spinning and blood began to ooze out of the walls and ceiling. The bedroom door then flew off its hinges and I saw a man, a woman and three children in Victorian dress, covered in blood. Then everything stopped as quickly as it began. When my husband came home from the pub, I was so traumatised I could hardly tell him what had happened. Imagine how relieved and foolish I felt when he explained that it was probably just an air lock in the central heating pipes.

Marjorie Spleen, Crewe

I thought I'd seen a ghost the other day when I walked into the living room and saw my late husband floating in front of me, two feet off the ground. Then I remembered he'd hanged himself off a beam earlier in the day and I'd forgotten to cut him down! How silly I felt.

Edna Hardboard, Torquay

I'd always believed in ghosts until I saw one flying round my bedroom making howling noises. However, it turned out to be a sheet with an owl under it. Needless to say, I stopped believing in ghosts there and then.

Ethyl Acetate, Surrey

Kids Say the Funniest Things about Ghosts!

...We were sitting down to eat our tea the other night, when every object that wasn't fastened down suddenly flew into the air and began to spin round the room wildly. Plates, cups, knives...even the microwave oven joined in this unholy dance, whilst the lights and TV switched on and off and doors, drawers and windows opened and slammed shut, pushed with great force by an unseen hand. My 4-year-old grandson was terrified, and hid under the table, shouting "Help! There's a polterghost in the room!" How we chuckled. He meant to say 'poltergeist'!

Edna Football, Goole

..."Granny, why is there a tall, cowled figure with a scythe standing behind you, beckoning you with a bony finger and filling the room with an all-pervading stench of death and decay?" asked my 4-year-old grandson the other day when he was visiting me in hospital. When I looked round, there was nobody there!

Edna Doomed, Dundee

Spookdoku

No. 3,285,483
Scare rating ★★★☆☆

The World's Most Frightening Number Puzzle!

Fill in the grid from beyond the grave so that each ghostly row, spine chilling column and ghoulish 3x3 square contains all the digits 1-9... **IF YOU DARE!**

			2		1	6	4	
	8							
7			9	6				
	2					4		
		2					2	
1			8					
						9		
			3					3
4				9				

28

GOD YOU'RE EMBARRASSING

Celebrity S

THE medical textbooks are littered with bizarre accounts of transplant patients who have taken on the characteristics of their donors. Doctors report some organ recipients starting to crave the favourite foods of their benefactors, whilst others develop interests which eerily echo those of the dead people who bequeathed them their body parts.

So-called Organ Memory Syndrome is a process that is still not fully understood by scientists; indeed some hardened sceptics claim it doesn't exist at all. However, one thing's certain; it is an un-nerving experience to come round after a major operation only to start experiencing the emotions, thoughts and memories of someone you never even met.

One person who is certain that Organ Memory Syndrome **DOES** exist is Lewisham man Gordon Boxtree, who has had more than **THIRTY** major organ transplants over the last decade. Flashbacks to the lives of his organ donors are an everyday occurrence for Gordon. And what makes his story even more remarkable is that his replacement parts were removed from recently-dead **STARS**.

He told us: "I've had every transplant in the book - hearts, lungs, kidneys the lot. And let me tell you, the list of my organ donors reads like a Who's Who of showbiz!"

Transplant surgery changes most patients' lives for the better, but Boxtree says his star-studded swap-ops have turned his life into a living hell. And now, in these exclusive extracts from his explosive new autobiography **'Living with OMS - A Survivor's Story'** *(Pikelet Books, £8.99) he blows the lid off the series of traumatic events he has suffered at*

HEART ATTACK: Benny transplant turned Gordon into sex fiend.

EXCLUSIVE!

the hands of the dead stars' organs.

"The first time I suspected I was suffering from OMS was in 1996. I had recently had a heart transplant at Lewisham Hospital, and I was feeling full of beans. I decided to go for a walk through my local park, but I must have taken a wrong turning or something, because I ended up in the grounds of the local nursing college halls of residence.

"I'm not quite sure what happened next. A sexy young nurse walked past the bush where I was hiding, and I suddenly felt an overwhelming urge to start chasing her. I ran after her at high speed through the gardens, weaving round the trees until I eventually caught up with her and ripped her dress off. The poor girl was left standing there in her underwear.

"I knew what I was doing was wrong, but I was unable to stop myself. It was almost as if I was being possessed by another personality. Luckily, the police arrived quickly and, following another short chase, I was arrested.

"Later, whilst preparing my defence I phoned the hospital to ask who my organ donor had been. When they told me, my blood ran cold. For I had been given the heart of TV funnyman **BENNY HILL**. I am certain that it was Organ Memory Syndrome from Hill's heart that caused me to behave in the way that I did."

However, the judge at Gordon's trial refused to accept his plea of diminished responsibility due to Organ Memory Syndrome and found him guilty of Indecent Assault. Boxtree's record of similar offences also counted against him. He was sentenced to 6 months in prison and put on the Sex

DEAD FAMOUS: Showbiz spare part surgery victim Boxtree, yesterday.

Offenders register.

That was the first time Gordon fell foul of phantom memories from transplanted organs. But it certainly wasn't to be the last.

"Like every freshly-released convict, when I got out of prison I vowed that I would never break the law again. And when I got into my car to drive to the pub to celebrate my first

> ## "I've had every transplant in the book and the list of my organ donors reads like a Who's Who of showbiz!"

day as a free man, the last thing I expected was to get into trouble with the police.

"Throughout the afternoon I had quite a lot to drink, and when I set off to walk the eight miles home as I usually do, I intended to leave my car safely in the pub car park. However, I was suddenly gripped by an overwhelming compulsion to get

into it and drive home. The feeling came from nowhere. I knew I was incapable of controlling a vehicle, yet there was nothing I could do to stop myself getting behind the wheel and turning the key.

"The next thing I knew I was being cut from the wreckage of my car, which was upside down in the front of a dry-cleaners' shop. Apparently I had crashed following a police pursuit through the town centre at speeds of up to 100mph. Luckily, I had clipped a bus queue whilst negotiating a roundabout the wrong way and somersaulted into a parade of shops before I could do too much damage.

"In the police cell the next morning, I suddenly realised what must have happened. The day before I had undergone a liver transplant, and the organ donor had been Formula 1 racing driver **JAMES HUNT**. My OMS had caused me to act as if I was on the starting grid of a Grand Prix. As far as my new liver was

pares

Top of the Ops
Just some of the transplants that have turned Boxtree's life upside down.

FIGHTING FOR BREATH: Giant Haystacks's lungo gavo Gordon red mist.

BAD NIGHT FROM HIM: Barker's kidneys turned Boxtree into burglar.

LIVER AND LET DRIVE: James Hunt's hepatic organ took control of the wheel.

CARDIAC ARREST: Benny Hill's saucy ticker landed Gordon in the nick.

concerned, the panda cars chasing me through the streets were being driven by Emerson Fittipaldi, Niki Lauda and Michael Schumacher.

"Sadly, the police weren't very sympathetic to my medical condition, and they threw the book at me. I found myself back in prison, serving 4 years for drunk driving, vehicular manslaughter and assaulting a fireman with intent to cause actual bodily harm."

When he was released, Boxtree thought his OMS troubles were over. But nothing could have been further from the truth.

"For a week or two after coming out of jail, everything was fine. Then I got a nasty cough and my doctor told me I needed a lung transplant. Luckily for me, suitable donor organs were available. I couldn't believe it when the surgeon told me the body they had been removed from, for it was yet another star. This time my anonymous ben-

efactor was heavyweight wrestler **GIANT HAYSTACKS**!

"The next day I got home, feeling on top of the world and I decided to take my dog for a walk down to the bookies. However, as I was going through the precinct I saw a man giving my dog a funny look, so I stopped to find out what his problem was. He told me he didn't want any trouble.

"I ran after her and ripped her dress off. The poor girl was left standing there in her underwear."

"I'm not usually a violent person, and normally I would have left it there. But this time something was different. Giant Haystacks was never a man to back down from a fight and I could feel his donated lungs egging me on to launch an attack. Now, in my new organs' mind's eye this innocent bystander had turned into his arch enemy Big Daddy, whilst the

precinct had turned into a wrestling ring.

"There was nothing I could do to stop myself. I knocked his walking stick out of his hand and grabbed him in an armlock. I punched him repeatedly in the face, and when he went down I started to kick him in the ribs, groin and throat. I'm not proud of what Haystacks's lungs made me do, but until you've experienced an attack of celebrity OMS, you don't know how overwhelming these compulsions can be."

Through no fault of his own, Boxtree had ended up on the wrong side of the law once again. Next time his doctors told him he needed a kidney transplant, he decided to take precautions.

"Once bitten twice shy, or so they say. So this time I insisted that my surgeon told me who my donor was before I agreed to the surgery. And when he explained that my new kidney had been harvested from the cadaver of comedy legend Ronnie Barker I was delighted. Barker was basically a good man, and I thought that the worst I could expect would be to start mispronouncing my words or perhaps dressing up in drag and putting new lyrics to well-known songs. I agreed to the op there and then.

"So you can imagine my horror when I found myself later that night breaking into my neighbour's house and stealing a television and fifty pounds cash. I couldn't believe what I was doing. Except for a few minor brushes with the police and a handful of stints inside, I'd never broken the law in my life, yet here I was kicking a door in, stealing from a friend and defecating on her living room carpet.

"I'd forgotten all about Barker's character from his long-running sitcom 'Porridge'. As I explained to the police, it wasn't loveable Ronnie's kidneys making me burgle the house, it was those of his character, the housebreaking habitual criminal **NORMAN STANLEY FLETCHER**! But they didn't believe me, and before I knew it I was back inside. Unfortunately, by then my OMS had worn off, so I was unable to accept imprisonment in the same casual manner as Fletch."

Gordon hopes that his book will draw attention to the plight of him and his fellow OMS sufferers. He told us: "Perhaps one day in the future a cure can be found for this dreadful condition. Until then, is it too much to hope that the police, magistrates and probation service could show a little more understanding? After all, I am not responsible for my actions. I am just a puppet of the dead stars' organs."

Next Week: Gordon is arrested for shoplifting after receiving a blood transfusion from a famous teatime TV show presenter.

American Re-Brand

SUDDENLY SUBIQUITOUS faux-libertine Russell Brand has added another feather to his cap by selling the format of himself to American television.

Cockney waif impersonator Brand is set to net £2m from the sale, which has been snapped up by Fox TV. The network is hoping their purchase will emulate the success of recent US remakes of British hits such as *The Office, Little Britain* and *Badger and Badger*.

BRAND

Brand will be recast and substantially rewritten to appeal to stateside tastes, but executives have promised that the *Big Brother's Big Mouth* presenter will retain his trademark neckerchief, straggly hair and twig legs.

PRODUCT

Ali Gstein, head of Overseas Property Development at Fox, told *Variety* magazine: 'Ever since Russell's face moved to the right hand column of page three of most British tabloid newspapers, we've been dying to get his format into our portfolio.

'Our thinking is if we can take his format and – here's the clever part – add some jokes, as if he was a stand-up comedian, we're on to a winner.'

The network hopes to have its own version of Brand, *Russ B*, on air in time for next 'Fall', a US version of the colourful British season autumn. Current stateside favourites to play the popular foppish ladykiller include *Roseanne*'s John Goodman, *Diff'rent Strokes*' half pint Gary Coleman and man-like former Golden Girl Bea Arthur.

JACK BLACK in THE CASE OF THE CROOKED COUNCILLOR

THE WHITSUNTIDE HOLIDAYS WERE HERE ONCE MORE AND BOY DETECTIVE JACK BLACK AND HIS DOG SILVER WERE STAYING WITH AUNT MEG AT HER COTTAGE IN THE UNSPOILT, ILLEGAL IMMIGRANT-FREE VILLAGE OF TWEEBURY-ON-THE-NICE.

IT'S LOVELY TO HAVE YOU FOR THE HOLIDAYS AGAIN, JACK. AND I'VE MADE YOUR FAVOURITE TEA TO WELCOME YOU BACK.

BOILED BEEF AND CARROTS?

WITH LASHINGS OF GRAVY!

OH YUM!

WOW! WHAT A FANTASTIC CAR!

YES, ISN'T IT. I GOT IT LAST WEEK.

I DON'T MEAN TO BE RUDE, AUNT MEG...

...BUT HOW CAN YOU AFFORD TO BUY A CAR LIKE THIS ON A WIDOWS PENSION?

MEG 1

OH, I DIDN'T BUY IT, JACK, HEAVENS NO. MR RICHENBACKER GAVE IT TO ME.

MR RICHENBACKER?

YES, HE'S THE BOSS OF TOXICORP INDUSTRIES.

THEY WANTED TO BUILD A NUCLEAR REPROCESSING PLANT AND RADIOACTIVE WASTE DUMP ON THE PLAYING FIELD OF THE VILLAGE PRIMARY SCHOOL.

I DON'T UNDERSTAND. WHAT'S THAT GOT TO DO WITH THE CAR?

DON'T FORGET I'M ON THE PARISH COUNCIL. MR RICHENBACKER PROMISED ALL THE COUNCILLORS A NEW BENTLEY AND A £25,000 CASH BACKHANDER IF WE GRANTED HIS COMPANY PLANNING PERMISSION.

MEG 1

THAT'S BRILLIANT! I WANT TO BE A PARISH COUNCILLOR WHEN I GROW UP, AUNT MEG.

NOT SO FAST JACK, IT'S NOT THAT SIMPLE. I'M AFRAID WE MAY HAVE TO RETURN THE CARS AND THE MONEY.

WHAT?...BUT WHY?

PLANNING PERMISSION HAS TO BE PASSED BY A UNANIMOUS VOTE FROM THE COUNCIL AND ONE OF US, MR ASHCROFT, IS BLOCKING THE APPLICATION. HE THINKS THAT NUCLEAR FUEL REPROCESSORS SHOULDN'T BE BUILT NEXT TO SCHOOLS.

WHAT!?! BUT THESE CARS ARE THE BEST MONEY CAN BUY?

I KNOW, JACK, I KNOW. BUT HE'S REFUSING TO BUDGE.

WHY DON'T YOU THROW HIM OFF THE COUNCIL?

I'M AFRAID WE CAN'T. YOU SEE HE HASN'T ACTUALLY DONE ANYTHING WRONG.

CAN'T YOU HAVE HIM KILLED, LIKE IN THE GANGSTER FILMS?

HO! HO! JACK. NOW YOU'RE LETTING YOUR IMAGINATION RUN AWAY WITH YOU.

LATER.

I'M OFF TO THE COUNCIL MEETING TO VOTE ON TOXICORP'S SCHEME. WOULD YOU LIKE TO WAVE GOODBYE TO THE CAR? ONLY I DON'T THINK I'LL BE COMING HOME IN IT.

OKAY.

AND I SUPPOSE I'D BETTER TAKE THIS TWENTY-FIVE GRAND WITH ME AS WELL.

THAT'S A LOVELY CAR, SILVER. AND I DON'T THINK WE SHOULD LET IT GO SO EASILY. COME ON, THERE'S DETECTIVE WORK TO DO.

WOOF!

IN NEXT TO NO TIME, JACK AND SILVER HAD REACHED THE VILLAGE HALL.

I THINK WHAT WE'RE LOOKING FOR WILL BE IN THE CAR PARK.

CLOSED COUNCIL MEETING TONIGHT NO PUBLIC ACCESS

THAT MUST BE RICKENBACKER'S CAR. AND THOSE MUST BE THE COUNCILLORS' BENTLEYS...WHICH MEANS THAT TATTY OLD 'LEFTIEMOBILE' MUST BELONG TO ASHCROFT.

TOXICORP IND

FAT CAT

WELL, WELL, A SATCHEL?

I THINK WE NEED TO TAKE A CLOSER LOOK.

MEANWHILE, INSIDE THE VILLAGE HALL.

WELL, IF WE CAN'T PERSUADE YOU, ASHCROFT, I SUPPOSE WE'D BETTER TAKE THE VOTE.

YES, I SUPPOSE WE HAD.

AND I'D BETTER TAKE BACK ALL THE CASH AND THE CAR KEYS.

ALL THOSE IN FAVOUR OF GRANTING TOXICORP PERMISSION TO BUILD A NUCLEAR REPROCESSING PLANT ON THE PRIMARY SCHOOL PLAYING FIELDS, SAY AYE.

AYE!

AYE!

AYE!

AYE!

AYE. ALL THOSE AGAINST SAY NO...

SUDDENLY.

STOP THIS MEETING!

WHAT THE!?!

IT'S ASHCROFT. HE IS NOT ALLOWED TO VOTE ON THE MATTER OF TOXICORP'S PLANNING PERMISSION.

NOT ALLOWED TO VOTE? HOW DO YOU MEAN?

I FOUND THIS SATCHEL IN THE BACK OF HIS CAR.

A SATCHEL!?! I DON'T UNDERSTAND, JACK?

THE SATCHEL JUST SPARKED MY CURIOSITY. AND IN THE GLOVE BOX I FOUND THIS! A SCHOOL REPORT FROM TWEEBURY-ON-THE-NICE PRIMARY SCHOOL...

...IN THE NAME OF BECKY ASHCROFT!

GOOD GOD!

ASHCROFT HAS A DAUGHTER AT THE PRIMARY SCHOOL ON THE FIELDS OF WHICH TOXICORP WANT TO BUILD THE NUCLEAR REPROCESSOR...

I...ER...YES...BUT...

ASHCROFT HAS A VESTED INTEREST IN THIS MATTER WHICH HE HAS NOT REGISTERED WITH THE COUNCIL, THE PENALTY FOR WHICH IS EXPULSION FROM THE COUNCIL WITH IMMEDIATE EFFECT!

IT'S WORSE THAN THAT, JACK. I BELIEVE A CRIMINAL OFFENCE HAS TAKEN PLACE.

SHORTLY.

COME ON, YOU LEFTY BASTARD.

WELL, THAT'S ASHCROFT AWAY TO PRISON, THANKS TO YOU, JACK.

WHAT WILL HAPPEN TO HIS DAUGHTER, AUNT MEG?

OH, DON'T WORRY ABOUT HER. SHE'LL EITHER GO INTO CARE OR JUST LIVE ON THE STREETS OR SOMETHING.

LISTEN, WHAT DO YOU SAY WE RECONVENE THE MEETING AND PASS MY PLANNING APPLICATION?

IT'S NOT THAT SIMPLE, MR RICHENBACKER. YOU SEE, THE PARISH COUNCIL MUST HAVE A FULL COMPLEMENT OF SIX MEMBERS IF A VOTE IS TO TAKE PLACE.

WHY DOESN'T JACK JOIN THE COUNCIL?

YES! I'LL VOTE FOR THE APPLICATION.

OH, WOULD THAT YOU COULD, JACK. BUT ALAS YOU MUST BE AT LEAST 18 TO SIT ON THE PARISH COUNCIL.

OH. THAT'S A SHAME.

WAIT A MINUTE, I MIGHT BE TOO YOUNG TO VOTE... BUT SILVER ISN'T

JACK, JACK. SILVER'S EVEN YOUNGER THAN YOU...HE'S ONLY THREE.

YES, WHICH MEANS HE'S TWENTY-ONE IN DOG YEARS!

HA HA! I THINK WE'VE FOUND OUR SIXTH PARISH COUNCILLOR.

FIVE MINUTES LATER.

ALL THOSE IN FAVOUR OF GRANTING TOXICORP PERMISSION TO BUILD A NUCLEAR REPROCESSING PLANT ON THE PRIMARY SCHOOL PLAYING FIELDS, SAY AYE...OR WOOF!

AYE!

WOOF!

HEH! HEH! THAT'S MY DOG!

SHE'S A PEDIGREE, Y'KNOW. SHE'S CALLED 'COOCHIE COOCHIE LADY MONTIFIORE OF BRIGADOON...

...BUT HER PET NAME'S GOIN' T' BE BEYONCÉ

WELL, I'M OFF T' THE BAR. THE USUAL, IS IT, GIRLS?

AYE!...AN'GET SUMMAT TO EAT F' BEYONCÉ, WILL Y', BAZ?..

...I'VE NOT FED HER TODAY

SHE'S GOIN'T' COME EVERYWHERE WI'ME. PARIS HILTON TAKES HERS EVERYWHERE WI'HER...ALL THE FILM PREMIERES AN'A-LIST HOLLYWOOD PARTIES...

I'M TAKIN' BEYONCÉ T'DAVE'S DARTS NIGHT AT THE RED COW. THEY RAFFLE A MEAT PLATTER

ARE YOU GOIN'T' TAKE HER TO OBEDIENCE CLASS, SAN? TEACH HER T' COME BACK WHEN Y'CALL HER?

NO...SHE'S JUST GOIN'TO LIVE IN ME 'ANDBAG, SO THERE'S NOT MUCH POINT

'ERE Y' GO, GIRLS...TWO CUNTBUSTERS F'YOU, A PINT OF COOKIN' F'ME, AN'A BAG OF MONSTER MUNCH F'BEYONCÉ

SHE'LL LIKE THESE. 'NICE 'N' SPICY' FLAVOUR, SAN

RUSTLE! RUSTLE!

HERE Y' GO, BEYONCÉ, CATCH!

SHE LOVES 'EM

OY! PACK IT IN. Y'CAN'T GIVE A PEDIGREE DOG FUCKIN' MONSTER MUNCH

DIDN'T THEY 'AVE WALKERS SENSATIONS?

LATER...

TIME GEEE-ENTLEMEN PERRRRR-LEEEEASE!

HEY, LOOK. SHE'S MENTAL FOR THESE. THIS IS HER TENTH BAG

BARP!

C'MON...LET'S GET TO ABRA-KEBABRA BEFORE THE QUEUES

ABRA-KEBABRA

SO...

'ERE, SAN! SHE LOVES THIS KEBAB MEAT WI'CHILLI SAUCE, SHE DOES

AYE! JUST LOOK AT HER WOLFIN' IT DOWN

Y'D THINK IT'D BE TOO SPICY FOR HER, WOULDN'T YER...I'LL BE SHITTIN' THROUGH THE EYE OF A NEEDLE T'MORROW

NO. CHIHUAHUAS ARE MEXICAN DOGS, SAN, SEE....CHILLIS IS WOT THEY EAT IN THE WILD

HERE Y'GO, BEYONCÉ. GET THAT DOWN YER NECK...HEH! HEH!

TOO HOT F'ME, THAT ONE

SHORTLY...

PUT TELLY ON, BAZ. GIZ A FAG, SAN, I'M FUCKIN' GASPIN'

HERE Y' GO, TRAY

TA, SAN...SNIFF!...SNIFF!...SNIFF!

'ERE BAZ...'AVE YOU FARTED?

NO, IT'S NOT ME...I THOUGHT ONE OF YOU TWO 'AD DROPPED YER ARSE, BUT I WAS TOO MUCH OF A GENTLEMAN TO ASK

SNIFF! SNIFF!...EELIRRRSH! SAN!..ELIRSH!...THERE'S ALL SHIT ON Y' FAGS

EH?

AW FUCK!...BEYONCÉ'S PEBBLEDASHED THE INSIDE OF ME BAG...

...THE DIRTY FUCKIN' MUTT! IT'S ALL OVER ME PURSE...ME LIPPY...ME TAMPONS...EVERYTHING

FUCKIN' THING!

SLING!

YELP!

IT'S NOT BEYONCÉ'S FAULT...I BET IT WERE THE PLANTERS DRY ROAST...OR THAT AFTER-SHOCK YOU GIVE HER.

£9.99 THAT BAG COST ME...NOW IT'S FUCKIN' WRECKED!

IT'S NOT...

...A COUPLE OF SQUIRTS O' FEBREZE AN' IT'LL BE GOOD AS NEW

FUCKIN' DOG!...I WISH I'D NEVER BROUGHT THE FUCKIN' THING

AW, DON'T BE LIKE THAT, SAN...

MAN'S BEST FRIEND, Y'KNOW...HIS DOG

AYE, REMEMBER GREYFRIARS BOBBY, SAN?...THE LITTLE SCOTTY DOG WHOSE OWNER DIED, AN'HE SLEPT BESIDE HIS GRAVE EVERY NIGHT...NEVER LEFT HIS MASTER'S SIDE.

AYE! BEYONCÉ'S JUST LIKE THAT FER YOU, SAN...LOYAL TO THE END SHE'LL BE...

...NO MATTER WHAT 'APPENS, SHE'LL NEVER LEAVE YER 'ANDBAG

YER RIGHT, TRAY..A DOG'S MAN'S BEST FRIEND...AN BEYONCÉ IS SAN'S BEST FRIEND

WHERE IS SHE?..I WANT T' GIVE HER A CUDDLE...

BEYONCÉ...WHERE ARE YOU?..

BEYONCÉ...COME ON!...I'VE GOT SOME MONSTER MUNCH!

BEYONCÉ...

BEYONCÉ...COME TO MUMMY...

Letterbocks

Letterbocks, Viz Comic, PO Box 656, North Shields, NE30 4XX Email: letters@viz.co.uk

I'M A terrorist, and when ID cards come into force I will probably employ great cunning and not declare that as my job. I'll probably say I'm a grocer or something.

A Terrorist
e-mail

IF ONLY the government had banned cigarette smoking in bars and restaurants in 1968 instead of legalising homosexuality. Then we might still be hearing the dulcet tones of Roy Castle playing his trumpet and Michael Barrymore would be in prison instead of making a successful comeback.

Chris Keenan
e-mail

SINCE causing the death of Princess Diana, the paparazzi have had a bad press. But let's not forget that it was one of them who headbutted Jay Kay and another who knocked one of Liam Gallagher's teeth out.

Gary Parslow
e-mail

RECENTLY, we had Michael Winner in our restaurant, but unfortunately the staff were out of love gravy as Jeremy Clarkson had been in ten minutes earlier.

Neil Kray
e-mail

I'M GOING to have to agree to differ with Prince Charles's assessment of his

He's high on drugs!

role in public life. Whereas he sees himself as a political dissident operating on the fringes of the zeitgeist, I see him more as a useless jug-eared toff who gets paid out of my taxes to play the cunt.

Moz, e-mail

MY HUSBAND plays a joke on me every April Fool's day. Last year I was determined not to be caught out, but lo and behold he tricked me again. Knowing I like cats, he woke me at 3.00am and told me there was a basket of kittens stuck on our chimney. I immediately climbed out of the bedroom window and shinned up the drainpipe onto the roof. When I got there and saw nothing but the television aerial I realised I had been had. However, the joke wasn't over. When I got back into the bedroom the cheeky devil had filled my slippers with broken glass. I'm determined he won't get me this year.

Ethel Alcohol
Sutton

THERE'S a bloke who has been coming into our

local for the last month who stands over by the cig machine. My mate thinks he's off the telly. Do any of your readers have a clue who he could be?

Andy Bryant
Bristol

*Who do you think the mystery famous bloke is by the cig machine in Andy's local? Perhaps it's him who played Charlie Fairhurst in Casualty. Or perhaps it's the bloke who used to read the weather on the big floating map on GMTV. Write in with your suggestions, and we'll pass them on to Andy.

I'M shocked that George Michael has been accused of doing drugs. I know that he has sex in toilets, but it's still a bit of a shock, isn't it?

Andy Sands
e-mail

WHY IS IT Tampax adverts always show women ice-skating, dancing or playing volleyball? The only activity my missus partakes in at that time of the month is biting my head off.

Tony Moon
e-mail

JOHN Smith is supposed to be Britain's most common name. However, I only know one John Smith, yet I know two David Johnsons. Statisticians don't know everything.

Gary Smith
e-mail

I RECENTLY saw a Grand Prix race where David Coulthard ran out of petrol on the last lap. He should get a VW like mine which has a gauge which tells you how much petrol you've got left. It's even got a little red light that comes on when you're down to your last gallon. That way he could have stopped off at the nearest petrol station to top up, and

if he felt hungry after all that driving he could have bought a scotch egg at the same time.

Gordon
Aberdeen

IN RESPONSE to Steven Mayne's comments about Charles and Eddy (Letterbocks page 22), they have indeed left it rather too late to release a follow-up single, as Charles out of Charles and Eddy died of cancer in 2001. Eddy out of Charles and Eddy could probably have released a tribute single, perhaps a re-recorded version of the number 1 hit in 16 countries *Would I Lie to You*, but he's probably missed the boat on that one now as well.

Paul Twist
Wigan

GAUDY, open-fronted amusement arcades as found in seaside towns could learn a lesson from their more sophisticated city centre cousins. A window display of dark velvet drapes, juxtaposed with neo-classical

white and gold feline figurines adds class to the world of obsessive gambling.

Sigmund Fimber
e-mail

I RECENTLY gave birth to my first baby, a boy, and my mum came round to see him. She gave me a frosty look when I told her to cradle the baby's head when she held him, reminding me that she knew all about babies having brought me and my two brothers up. Later on, she offered to change and feed him whilst I made a cup of tea. I couldn't believe my eyes when I came back in. She had put his nappy on his head and stuck a Farley's rusk up his arse! She laughed when I pointed out her mistake. "Well it has been a long time since you were a baby," she said.

T Warburton
London

THEY SAY that an apple a day keeps the doctor away. Not my doctor, it doesn't. He loves apples.

D Tartt,
London

I WAS recently having my photograph taken at a wedding. The photographer shouted 'say cheese' in order to get everyone smiling. However, my mother had choked to death on a piece of cheese just a week before, so his request had the opposite effect as I immediately burst into tears!

R Tufnall
London

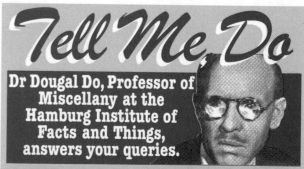

TOAST BAG

It's the POST with the MOST when it comes to TOAST

ACCORDING to Sod's law, toast always lands buttered side down. To get round this, I eat my toast dry, so it doesn't matter which way it lands if I drop it. Then I then eat the butter separately with a spoon.

Dr J Kingbast, Tewksbury

MY HUSBAND worked as a postman for fifty years. He has now retired, but still gets up at 4.00am and brings me a cup of tea and a slice of toast. He jokes that he used to deliver the POST every morning, now he delivers the TOAST every morning. However, it is not strictly true, as he worked in the Mount Pleasant Sorting Office and has never pushed a letter through a door in his life.

Edna Aneurism, London

I LAUGH when I hear young people complaining about how their electric toasters have broken. I was given a toasting fork as a wedding present in 1936. I have used it every day since and it has never let me down. And what's more, the toast tastes better.

Edna Vulvitis, Bracknell

LIKE MANY of my generation, I deplore the fact that the word 'toast' has been hijacked by so-called musicians. In my day, toasting meant grilling a piece of bread that one would eat at breakfast time. These days it means ranking up a phat sound on a ragga dub beat tip. Once again, as happened with gay, queer and cottage, a perfectly good English word has been lost to the language. And fist.

Brigadier Hepscott-White, Jedburgh

PS. And rim.

I SCREAM with hysterical laughter for several minutes every time I hear someone use the phrase 'warm as toast.' That's because sometimes you can have toast cold, for example when eating pate, or having breakfast at a Holiday Inn Express.

Francis Crabs, Crastor

WHEN MY father went off to the trenches during the First World war, my mother gave him a piece of toast for the journey. He put it in the breast pocket of his tunic and said to my mother 'I'll eat it when I get back'. Two years later on the Somme, a German bullet hit the pocket of his jacket. Fortunately, he wasn't wearing it at the time. His best friend had borrowed it and the bullet went straight through the toast and into his heart, killing him instantly. When he got back from the war, my father showed us children his lucky piece of toast with the bullet hole in the middle.

Edna Pleurodynia, Sheffield

Miriam

MIRIAM ANSWERS YOUR TOAST PROBLEMS

Dear Miriam...

I CAME HOME from work early recently and caught my husband making himself some toast. He was in the kitchen and had a recipe book spread open on the table. I was shocked.

I am 32 and he is 34 and we have been married for ten years. In all that time I have made his toast and he always seemed to enjoy it. To catch him making his own toast shocked me. When I confronted him about it later, he claimed at first that he was just testing the pop-up mechanism of the toaster. However, he eventually admitted that he had been a bit peckish and was making toast. He says that I am making a big deal about it.

The first time I tried to make toast for him afterwards it was a complete disaster. I burnt it and ended up in tears. I haven't been able to make him any toast now for about a month.

He says he still loves my toast and wants me to make it for him again, but I am so confused. Please help me, Miriam.

MW, London

Dear MW,

Sorry, but there is nothing wrong with a man making himself a bit of toast now and again, even when he has got a wife to make it for him. It doesn't mean he loves your toast any less. However, it may be that after ten years of marriage your toast has become a little dull. Try making him some with different toppings, adding a bit of Worcester sauce to the cheese and so on. Experiment a little. You may find that you actually like it.

TOAST Word
by Polyurea

EASY

Across
2. Grilled bread, often eaten with baked beans. (5)

Down
1. Machine for making toast. (7)

CRYPTIC

Across
2. Marten mixes up toast order. (5)

Down
1. Sat to grill bread. I'll drink to that. (5)

LAST WEEK'S ANSWERS: EASY *Across* 1. Toasting Fork *Down* 2. Pop Up Toaster. **CRYPTIC** *Across* 1. Saxophone. *Down* 2. Toast

WE ♥ YOUR TOAST POEMS

The food that I love most,
Is not a chicken roast
Lovely fish and chips
Will never pass my lips
And I would rather not
Eat sausages quite hot
A great big birthday cake,
does not me hungry make,
For the food I love most,
And this I really boast,
Is a lovely slice of... toast!

Edna Senile-Dementia Wales

When I was a little girl
With my hair a mass of curl,
There were no jumbo jets,
Or modern internets,
Policemen all had smiles,
And there was no paedophiles,
We went to Sunday school,
Because that was the rule,
Though Hitler's bombs did fall,
We were not sad at all,
For life was bright and gay
With toast for tea each day!

Edna Massive-Stroke Luton

Edna and Edna's lovely poems win them £80,000 cash and a Mercedes 560SEL each.

Mr. Logic

hmmm...

HE IS AS OF NEURALGIA ABOUT THE FUNDAMENT

£ EVERYTHING'S A POUND

hmmm...

'OW MUCH ARE THESE BATTERIES?

POUND.

WHAT ABOUT THESE BRILLOS?

POUND.

DOES THE MONIKER OF THIS PREMISE INDICATE THE FISCAL TARIFF LEVIED ON THE COMMODITIES HEREIN, OR IS IT MERELY ONE OF NO PERTINENCE?

WHAT?

IS THE TITULATION OF THIS ESTABLISHMENT AN ACCURATE REFLECTION OF THE MONETARY WORTH OF ITS VENDIBLES, OR DOES IT BEAR NO RELEVANCE THERETO?

ER...I...

I THINK HE WANTS TO KNOW IF EVERYTHING IS A POUND.

OXFORD PROFESSOR OF ENGLISH

BOG BRUSH SPECIAL OFFER £1!!!

OH, YES. YES IT IS. EVERYTHING IN THE SHOP IS A POUND.

I ASSUME THAT THE POUND HERE REFERRED TO APPERTAINS TO THE COST OF THE ITEMS, AS OPPOSED TO ITS WEIGHT AVOIRDUPOIS.

ER...YES.

hmmm. THEN SHOULD THE SHOP NOT MORE CORRECTLY BE TERMED "EVERYTHING **COSTS** A POUND."

WELL, I SUPPOSE...

SQUEAK! SQUEAK!!

TWO MINUTES LATER...

?

SQUEAK! SQUEAK!

MUCH LATER...

£18,234 PLEASE.

PHEW!

BLEEDEEP!

I THINK YOU MAY HAVE ERRED. YOU HERETOFORE DISCLOSED THAT THE COST OF EVERYTHING IN THE SHOP WAS £1.

WHAT!?!...

...NO. EACH! A POUND **EACH**!

hmmm.

THEN "EVERYTHING IS A POUND" IS A COMPLETE MISNOMENCLATURE. THIS ESTABLISHMENT SHOULD MORE ACCURATELY BE CALLED "**EACH** THING COSTS A POUND."

OH. WELL, I'M VERY SORRY, I'M SURE.

SO, TO CLARIFY, I CAN BUY ANY ONE ITEM IN THIS SHOP FOR ONE POUND...?

YES, THAT'S RIGHT.

hmmm.

...THAT BEING THE CASE. I SHALL PURCHASE THE TILL, PLEASE.

NO, THAT'S NOT **STOCK**. IT'S NOT FOR SALE.

hmmm! SO, IN ORDER TO COMPLY WITH THE SALES OF GOODS ACT (1966) THIS SHOP SHOULD BE NAMED "EACH INDIVIDUAL ITEM OF **STOCK** DISPLAYED FOR SALE WITHIN THIS PREMISE RETAILS FOR THE SUM OF £1 STERLING."

SECURITY TO TILL, PLEASE, SECURITY TO TILL.

...OR MOREOVER, SO AS TO AVOID ANY CONFUSIONS WHATSOEVER AS TO WHAT CONSTITUTES STOCK, "EACH INDIVIDUAL ITEM OF STOCK (EXCLUDING FIXTURES OR FITTINGS AND GOODS NECESSARY FOR TRADING) DISPLAYED FOR SALE WITHIN THIS PREMISE RETAILS FOR THE SUM OF £1 STERLING" WOULD BE A MORE APT NAME FOR THIS SHOP.

£1

£ EVERYTHING'S A POUND

...AND **STAY** OUT!

PUNT!

FULCHESTER TRAVEL AGENT

OPEN

BUMP!

THUMP!

CONGRATULATIONS!...

OPEN

...YOU ARE FULCHESTER TRAVEL'S **ONE MILLIONTH CUSTOMER!**

CLOSED

CLAP! CLAP!

FLASH!

HOORAY!

YOU WIN AN ALL EXPENSES PAID HOLIDAY TO THE COSTA DEL SOL, COURTESY OF FULCHESTER TRAVEL.

TICKET

A WEEK LATER...

€ TODO ES UN EURO

...4 ESTANCIA FUERA...!

BOTA!

IT'S VALENTINES DAY TODAY

SKIP

I CAN'T WAIT TO SEE HOW MANY CARDS I'VE GOT

NOT A SINGLE SOLITARY ONE. LOOKS LIKE NO ONE FANCIES ME.

BARE

GOD I'M DEPRESSED.

I KNOW — I'LL KILL MYSELF. THEN WHEN I'M DEAD, ALL THE GIRLS WILL BE SORRY THAT THEY WEREN'T NICER TO ME.

THAT'S ALMOST AS GOOD AS BEING LIKED.

I'VE COME TO SUNNY CALIFORNIA IN ORDER TO POP MY CLOGS.

FULCHESTER AIRLINES

THE STATE GUVERNOR IS ARNOLD SCHWARZENEGGER, AND HE'S MAD KEEN ON EXECUTING PEOPLE.

I JUST NEED TO COMMIT A HOMICIDE AND I'LL BE SENT TO THE ELECTRIC CHAIR IN NEXT TO NO TIME.

AH. THIS CHAP WILL DO.

AHEM. GIVE ME YOUR GOD DAMNED WALLET, YOU MOTHER. NO? OK THEN, TAKE THIS!

BANG

HOT DANG!

I'LL COME QUIETLY, OFFICERS.

HEH HEH. BETTER PLUG IN OL' SPARKY ~ FRIED SYD IS ON THE MENU.

NO NEED FOR THAT, BUDDY. WE'RE ARRESTING THIS HERE BLACK FELLER FOR THE MURDER. HE'S HAD A BANG ON THE HEAD, AND HE DON'T KNOW WHAT THE HELL'S GOIN' ON.

WHERE AM I?

HE'S A-GONNA DIE LIKE A DAWG!

FULCHESTER AIRLINES

BAH!

FLIGHTS BACK TO BRITAIN

BACK TO THE DRAWING BOARD.

AT HOME

IN FACT, IT'S QUITE LITERALLY "BACK TO THE DRAWING BOARD". I'VE A SURE-FIRE SCHEME TO SNUFF MYSELF OUT.

SKETCH

I'M DRAWING AN INFLAMMATORY PICTURE OF MUHAMMAD.

NOW TO SHOW MY PICTURE TO THIS SMALL MINORITY OF FUNDAMENTALIST ISLAMIC EXTREMISTS WHO ARE NOT REPRESENTATIVE OF MOST MUSLIMS IN FULCHESTER.

DEATH TO THOSE WHO INSULT ISLAM

GRRR!

HO HO! MY HEAD WILL BE SLICED OFF MY SHOULDERS BEFORE YOU CAN SAY 'JACK ROBINSON'.

HERE ~ WHAT DO YOU THINK OF THIS, THEN?

GRRR!

DEATH TO THOSE WHO INSULT ISLAM

SAY, THAT'S PRETTY GOOD, SYD. WELL DONE!

YES, IT'S AN EXCELLENT LIKENESS.

HUNH?

BAH! I GOT CONFUSED AND ACCIDENTALLY DREW A PICTURE OF **MUHAMMAD ALI** THE AMERICAN BOXER WHO USED TO BE CALLED CASSIUS CLAY.

THAT WON'T OFFEND ANYONE

JUST TO RECAP ~ IT'S A PICTURE OF THE **BOXER** MUHAMMAD ALI, WHO WAS BORN IN 1942 IN LOUSVILLE, KENTUCKY AND FAMOUSLY BEAT GEORGE FOREMAN IN THE 1974 "RUMBLE IN THE JUNGLE" BOUT.

ABSOLUTELY NOTHING TO GET UPSET ABOUT.

OH WELL. I SUPPOSE I COULD JOIN ONE OF THOSE SUICIDE CHATROOMS ON THE INTERNET, WHERE PEOPLE DISCUSS METHODS OF DOING THEMSELVES IN.

TAP TAP TAP

HMM, ON SECOND THOUGHTS, PERHAPS NOT. I MAY BE SUICIDAL, BUT I'M NOT **THAT** TRAGIC.

HANG ON, THOUGH ~ WHAT'S THIS?

PING

FIND A DATE

AN ADVERT FOR AN ONLINE DATING SITE. THIS COULD BE WORTH A LOOK.

TWO WEEKS LATER

GUESS WHAT, READERS? I'VE EMBARKED ON AN ONLINE ROMANCE WITH A REALLY NICE GIRL WHO LIVES IN AMERICA.

HI SYD!

LOVE CANDY-SUE

HER NAME IS CANDY-SUE, AND SHE SAYS SHE REALLY FANCIES ME.

I'M OFF TO AMERICA TO FINALLY MEET CANDY-SUE. I'M SO HAPPY ~ LIFE IS SWEET AGAIN.

TICKETS FOR FLIGHTS

A TICKET TO CARBONDALE, ILLINOIS, PLEASE.

SIX MONTHS LATER IN CARBONDALE, ILLINOIS

HOLY CRAP! LOOK AT ALL THE SEVERED HEADS IN THIS FRIDGE!

redrum

THE CRAZY BITCH HAS BEEN LURING GUYS HERE THROUGH AN INTERNET DATING SITE FOR YEARS.

Twok the Night Before Christmas

'Twas the night before Christmas
and all through the flat.
Not a creature was stirring...

Except for a Rat.

The stockings were hung
by the chimney with care...

...Which Ratboy shat into,
Just for a dare.

A bundle of toys he suddenly saw,
And he realised he could take them
and sell them for draw.

His eyes how they twinkled,
His fingers how light,
And he took every gift
that was in his sight.

Away to the window he flew
like a flash:

WHO WANTS TO BUY PRESENTS OR SWAP THEM FOR HASH?

More rapid than eagles
the little cunts came,
And he whistled and shouted
and called them by name,

HOW TASHA! HOO NOSHA! HOO GAVIN AND GAZZA! ON SMACKHEED! ON FUCKFACE! ON BOBBA AND SHAZZA!

I called the police up,
They couldn't give a shit.
They gave me a victim support number,
And that was about fucking it.

The kids suddenly saw me
Making the call:

HOW, NASH AWAY! NASH AWAY! NASH AWAY ALL!

But I heard him exclaim,
As he ran out of sight:

I SHAGGED YER MAM AND YER MAM WAS SHITE!

ASK ANYONE on the street to name their two favourite Captains and they'll reply without a moment's hesitation "Kirk and Birdseye". Captain James T. Kirk, Commander of the Starship Enterprise, has been a fixture on our screens for 40 years, as has his fish finger-frying ad-break counterpart Captain Birdseye. Both have voyaged to exotic locations; clean-shaven Kirk to distant galaxies to fight alien monsters, be-whiskered Birdseye to suspiciously breezy-looking tropical beaches to cook fish fingers for his crew of youngsters. But whilst everyone agrees they're the top two Captains in the world, which one is the best... and more importantly, which one is the worst? It's time to tot up the scores once and for all, as we present....

THE CLASH OF THE CAPTAINS
KIRK   VERSUS   BIRDSEYE

Travelling at Warp Factor Seven, Kirk regularly clocked up ten billion miles before breakfast boldly going where no man had went before. In fact, at the end of his five year mission to seek out strange new worlds, it is estimated that Kirk had covered a staggering 6.02×10^{28} light years - that's more miles than there are atoms in the Galaxy. With such an impressive tally, Kirk opens the contest with a substantial score.	**9** **ROUND 1 TRAVEL** **6**	In comparison with the Starship Enterprise, Captain Birdseye's ship the Fish Finger trawls the sea at a snail's pace. At the helm of his trusty three-masted schooner, the cheery skipper and his crew of unchaperoned children have circumnavigated the globe thirty-six times in search of the tastiest fillets of white cod. However, Birdseye's career total of around a million miles is still less than the distance covered by Kirk every two-thousandth of a second.
Wherever he went, Captain Kirk was for many years plagued by Klingons - members of a warlike race with Cornish pasty heads. But many other enemies threatened the safety of him and his ship, including Romulans, Khan, Tribbles and Cybermen. Indeed, it was a rare episode of *Star Trek* that didn't finish up with Kirk beaming down onto an alien planet to have a good old-fashioned fist fight with a more-or-less man-sized space monster.	**8** **ROUND 2 ENEMIES** **7**	Every seaman's worst fear is an attack by pirates, and for Captain Birdseye that nightmare came true in the seventies, when his advertisements were repeatedly attacked by his arch enemy, pirate Captain Jack. Unlike traditional pirates who murder and rape, forcing their innocent victims to walk the plank, Jack was hell bent on pinching fish fingers. However, his plans were invariably thwarted by Birdseye's pre-pubescent crew, whom the bachelor Captain rewarded with a good old-fashioned nosh-up!
Wherever he went, Captain Kirk was for many years plagued by Klingons - small pieces of faecal matter adhering to the hair in his buttock cleft. However, in recent times he has taken to eating a fibre-rich diet of Kellog's Bran Flakes. As a result, it is believed that the Captain's logs now move twice as fast through his bowels and leave much less mess around his anus. Kirk's phaser is set to stun, and so is the state of his nipsy. It's a good performance from the Starship Commander's starfish in this round.	**7** **ROUND 3 ANAL HYGIENE** **5**	Subsisting on nothing but fish fingers, Birdseye's diet is very imbalanced. Nutritionally speaking, the only fibre he is getting is from the small slice of lemon placed on the side of the plate as a serving suggestion, and clarty motions are the inevitable result. In a 200-year-old sailing ship, washing facilities are going to be primitive at best, with the Captain probably forced to regularly share his bath with several of his young friends. Browneye hygiene is going to be a problem for Birdseye, and consequently he scores poorly.
Being in charge of a giant starship crewed by members of every race and species imaginable tested Captain Kirk's relationship skills to the limit. Acting as a referee between the emotionless logic of Vulcan Dr Spock and the fiery temper of Scottish 'Bones' McCoy took up most of each episode. On a larger scale Kirk would often bring peace to war-torn planets, using his diplomatic skills in a way that would leave modern day peacemakers such as Kofi Annan, Nelson Mandela and George W Bush shaking their heads in awe.	**8** **ROUND 4 RELATIONSHIP SKILLS** **7**	Keeping discipline on a traditional square-rigged sailing ship was usually the responsibility of a detachment of six tough marines. Punishments were swift and harsh, with offenders being made to 'kiss the gunner's daughter', as well as being flogged with the cat, keelhauled or even hanged off the yard arm. But since Captain Birdseye is the only adult on the Fish Finger, discipline is left to him alone. A few gentle smacks on his innocent young crew's bare bottoms or on the backs of their young legs are often all that is needed to keep them in line.
In a famous episode of *Star Trek,* Kirk and the rest of the Enterprise's crew were struck by an alien space virus that caused them all to age a thousand times faster than they normally would. Fortunately for the Captain, Dr McCoy managed to find an antidote with about five minutes of the show to go, and so everyone was returned to normal. In the programme, the senile Kirk was a very wrinkly, white-haired old man who made gumming movements with his mouth. However, in real life he has aged quite differently. In his latest Bran Flakes adverts he is remarkably wrinkle free, his hair has stayed its original colour, and he just looks like he's been crying a lot.	**7** **ROUND 5 AGEING** **5**	As any jolly Jack Tar will tell you, a life on the ocean wave can take its toll on the complexion. Constant exposure to salty spray and bitter winds whilst a-combing the seven seas for the choicest fillets of white cod can quickly lead to a prematurely-aged look. However, Captain Birdseye's youthful crew clearly keep him feeling like a youngster every day, whilst a little bit of him no doubt rubs off on them too. But there's an even easier way for the veteran seafarer to stay looking ever-youthful. Ad chiefs recently sacked the man who'd played him for decades, and replaced him with a stubbly young man who didn't look anything like a Captain.
Oh dear, not once in the entire 71 episodes of *Star Trek* did Kirk ever appear wearing a hat which clearly denoted his rank. A disastrous round for the titfer-less Commander of the Starship Enterprise.	**0** **ROUND 6 CAPTAIN'S HATS** **10**	Birdseye is never to be seen without his traditional Captain's cap. And just to avoid any confusion, not only does it say 'Captain' on the front, it's also got a picture of himself leering through a lifebelt on the badge.

Captain Kirk may have fought off every alien in the Universe, but in the end he couldn't beat a fishy-fingered octogenarian with a predilection for children. In the only battle that counts, the battle of the Captains, he let down his defensive shields down, and millions of trekkies around the world too.

CONCLUSION 39 40

Shiver me timbers and splice the main brace. It's time to break out the ship's rum to drink a toast the winner. It's three cheers for Captain Birdseye as he flicks two fish fingers at his space age rival. He's given Kirk a proper battering, and left him looking a bit (bread) crumby.

Next week: Mr T versus Mr Sheen

41

SUNDAY...

DO COME IN, BILL, DO COME IN... HOW LOVELY TO SEE YOU

AND, GOODNESS, ANGELICA. WHAT A PRETTY DRESS YOU'RE WEARING

HELLO THERE, CISSY

GOSH...LOVELY FLOWERS, BILL. THANK YOU

≥PECK!≤

EUURGH! I'M GOING TO SPEW!

WATCHING TWO WRINKLIES SNOGGING... DISGUSTING. LIKE WATCHING TORTOISES DOING IT AT THE ZOO

WELL IT TURNED MY STOMACH!

OH, I'M SORRY MY PRINCESS. IT WAS JUST A PECK

IS THAT AN X-BOX 360 NET PLAY?

MIND YOUR OWN BUSINESS

IS IT?

YES...I GOT IT FOR THINKING ABOUT LETTING MY MUM MARRY YOUR DAD

DID YOU HEAR THAT, FATHER!?!...HE GOT THAT FOR LETTING HER MARRY YOU!

OH..ER THAT'S NICE

I WANT ONE OF THEM TOO. NOW!

OH, ER...OKAY MY PRINCESS. I'LL JUST BE TEN MINUTES.

YOU'LL BE FIVE MINUTES OR THE WEDDING IS OFF!

5 MINS LATER...

MY X-BOX 360 IS NEWER THAN YOURS...AND I'M BETTER AT GRAND THEFT AUTO THAN YOU.

SEETHE!

I'VE RAN OVER 18 PEOPLE AND YOU'VE ONLY RAN OVER 6

AH!. LOOK AT THEM PLAYING TOGETHER

HEY, YO MUTHA FUCKIN' ASSWIPE

WOO-WOO

WELL, IT'S LOVELY TO SEE YOU TWO GETTING ON SO WELL. WOULD YOU LIKE TO SHARE A BOWL OF SMARTIES?

SHARE? NO...I WANT A BIG BOWL ALL OF MY OWN

I WANT A PUDDING BOWL FULL

A WASHING UP BOWL FULL

SO...

HERE WE ARE...TWO BOWLS OF SMARTIES

ONE FOR TIMMY... AND ONE FOR ANGELICA

MY GOD!...THESE ARE ORANGE! I HATE ORANGE, WOMAN

THUMP!

I'M SORRY, CISSY, BUT ANGELICA IS ALERGIC TO TARTRAZINE...IT BRINGS HER OUT IN A TANTRUM. BUT SHE LOVES THE BLUE ONES WITH FCF E133

I WANT BLUE!

GET ME BLUE ONES, OR YOU CAN FORGET ABOUT THIS WEDDING

YES..WELL, TALKING ABOUT WEDDINGS...WILLIAM AND I WOULD LIKE TO HAVE YOUR BLESSING BEFORE WE...

SHUT UP! IT'S TIME FOR DR. WHO

OH, THAT'S TIMMY'S FAVOURITE

DADDY! I CAN'T SEE...TELL HER TO TELL HIM TO MOVE

ER...CISSY... ER... COULD YOU ER...ASK...

I CAN'T SEE THE TELLY!

I COULDN'T ASK HIM TO MOVE, BILL ...HE LOVES TO WATCH DR. WHO TWO INCHES FROM THE SCREEN

HE'S IN THE WAY OF THE TELLY, DADDY...

...AND IF YOU THINK I'M LETTING YOU MARRY HER WHEN SHE WON'T MAKE HIM MOVE SO I CAN SEE THIS

...THEN YOU'VE GOT ANOTHER THINK COMING

SHORTLY...

EX-TER-MIN-ATE!! EX-TER-MIN-ATE!!

IT'S A BIG STEP FOR THEM, CISSY...BUT I'M SURE THEY'LL GIVE US THEIR BLESSING SOONER OR LATER...

YES.

...WE'LL JUST HAVE TO BE PATIENT

20 YEARS LATER...

WOMAN...SHE'S GOT A PLAYSTATION HOLOGRAM 20,000 VIRTUAL CYBER HAT...YOU'D BETTER GET ME ONE, OR YOU CAN KISS YOUR WEDDING PLANS ON THE ARSE

YES, MY POPPET.

I'VE BEEN APPOINTED PROFESSOR OF BRAINY BOOKS AT OXFORD UNIVERSITY, READERS.

AT LAST I HAVE FULFILLED MY POTENTIAL, AND ACHIEVED SOMETHING WITH MY LIFE.

HM. THE THESIS EXPATIATED BY THIS AUTHOR APPEARS TO BE SOMEWHAT PLEONASTICALLY NEOLOGISTIC.

EXCUSE ME!

DON'T TELL ME. LET ME GUESS. THIS ISN'T OXFORD UNIVERSITY AT ALL... IT'S A HAT SHOP.

AND FAR FROM BEING A BRAINY PROFESSOR, I AM IN FACT A USELESS SHIT-FOR-BRAINS. AM I RIGHT?

NO TERRY, YOU'RE WRONG. THIS IS OXFORD UNIVERSITY ~ IT'S THE DEPARTMENT OF HAT STUDIES.

OH, RIGHT.

SO... DOES THAT MEAN THAT I AM A PROFESSOR AFTER ALL, THEN?

OF COURSE NOT, TERRY! YOU'RE A THICK CUNT WHO HASN'T AN OUNCE OF SENSE

...AND FOR THAT REASON, WE HAVE BROUGHT YOU HERE TO TEST OUT THIS NEW DUNCE'S HAT.

JUST POP IT ON YOUR HEAD, PLEASE

NOW THEN. WE WANT TO SEE IF THIS CONICAL PAPER HAT CAN WITHSTAND THE IMPACT OF A FOUR POUND LUMP HAMMER.

ARE YOU READY?

YEP. FIRE AWAY.

GRUNCH

FINE! IT DIDN'T WITHSTAND THE IMPACT AT ALL.

COME BACK AGAIN TOMORROW, TERRY, AND WE'LL REPEAT THE EXPERIMENT WITH A PICK AXE.

OXFORD UNIVERS DEPT. OF HAT ST.

RIGHTO. SEE YOU TOMORROW. OOYAH!

SHORTLY

THERE MUST BE MORE TO LIFE THAN BEING BEATEN OVER THE HEAD EVERY DAY. I'M IN A RUT.

I NEED TO BE CHALLENGED ~ TO BE GIVEN THE CHANCE TO PROVE I CAN DO SOMETHING WITH MY LIFE.

TERRY... HARKEN TO ME, O TERRY...

FUCK ME! WHO'S THIS?

I AM KNOWN AS GORDOLF THE WISE, AND I HAVE CHOSEN YOU, TERRY, TO EMBARK UPON A QUEST ~ A QUEST THAT WILL TEST YOUR WITS AND INGENUITY TO THEIR VERY LIMITS!

ARE YOU PREPARED TO MEET THAT CHALLENGE?

YES! YES, I AM... ....I THINK

THEN HARKEN! FOR THE OBJECT WHICH YOU MUST SEEK IS YOUR OWN ARSE

GO FORTH AND FIND IT USING BOTH OF YOUR HANDS AND THIS, THE FLASHLIGHT OF KUTHOR!

RIGHT. THIS SHOULDN'T BE TOO HARD.

BUT FIRST OF ALL, I NEED TO WORK OUT HOW TO SWITCH ON THIS FLASHLIGHT... HMM...

TWO HOURS LATER.

NOPE. THIS FLASHLIGHT HAS GOT ME FLUMMOXED. I CAN'T SEE HOW YOU SWITCH IT ON AT ALL.

WELL NEVER MIND, PERHAPS I CAN COMPLETE MY QUEST WITHOUT IT.

NOW, LET'S SEE I MUST SEEK... ERM... ERM... I MUST SEEK...

WOULD YOU BELIEVE IT? I'VE FORGOTTEN WHAT IT IS I WAS SUPPOSED TO BE LOOKING FOR

LET'S FACE IT. I'M A COMPLETE WASTE OF SPACE.

I'M JUST A PIG-IGNORANT GORMLESS GIT WITH NOTHING WORTHWHILE TO OFFER SOCIETY.

EXCUSE ME ~ BUT WE'RE LOOKING FOR A PERSON OF YOUR CALIBRE.

I THINK WE HAVE JUST THE JOB FOR YOU, YOUNG MAN...

AND LATER

THIS IS BBC RADIO FOUR

AND NOW IT'S TIME FOR 'THOUGHT FOR THE DAY' WITH THE RIGHT REVEREND TERRENCE FUCKWITT, BISHOP OF FULCHESTER...

EVERY DAY I LOOK AROUND ME AT THIS WORLD IN WHICH WE LIVE...

AND I THINK TO MYSELF: 'BUGGER ME! I HAVEN'T GOT THE FOGGIEST NOTION WHAT THE FUCK IS GOING ON'

WITH HIS TWINKLY Irish smile and his loveable brogues, TV presenter Eamonn Holmes has carved himself a niche in the world of inconsequential broadcasting. Whether he is cowering behind co-presenters on *The National Lottery Jet Set,* or failing to engage countless interviewees in conversation on cheap daytime TV shows, Eamonn is rarely off our screens. We think we know everything about him, but is there a hidden depth behind the bland, shallow facade that we see on TV? It is a question infinitely more interesting than all the things he has ever said put together... and once again, the answer is all in the name...

EATING

IN BETWEEN filling the TV schedules with half-arsed programmes, Eamonn likes to eat food... a lot of food! And he loves nothing more than Battenburg cake. "I can't get enough Battenburg," he told his website Eamonn.tv. It has been said that in a week, Eamonn pushes enough Battenburg slices into his face with his pudgy fingers to make a board big enough to play 350 games of chess.

ALLERGY

ON TV, Eamonn's inane smile hides a tragic secret. For the journeyman presenter was born with a lethal food allergy. Throughout his time at TVAM, canteen staff were under strict instructions not to serve him any fresh fruit, as one bite could kill him within seconds. In fact the only fruits Holmes can eat without dropping dead are toffee apples, banana fritters and Terry's chocolate oranges. And strawberry bonbons.

MEDIOCRITY

EAMONN first hit our screens in the early nineties, and a rollcall of his TV credits reads like a Who's Who of broadcasting cat litter. Programmes such as *Holiday Outings, Pot Black Timeframe,* and his lunchtime general knowledge quiz *SudoQ* all faded from memory even before their end credits finished rolling. Entertainment scientists have calculated that if awards were given for mediocrity, Holmes would need a cabinet the size of ten Albert Halls to house all his trophies.

OVERWEIGHT

VACUOUS TV host Holmes has struggled to keep his weight down for years. According to doctors, a normal Body Mass Index (the ratio of a person's weight to the square of their height) is between 18 and 25. With a BMI of 44.8, Holmes lies somewhat outside the normal range, although that doesn't necessarily indicate obesity. "It could be that I'm simply of an extremely athletic build, because muscle weighs more than fat," he told his website Eamonn.tv, whilst licking Battenburg crumbs off his fat fingers.

NAKED

AMAZINGLY, Eamonn's missus Ruth has never once seen her chubby hubby in his birthday suit. The bashful broadcaster never takes his clothes off, and even showers in his vest, pants and socks. And when it comes to bedtime, Mrs Holmes still doesn't get an eyeful of Eamonn, as his bedroom has a Victorian bathing machine into which Eamonn climbs in order to don his jim-jams. His wife then pulls it alongside the bed so he can slip under the duvet whilst retaining his modesty.

NUDIST

EAMONN is a keen nudist, and when he's not fronting televisual polyfilla, he'll likely as not be found playing volleyball in the buff at his local nudist camp. Holmes loves the sense of freedom that going without clothes gives him, but there is a downside to his saucy behaviour. "Last year at the nudist club barbecue, I was having a wee through a knot-hole in the fence when a short-sighted chef mistook my you-know-what for a sausage. Before I knew what happened, he'd pricked it with a fork, cooked it over the hot coals for ten minutes and given it to the lady Mayoress in a bread bun!" he told his website Eamonn.tv.

HORROR FILMS

EAMONN loves to watch scary films about ghosts, monsters and frankensteins last thing at night. "I love the horror film genre. As a boy, I was brought up on the films of Bela Lugosi, Boris Karloff, and the Hammer studios, and it's a love that stayed with me all my life," he told his website Eamonn.tv. However, his wife Ruth has had to pull the plug on her fella's late-night fright fests. "He kept on having nightmares and wetting the bed," she told her website Eamonnswiferuth.tv

OESOPHAGUS

LIKE MANY stars, Eamonn has succumbed to the lure of the plastic surgeon's knife. But he has not had a facelift, a tummy tuck or an anal bleach - he's had his oesophagus surgically widened. The two hour procedure stretched the TV presenter's gullet to the width of a drainpipe, enabling him to insert whole Battenburg cakes into his stomach without wasting precious time chewing.

LACTATION

EAMONN suffers from a rare medical condition that causes his breasts to secrete cottage cheese whenever he hears a baby cry. "I remember presenting a feature about prams on GMTV once, and there were babies crying all over the studio. I had to change my shirt six times, and under the studio lights, the smell of curdled cottage cheese was unbearable," he told his website Eamonn.tv

MISFORTUNE

EARLY IN childhood, Eamonn suffered a terrible misfortune. At the age of ten, he wrote to *Jim'll Fix It* to ask if he could look round a Battenburg cake factory to see how his favourite food was made. Unfortunately, his letter wasn't chosen. Twenty years later, on his first day as a cub reporter for Ulster TV, he was sent to a cake factory to report on a story about a kitten who had fallen into a giant vat of marzipan. "They needed a volunteer to eat a tunnel through the marzipan to the stricken cat. No prizes for guessing who stepped forward!" the overweight nonentity told his mother-in-law's website Eamonnswiferuthsmam.tv

ERECTILE DYSFUNCTION

17% OF MEN suffer from some form of impotence, so there is a 1 in 6 chance that Eamonn's performance between the sheets is as disappointing as it is on screen. But doctors say that the likelihood of erectile dysfunction is increased in men who are middle-aged, overweight and who have failed to achieve anything worthwhile in their lives. "I'll put my shirt on Eamonn Holmes not having got it up for years," says Morris Moskovitch, Cambridge University's Professor of Speculative Urology.

SOILED UNDERPANTS

EAMONN'S only memorable television broadcast occurred when Fathers for Justice campaigners invaded the set of *The National Lottery Jet Set* on May 20th 2006. A shaken Holmes cowered behind co-presenter Sarah Cawood, before scurrying out of the studio. He was seen several minutes later, hiding a pair of excrement-filled underpants behind a bush in the Blue Peter Garden. "Yes, I did soil my pants, but it wasn't because I was frightened. I'd foolishly eaten four packets of Smints just before going on air," he told his underpants' website Eamonnskegs.tv

Have They Got Tattoos for You?

Body Art Secrets of the BBC Newsroom

THE-SOBER-suited BBC newsreader has been a familiar fixture on our TV screens for many years. Names such as Richard Baker, Peter Woods and Robert Dougall evoke a staid, civilised image which is in keeping with Lord Reith's original vision. In the BEEB's earliest times, presenters were required to wear a dinner suit whilst reading the headlines... *and that was just on the radio!* But more recently the rules have been relaxed, and journalists are now occasionally allowed to deliver their reports whilst dressed casually, perhaps wearing jeans or an open-necked shirt.

But one regulation, stating that no newsreader may display body-piercings or tattoos on screen, is still as strictly enforced as ever. And it's a rule that has led to many of the country's leading newscasters being forced to cover up bizarre body adornments. Here, in an article the BBC *TRIED TO BAN* we take an eye-opening peek behind the scenes to reveal who's hiding what in the BBC newsroom...

Lip Up, Chatty

Dermot Murnaghan is a familiar face that we welcome into our living rooms every morning. Yet few viewers realise that, offscreen, the mild-mannered breakfast sofa chat king sports a twelve-inch plate lip. Murnaghan first got the circular facial ornament after visiting the Amazon basin to film a report about Brazilian deforestation in the 1980s. *"I saw one on a tribal chief and knew there and then that I had to have one. It was the coolest thing ever,"* he told the Radio Times. *"The witch doctor used a sliver of bamboo to cut a four-inch hole under my bottom lip before stretching it wide enough to slip the frisbee-sized plate inside, all without anaesthetic. It really hurt, but it was worth it when I looked in the mirror back at the hotel,"* he added. Murnaghan always takes his plate out before going on air, but one morning last year Breakfast Time viewers nearly got more than they bargained for. *"I'd overslept, so I only had time for a quick shave and a cup of tea on my way to work,"* he told us. *"I got to the studio just in time and we were one second from going on air when the producer spotted that in my hurry I'd left my plate lip in. Natasha, like the true professional she is, didn't miss a beat. She seamlessly covered for me while I took out my plate and hid it under a cushion on the breakfast sofa!"*

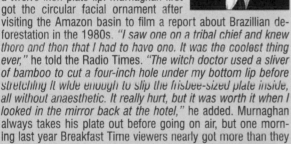

Tattoo Huw

Huw Edwards rarely cracks a smile when reading the news. That's because he's terrified that if he did, his makeup would crack and his secret would be revealed. For more than 98% of the Welsh newsman's face is covered with complex Polynesian tribal tattoos which he is forced to disguise with thick concealer before going on air. Indeed, according to a BBC insider, Edwards must spend an incredible *THREE HOURS* prior to every broadcast having flesh-toned pancake applied to his skin before he looks normal enough to go in front of the cameras. The source told us: *"Huw had the tattoos done following a £1 bet with a soundman whilst covering a G8 summit in Tahiti. He's bitterly regretted it ever since, of course, and the irony is that the soundman got a job at ITN a week later, so Huw never even got his pound!"*

News Anchor

Another newsreader who is forced to hide her body art whilst on screen is veteran presenter **Moira Stuart**. A BBC source told us: *"In the latter years of the eighteenth century Moira was press-ganged into the Royal Navy and spent several years as a deckhand on a three-masted frigate, the HMS Renown. In 1796, whilst her vessel was being re-fitted in Tunis, she and her crewmates got drunk on rum and she foolishly agreed to get the name of her ship and an anchor tattooed prominently on each forearm."* Now, more than two centuries later, these crude tattoos are still clearly visible and so Moira - nicknamed Popeye by newsroom pals - is under strict instructions to wear long sleeves whilst reading the headlines.

Bottom Marks for Paxo

You may have wondered why you rarely see BBC grand inquisitor **Jeremy Paxman** with his shirt off, and when you do it's never from behind. The reason is that the combative Newsnight host's back and buttocks are covered in raised, patterned scars called keloids. *"I was on safari in the Masai Mara when my jeep broke down hundreds of miles from anywhere,"* he told us. *"It was going to take the AA over three weeks to reach me, but luckily a couple of passing tribesmen took me back to their village. We got on really well, and they offered to initiate me into their tribe. I was sure they would be offended if I refused, but if I'd known what the initiation ceremony involved, I think I would have politely turned them down!"* he added. Paxman was drugged with a potent infusion of roots and poison berries, and spent the next four days tied face down in a mud hut whilst tribal chiefs made thousands of tiny slits in his skin, into which they they pushed pea-sized pieces of ash. *"When the drugs wore off and my hallucinations stopped, the pain was indescribable,"* Paxman continued. *"Let me tell you, I was glad when the AA eventually turned up and fixed my flat tyre,"*

And Spinally

Ever wondered why **Fiona Bruce**, the ice-cool New at Ten beauty keeps her head so still when reading the news? According to BBC insiders it's because Fiona is one of the few women in Britain to wear Burmese rings which stretch her neck to then incredible length of 2 foot 6. Bruce underwent the neck stretch procedure after watching a World About Us programme featuring the Giraffe Women of Burma. She now has 120 rings on her neck which she must keep on for life. *"The vertebrae are stretched so far apart that if the rings were removed, her head would flop onto the newsdesk and she would die,"* a BBC bar source told us. To disguise the neck when reading the news, Bruce kneels down behind a foam rubber torso specially created by boffins in the BBC special effects department. To add realism the man who used to operate Grodon the Gopher works a pair of artificial arms to shuffle the papers.

Bill's Not Cock-a-Hoop

Deadpan morning news man **Bill Turnbull** showed unexpected mettle when he foxtrotted his way to an early exit on Strictly Come Dancing. But Turnbull, 57, has another bit of metal that is even more unexpected and that he certainly doesn't show on screen. For unbeknownst to everyone except his wife, Turnbull sports a Prince Albert - a sort of metal ring punched through the side of his bellend and out his hog's eye. *"I can't think what possessed me to have it done,"* he told Smash Hits in 1994. *"It was excrutiatingly painful, I can't piss without leaving a wet patch on my trousers and my cock's forever setting airports alarms off,"* he added.

FRU T. BUN
THE MASTER BAKER & HIS GINGERBREAD SEX DOLLS

...ARE YOU SURE YOU CAN'T COME TO THE EYE HOSPITAL WITH US, DEAR..?

NO. I'M AFRAID I CAN'T...

≡GROAN≡

...NOT WITH THIS HEADACHE.

...BUT LITTLE CHELSEA'S HAVING AN OPERATION TO CORRECT HER SQUINT... YOU SHOULD BE THERE FOR HER, YOU KNOW, FRUBERT.

≡SIGH≡

DO YOU THINK I DON'T **KNOW** THAT? DO YOU THINK IT'S NOT EATING ME UP INSIDE THAT I CAN'T BE THERE FOR MY OWN DAUGHTER'S OPERATION?

I JUST THOUGHT...

OH MY **GOD**..! MY HEAD..! YOU'RE MAKING MY MIGRAINE WORSE..! OOH, THE PAIN!... **THE PAIN!** I NEED TO LIE DOWN..!

...ACTUALLY, I'LL NEED TO STAY HERE ALL DAY, I SHOULD THINK.

I'M SORRY, DEAR. I DIDN'T MEAN TO UPSET YOU. IF YOU GIVE ME THE VAN KEYS, WE'LL BE OFF...

WHA..?!

THE **VAN**?! NO, YOU CAN'T HAVE IT... I NEED THE...ER...I MEAN IT'S BROKE... AND IT HASN'T GOT AN MOT...ERM... AND IT'S RAN OUT OF PETROL... ERM... ER...

ANYWAY, I'VE LOST THE KEYS.

...NOW HURRY UP OR YOU'LL MISS YOUR BUS...

ERM... RIGHT, FRU. I'LL RING YOU AND LET YOU KNOW IF CHELSEA HAS COME THROUGH THE SURGERY...

NO! NO!

I'LL BE RESTING... DON'T WAKE ME UP.

OOH, ME HEAD.

SLAM!

HEY! WELL WHAT DO YOU KNOW..? FRU T'S MIGRAINE JUST GOT BETTER..! HEH! HEH! YOU SLY OLD MASTER BAKER, YOU!

...IT'S ALRIGHT, MY DEAR. YOU CAN COME OUT NOW... THEY'VE GONE.

2 MINUTES LATER...

BUS STOP

MUMMY! MUMMY! ...DADDY! ...**DADDY!**

NO, CHELSEA LOVE. I TOLD YOU. DADDY CAN'T COME, HE'S POORLY.

NO, LOOK... **DADDY..!**

WHAT!? NO, IT CAN'T BE...IT **IS**. IT'S FRUBERT'S VAN! WHERE'S HE OFF TO..?

BUS STOP

DADDY! DADDY!

...AND WHO'S THAT WITH HIM..?

Restaurant d'Amour

SHORTLY... ...A DOZEN OYSTERS, PLEASE... AND A BOTTLE OF CHATEAU LAFITTE CHAMPAGNE.

RÉSTA

WELL, MY DEAR... HERE'S TO A MEMORABLE... **SHIT!** IT'S THE MISSUS!

ERM...NOW, DEAR... THIS ISN'T WHAT IT SEEMS... I CAN EXPLAIN EVERYTHING...

WHAT!?!

OH YES!? WELL WHAT ARE YOU DOING HERE? AND **WHO** WAS THAT WOMAN YOU CAME IN WITH..?

A WOMAN!?! ...IT'S **YOU** WHOSE EYES ARE ALL SPAZZY, NOT CHELSEA'S.

BUT...

RÉSTA

IF YOU **MUST** KNOW, I'M HAVING LUNCH WITH MR. TRAVIS - THE BIGGEST FLAPJACK BUYER IN THE NORTH..! I WAS JUST ON THE CUSP OF SECURING A TIFFIN CONTRACT WORTH A HUNDRED POUNDS A YEAR..!

I'M SORRY, FRUBERT DEAR... I JUST THOUGHT FOR A MINUTE YOU WERE...

WELL, I **WASN'T**. NOW, IF YOU WERE ANY KIND OF MOTHER, YOU'D GET **HER** TO HOSPITAL..!

Letterbocks

Letterbocks, Viz Comic, PO Box 656, North Shields NE30 4XX
Email: letters@viz.co.uk

PROFESSIONAL footballers have hit the headlines recently for indulging in gamesmanship - diving and playacting and so on. Well at least they are now limiting their disgraceful behaviour to the pitch these days. It wasn't so long ago that they were out beating up Pakistanis, dogging in car parks and gang raping women in hotel rooms. Let's give credit where credit is due.

T Harpic,
London

JAMIE Oliver has been telling people to 'try something new today'. So this weekend at my Chinese takeaway, I had a number 163 and 24 instead of my usual 122 and 47. And it was awful. So thanks for nothing.

S Hurle,
e-mail

ON A similar subject, I too took Jamie's advice. I usually get all my shopping from Sainsbury's, but after seeing his advert I thought why not, and went to Asda instead.

Spud
e-mail

WHY IS it, whenever another terrorist atrocity occurs, people start saying that the world has gone crazy? Don't they realise that, according to Seal, we're never going to survive UNLESS we get a little crazy. Now THAT, Alanis Morrisette, is ironic. Send her my fiver. And my pencil.

Richard Hadfield,
e-mail

IT'S GOOD to see Noel Edmonds back on TV enjoying sucess with *Deal or No Deal.* As well as the obvious financial bonuses, it must be good for Noel to be involved in a TV show where he gets to open a box without a contestant plummeting 100 feet to their death.

Joel Young,
e-mail

RECENTLY I was unfortunate enough to be stuck behind the Fun Lovin' Criminals in a queue at Gatwick Airport. However, after they had checked in, the various members of the group decided they did not want to sit next to each other after all and proceeded to hold up the rest of the queue for a good ten minutes while they farted around getting their seats changed. Have any other readers been pissed about by second-rate has-been bands?

Simon Day,
e-mail

✱ *HAVE you ever found yourself being inconvenienced by lacklustre pop celebrities? Perhaps you've been held up at the supermarket whilst Leo Sayer fannied about, going through his pockets looking for a frozen pizza money off voucher. Or maybe Huey Lewis and the News once lit a bonfire when you'd just hung your washing out. Let us know at the usual address; there's a crisp fiver for the sender of every letter we use.*

I WAS just settling down in front of my PC for a good wank when there was a power cut. Never mind, I thought, I'll put on a pornographic DVD instead. In the next horrifying moment I caught a glimpse of what the end of civilisation might really be like. It's going to be no joke, is it?

Stevo,
e-mail

WHY can't surgeons apply the same techniques they use on fatties' stomachs, and staple smokers' lungs? One drag would then be more than enough for even the most hardened faghound, thus saving the National Health Service billions. Do I win £5?

Dr. Dave Saunders,
e-mail

I'M unemployed, and I'm now on my fourth wank in two hours. It's starting to hurt, but I couldn't be happier.

John,
e-mail

MY FRIEND tuned in to the Channel 4 quiz programme *Fifteen to One* many years ago just as William G Stewart said: "I would like to apologise for what I said about the

actor John Nettles yesterday." My friend wasn't lucky enough to see the previous episode in which the comment had been made, and this has bothered him ever since. Can anyone help solve this intriguing mystery?

Christina Martin,
e-mail

WE ALL know what a self-serving useless bunch of good-for-nothing twats estate agents are. Well, in north London they've taken to underlining this fact by driving around in garishly-painted Minis and Beetles. However, last week I was astonished to see a new pinnacle of wankiness; one of these cars

---

End of a Good Life

MARGO LEADBETTER, the snooty neighbour from classic TV sitcom *The Good Life*, has died, at the age of 64.

Actress Penelope Keith, 65, who played Margo, told reporters that she was 'deeply saddened' to hear of her character's death.

POPULAR

The news was broken to friends by Bob Larbey, one of the writers of *The Good Life,* the hugely popular series which ran for four series between 1975 and 1978. "Bob phoned me in tears yesterday to tell me Margo was gone," said Keith. "I was shocked. We all are."

"As an actor, you often play a character who dies, but it usually happens while you're playing them. This is the first time one of my characters has died without me being there. I didn't even know this could happen," she added.

According to Larbey, Margo died at her Surbiton home following a heart operation. Her husband Jerry, played by Paul Eddington, who died in 1995, was at her bedside when she passed away.

TOP TIPS

DAYTIME TV viewers. Want to win those phone-in prizes? Follow this easy guide to answering multiple choice questions: (a) is the answer, (b) rhymes with the answer and (c) is in no way the answer.

Christina Martin, e-mail

NEWSREADERS. Save time in broadcasts by simply reporting when Pete Doherty hasn't been arrested on some drugs charge.

Paul Skinback, e-mail

BOILED EGGS cut in half vertically, and with the yolk removed, make ideal miniature porcelain-style urinals for hamsters and guinea pigs.

Robert Healey, e-mail

MOVIE-GOERS. If you are late for the start of a film, and think the lights may already be dimmed when you enter the cinema, close one eye about the time you buy your ticket and then open it when you enter the auditorium. Hey presto, you won't be fumbling around in the darkness for the steps or seats.

Brian Derbyshire, Warrington

ANNOY SpecSavers staff by wandering up to their counter, squinting your eyes whilst looking up at the price board, and when they ask if they can help you, saying "Big Mac Meal, please."

Richard Karslake, Oxon

SLICING a Battenburg cake lengthways, both vertically and horizontally, makes four handy, long mini sponge cakes (one pair yellow, the other pink).

RO Williams, e-mail

MAKE your own inexpensive mints by leaving blobs of toothpaste to dry on a window sill. Use striped toothpaste to make humbugs.

Mark Hughes, Southampton

DOCTORS. Tired of licking stamps? Simply attach your stamps to the underside of your tongue stick before the patient says "Aah." Hey presto! Free saliva.

Moe, e-mail

MOVIE-GOERS. Just before your film ends, hold one eye wide open with your thumb and forefinger, so you won't be dazzled by the lights when you leave the cinema.

Brian Derbyshire, Warrington

proudly emblazoned with the legend "Property Response Vehicle". Can anyone top this for utter shouty arse-hole-ness?

Duncan, e-mail

AS A follower of crackpot L Ron Hubbard's Scientology religion, Tom Cruise apparently told his wife Katie Holmes that he expected her to give birth to their recent baby without uttering a sound. However, it's not long since Tom famously blubbed his eyes out when someone squirted a water pistol in his face at a film premiere. I'd like to see him shit out an eight pound pineapple in silence, the sanctimonious little twat.

Spud, Luton

JUST A thought. Why don't apes turn into humans any more?

Leeroy, e-mail

ROAD RAGE · POSTBAG ·

TO THE plumber in his van who cut me up on the city bypass. Having your mobile number on the side panel of your vehicle may be good for business, but please note that it may be useful to other persons too. It might be a good idea to switch your phone off when you go to bed from now on, as I am on nightshift again next week, and we don't want your blood pressure rising again at 3, 4 and 5am, do we?

Big Spo Edinburgh

THE OTHER day whilst driving through Alderley Edge in Cheshire, a woman driving a large 4x4 pulled up suddenly and unexpectedly in front of me to chat to a pedestrian friend. Fortunately, she had the foresight to display a 'Back Off! Twin Princesses on Board!' sign in her rear window. This reminded me to apply my brakes in an emergency fashion, and mount the pavement to avoid ploughing into the back of her vehicle. If only all women 4x4 drivers were so conscientious with regard to road safety.

Peter Lawson Email

Have Your Say

FRANCE'S Thiery Henry's shameful behaviour in the World Cup game against Spain, pretending he had been struck in the face, sickened the nation. It was no more than could be expected of a French car salesman, but it highlights the extent to which playacting has become part and parcel of the game. But what should be done to players who take dives during the game, and what steps could FIFA take to stamp it out? We went on the streets to find out what YOU thought...

...I think if footballers want to play the actor then they should be dressed for the part. Anyone caught indulging in theatrics should be yellow carded and forced to play the rest of the game wearing a doublet and hose and carrying a skull.

T Hennesey, Nottingham

...players like Henry are only human, and he may have reacted on the spur of the moment. He should not have been shown the yellow card for his actions as many have said, rather he should have been sent to a 'sin bin' for five minutes to reflect on his behaviour before returning to the game.

H Barnstorm, Leeds

...I believe that Mr Barnstorm (above letter) makes a good point, but I don't think that sitting in a 'sin bin' thinking is the best way to punish these players. Offenders should be given a short community service sentence by the ref, and have to spend ten minutes picking up litter in the stadium or painting the fence surrounding the ground before returning to the game.

Len Goatscheese, Hull

...for too long have FIFA adopted a softly, softly approach with these cheats. Any player caught diving during a game should be sent off the pitch, banned from football for life and put on the sex offenders register.

M Waddington, Goole

...expulsion from the game is the only thing that these players un-

derstand, but decisions should not be taken lightly. Perhaps FIFA could introduce a system whereby palyers are warned on their first offence, perhaps by being shown a yellow card. If they offend again, they should be shown a card of a different colour, perhaps blue or red, and ordered off the pitch.

Louis Playwood, London

...as a retired schoolteacher, I would like to see FIFA give the referee the power to beat any player guilty of diving. He should pull his shorts down, bend him over and give his bare behind six strokes of the cane in front of the whole stadium.

M Fibreboard, Nottingham

...I am a multi-millionaire businessman and I was about to replace my worldwide fleet of 8500 ageing company cars with brand new Renault Clios. However, after seeing Thiery Henry's disgraceful playacting in the France versus Spain game, I will be buying Seat Ibizas instead.

H Richenbakker, New York

...I think that if these footballers want to go diving then they should be dressed for the part. Anyone caught diving should be yellow carded and forced to play the rest of the game wearing a wet suit, flippers and an aqualung. If they commit a second, similar offence they should be given one of those old fashioned diving suits with lead boots and a brass helmet.

T Hennesey, Nottingham

...football has long since stopped being a sport. The

players are now businessmen and for them, time is money. If they are rolling around on the ground, they are not playing football and they should not be paid for that time. Then we'll soon see how injured they are. Henry spent thirty seconds pretending to be injured, so by my reckoning he should be £2768 short in his wage packet next week.

M Nantucket, Luton

No one can deny that Thiery Henry, Premiership Player of the season 2006, is a magnificent footballer, and that the French are wonderful people. But his actions brought shame on his nation, and I believe we should all stop going there on holiday, abandon all plans to adopt the Euro as our currency and pull out of the European Union.

G Sprake, Wolverhampton

I don't know what all the fuss is about. In this shamful episode, Thiery Henry is the real loser. In pretending to be hit in the face and being awarded a free kick that led to France's second goal and ultimate victory over Spain and progression into the quarter finals, Henry is only cheating himself.

J Plywood, Cornwall

I was watching the match on the telly and when I saw Henry pretend to get hit, I was so incensed that I put my foot through the screen and sent France the bill.

Renton Oerstryk, Hull

It's the Battle of the Animals
Yannick Noah's Ark

RECENTLY, the whole of London was captivated by Wilma, the bottle-nosed whale who lost her battle for life after swimming up the Thames into central London. Sadly that brave fight ended in death from dehydration after well-wishers lifted the plucky twenty-footer out of the water on a crane. But her sad end served to highlight the plight of whales all over the world; and ever since, these gentle giants of the seas have seldom been out of the news.

Britain has gone Whale Potty. In pubs and clubs across the land, the dwindling whale population has become the hot topic of debate. Whale charity Greenpeace has seen its numbers swell tenfold, and now three out of four Britons actively spend 10 hours per week saving whales.

But what about the only other member of the animal kingdom that begins with the letter 'W' - the humble **wasp?** These miniature marvels were buzzing around the planet 20 million years before whales were invented. They pollinate plants and kill garden pests, yet they are reviled by the British population. If a wasp were to drown in the Thames, it is unlikely that it would feature even on the local news.

So are we being unfair to the wasp? If there was only one place left on the ark when Noah got to the last but fourth letter of the alphabet, who do you think it should go to? Wasps or Whales?

We asked naturalists **Sir David Attenbor-ough** and **Bill Oddie** to look at all aspects of the lives of these two very different creatures. Here they plead the case for the mighty whale and the humble wasp being allowed onto the Ark. Tennis player **Yannick Noah** will listen to the cases for whales and wasps before deciding which species to allow aboard his namesake's fabled vessel.

STINGING

IT'S A good start for these enormous gentle giants. Whales are known throughout the world for their placid nature, and there has never been a report of a whale stinging anyone. In fact, whales do not even possess a sting - and it's a good thing too. Because if they did, scientists estimate it would be the size of a telegraph pole sharpened at one end, and would contain over 200 gallons of poison. That's sufficient venom to sting the buttocks of 600,000 people, enough to fill the grounds of every Premiership League club in the land. Except Sunderland, which would only be a quarter full as usual.

ALTHOUGH only small, these buzzing insects back a punch. Over half of their body weight is made up of their sting, and they like nothing more than to stick it in the bottoms of unsuspecting members of the public. And once it has delivered its painful payload, a wasp simply makes some more and flies off to find another hapless victim. Indeed, boffins estimate that over its lifetime, a wasp produces 200 gallons of poison. That's sufficient venom to sting the buttocks of 600,000 people, enough to fill the grounds of every Premiership League club in the land. Except Sunderland, which would only be a quarter full as usual.

NOT GETTING STUCK

TWO thirds of the earth's surface is covered by water, and you would think that with all the world's vast oceans to roam, the whale would rarely become stuck. But you'd be wrong, for these dim-witted denizens of the deep are constantly finding themselves floundering on beaches, gasping for water, or swimming in circles by Battersea Power Station looking for the way out to the ocean. And even when they are pushed back into the sea by beardy-weirdies, nine times out of ten these blubbery buffoons simply swim straight back onto the sand.

WASPS are truly the Houdinis of the animal world, being able to escape from all manner of sticky situations. Most wasps fly straight through cobwebs, and those that do get stuck don't need to struggle for long before they are off, depriving many a spider of his stripy dinner. Indeed, their only natural enemy is jam, which holds a fatal fascination for the wasp. Once one of his legs has become ensnared by the sticky preserve, there is no escape and a sweet, sugary death quickly follows. Bizarrely, however, they can escape from marmalade and lemon curd.

MUSICAL ABILITY

WHALES are the only animals who have topped the music charts, their songs featuring on albums such as *Out of the Blue* by ELO and many more. Rightly have whales been dubbed 'The Pavarottis of the Oceans'. Just like the Italian tenor, they are grossly overweight and can sing very loudly, their mating songs carrying for a distance of three thousand miles. But as well as lady whales, their haunting strains are also popular with earth mother-types who like to listen to CDs of whalesong whilst giving birth in PVC paddling pools surrounded by Laura Ashley tealights.

UNLIKE whales, wasps have little or no musical talent. Rightly they have been dubbed 'The Paul Rutherford out of Frankie Goes to Hollywoods of the animal world'. In fact, the only noise wasps can make sounds a bit like somebody in a mental hospital playing a kazoo. Scientist put this lack of an ear for music down to one thing - their lack of ears! Over the years, wasps' ears have evolved into antennae, pairs of wobbling Deely-Boppers on the top of their heads which are completely useless for hearing.

PLUMAGE

BY and large, whales are not noted for their colourful livery. All whales are grey, except the blue whale, which is blue, and the black and white killer whale, which isn't a whale at all, more a cross between a shark and a dolphin. A whale's neutral colouring means that it blends into its blue and grey surroundings so it can sneak up behind an unsuspecting plankton.

THROUGHOUT nature, the colours black and yellow together signify danger. As humans, we instinctively know to keep our distance from animals displaying these colours, such as wasps, hornets and tigers. And these colours are used in everyday life to signify places and situations it may be best to keep our distance from, such as sources of radioactivity, biological toxins, and certain down-market supermarkets.

HEARTINESS OF APPETITE

WHALES have an undeserved reputation for being greedy. In the Bible, Jonah and his technicolour dreamcoat were eaten by a whale. In Herman Melville's novel, Gregory Peck and his ship were gobbled up by Moby Dick. And in *Pinocchio*, Monstro the whale made a meal of Gepetto, his cat and Jimminy Cricket. But in fact, despite their gargantuan size, whales are the daintiest of eaters. It is an irony of nature that these jumbo jet-sized monsters like nothing more than to nibble on a plankton - a tiny fish no bigger than a grain of salt.

WASPS have voracious appetites, and unluckily for us, they eat the same things as we do. It is a sad fact that no British Bank Holiday picnic is complete without a swarm of the hungry marauders chasing everyone away before tucking into the contents of their hamper. So keen on stealing picnics are they, that wasps have rightly been called 'The Yogi Bears of the animal kingdom.' It is estimated that during its life, the average wasp scoffs over 300 Cadbury's mini-rolls, 250 rounds of jam sandwiches and 150 ice lollies, all washed down with 600 tins of fizzy pop.

SOCIAL STRUCTURE

WHALES have rightly been called 'The Tramps of the Ocean'. They don't have a house or any teeth, and they spend their time wandering round singing tuneless songs to themselves, occasionally under Battersea Bridge.

LIKE Humans, wasps live in highly complex social groups which would not function efficiently unless each performed their allotted tasks, such as tending larvae, looking for dropped lollipops and stinging people on the arse. Unlike humans, however, wasp society is quite backward since all members of the colony must kow-tow a single, self-appointed queen who sits about all day doing nothing.

SWATABILITY

WHALES remain one of the hardest members of the animal kingdom to swat with a newspaper. Thanks to a layer of blubber nearly 8 feet thick, these lengthy leviathans would not feel anything, even if beaten quite viciously. It has been calculated that in order to splat a blue whale, one would have to hit it with a *Daily Star* as big as a four football pitches, featuring a picture of Jordan on the cover with her tits as big as two St Paul's Cathedrals. This was found too impractical, and Japanese whale welfare research vessels now prefer to use explosive harpoons.

WASPS are the perfect size for swatting and thanks to their complex compound eyes they make easy prey. A wasp's vision of the world is like a continuous special effect from an episode of *Top of the Pops* from the 1970s - a continuous rotating kaleidoscope of tiny images. Instead of seeing one newspaper bearing down on him a wasp sees a thousand, and in order to get away he must choose the right one to fly away from. And woe betide any wasp who makes the wrong judgement. He'll be smeared across the wall like so much mustard before he can say Jack Robinson.

BREATHING UNDERWATER

UNLESS you're standing outside a Marine Biology Convention and they are having a fire drill, if you ask the man in the street whether a whale can breathe under water, he'll say yes. But he'd be wrong. That's because unlike fish, whales don't breathe water, they breathe air through their noses. And like Daniella Westbrook, they have one enormous nostril. But unlike her, it is on top of their head. Indeed, if you held a whale's head in a bucket of water for long enough, it would drown. However, scientists have calculated that it would take a man as big as Nelson's column to lift a whale, and he would need a bucket the size of the Albert Hall. With a handle on it as big as Sydney Harbour Bridge.

IF YOU hold a wasp's head under water, it will die. However, you'd better be prepared for a long wait, as its death will be due to old age, not drowning. That's because wasps do not breathe through their mouths, but through special snorkel-like tubes called spiracles which open out in their bottoms. This is why, when they are exerting themselves and panting for breath - for example whilst flying - they make a high-pitched farting noise. This unusual breathing technique is not without its risks; if a wasp with diahorrea were to attempt to wash its nipsy it would drown almost immediately.

ORIGAMI SKILLS

A WHALE'S brain is over 300 times bigger than that of a human, so you might think it could easily get to grips with the ancient Japanese art of paper folding. Flapping birds, jumping frogs and a man wearing a sampan hat in a rickshaw would all be well within the mental compass of these intellectual giants of the ocean. However, it is thought that the whale's enormous clumsy flippers, whilst excellent for swimming effortlessly through the oceans, would prove next to useless for creating crisp, diagonal folds in sheets of paper.

ANYONE who has ever knocked a wasps' nest from the roof of their shed with a stick, before covering it in petrol and setting it alight, will have marvelled at the intricate structure of this miracle of nature. With its thousands of hexagonal chambers and its intricate galleries, a wasps' nest is a paper structure infinitely more complex and beautiful than anything the greatest human origami artist could create. Unfortunately, since it is made from chewed-up wood pulp and wasp spit, it doesn't count, as the rules of this ancient oriental art forbid tearing the paper or using glue.

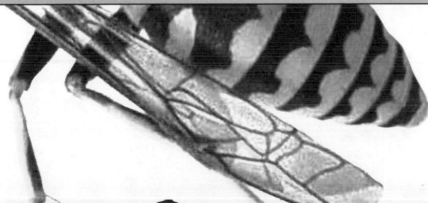

YANNICK NOAH'S VERDICT

"*In my long tennis career, I have seen some close matches. Borg versus Connors in the Wimbledon Semi in 1982, Yvonne Goolagong versus Chris Evert in the 1979 Australian Open, Vitus Geralitus versus Billie Jean King in the 1981 Davis Cup men's final. But none has been such a nail-biter as this titanic encounter. And after looking carefully at all the evidence, it's game, set and match... to WASPS. Like John McEnroe, these insects are fiery and bad tempered, but determined to get to the top. And like him, they are unpopular with people, but possess an indefinable star quality. Whales, on the other hand, like Betty Stove, are blubbery buffoons that occasionally have their moment in the limelight, but are destined to be the perpetual runners-up of the Animals Beginning with W Stakes. Consequently, there is no place for them aboard my great-great-great-great-great grandfather's ark, and they will have to perish in the flood along with all the wicked fornicators of the*"

Next week: Giraffes versus Gnats

ROGER MELLIE

THE MAN ON THE TELLY

ONE DAY... **KNOCK! KNOCK!**

AH! THAT'LL BE ROGER

COME IN!..

JUS' LIKE THAT!.. JUS' LIKE THAT!..

NOT LIKE THAT, LIKE **THAT**!.. AH-HA-HAAR!

ER...

...HI, ROGER

GLASS... BOTTLE... BOTTLE... GLASS... I WENT TO THE DOCTOR THE OTHER DAY...

ROGER... WHAT...?

TOMMY COOPER, TOM... GOOD, ISN'T IT?

ERM... YES, BUT... WHY?

DON'T SAY YOU'VE FORGOT, TOM. ...THIS SHOW YOU'VE GOT ME ON... WHO DO YOU THINK YOU ARE?...

I CAN DO FRANK SPENCER...

EDDIE WARING...

OOH, BETTY...

AYE, AYE! UP AN' UNDERRR...

IDI AMIN...

OKAY. STOP YOU THERE ROGER

HELLOO 'DERE!

THE PROGRAMME YOU'RE THINKING OF IS *WHO DO YOU DO*?... IT FINISHED IN THE LATE SEVENTIES

YOU SURE, TOM?.. IT WAS ON UK GOLD LAST NIGHT

NO, ROGER. THE SHOW WE ARE FILMING TODAY IS ALL ABOUT GENEALOGY

EH!?.. FORTUNE TELLING?

WHAT?.. NO... FAMILY HISTORY

EVERY WEEK A DIFFERENT CELEBRITY IS FILMED PRETENDING TO TRACE THEIR FAMILY TREE...

OH, NO, TOM. FUCK THAT. I'M NOT INTERESTED IN ALL THAT BOLLOCKS

WELL, HOLD ON, ROGER... THINK...

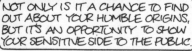

NOT ONLY IS IT A CHANCE TO FIND OUT ABOUT YOUR HUMBLE ORIGINS, BUT IT'S AN OPPORTUNITY TO SHOW YOUR SENSITIVE SIDE TO THE PUBLIC.

IT'S GREAT TELLY, ROGER. EVERY CELEB WORTH HIS SALT HAS DONE IT... BILL ODDIE... SHEILA HANCOCK... ERM... IAN HISLOP.. ERM ...ERM...DAVID BADDIEL...ERM ...COLIN JACKSON

THAT'S A FUCKIN' GALAXY OF STARS, TOM...

...NO. I THINK I'LL PASS ON THIS ONE. LIFE'S TO SHORT TO SPEND IT GOING THROUGH DUSTY PAPERS IN THE PUBLIC RECORDS OFFICE TO FIND GREAT GRANNY MELLIE DIED OF RICKETS WHEN SHE WAS TWO

OKAY, ROGER...

...SHAME THOUGH. THE PROGRAMME OFTEN UNEARTHS SOME SURPRISES

...JEREMY CLARKSON FOUND OUT HIS ANCESTORS WERE MULTIMILLIONAIRES IN THE GLASS INDUSTRY...

THAT AFTERNOON...

RIGHT, ROGER... WE'LL JUST TAKE THAT ONE MORE TIME. AND IF WE COULD LOSE THE 'FUCKING HELL' FROM THE FIRST SENTENCE...

RIGHTO, TOM

AND THE SECOND

PVBLIC RECORDS OFFICE

WHO DO YOU THINK YOU ARE?... ROGER MELLIE... TAKE THREE

AND ACTION!

I'VE ALWAYS BEEN FASCINATED BY MY ANCESTORS...

SO I'VE COME HERE – TO THE FULCHESTER PUBLIC RECORDS OFFICE TO FIND OUT MORE ABOUT JUST WHO THEY WERE

FINDING REFERENCES TO THE MELLIE FAMILY IS GOING TO BE LIKE FINDING A NEEDLE IN A HAYSTACK

I'M IN FOR A LONG NIGHT...

AND *CUT!*

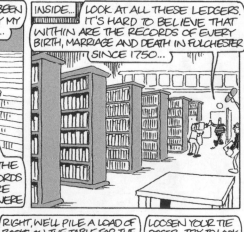

INSIDE... LOOK AT ALL THESE LEDGERS. IT'S HARD TO BELIEVE THAT WITHIN ARE THE RECORDS OF EVERY BIRTH, MARRIAGE AND DEATH IN FULCHESTER SINCE 1750...

RIGHT, WE'LL PILE A LOAD OF BOOKS ON THE TABLE FOR THE NEXT SHOT

HERE'S THE ONE YOU WANT

YOUR GREAT GRANDFATHER DIED OF DYSENTERY IN THE POORHOUSE... I'VE MARKED THE PAGE FOR YOU, MR MELLIE

LOOSEN YOUR TIE ROGER... TRY TO LOOK LIKE YOU'VE BEEN UP FOR TEN HOURS

...RIGHT, JUST READ ABOUT HOW HE DIED, LEAVE A NICE PAUSE... AND THEN WIPE AWAY A TEAR...

A **TEAR**, TOM? YOU WANT ME TO BLUB?

YES, ROGER... IT'S GREAT P.R.

JEREMY PAXMAN CRIED OVER HIS GREAT GRANNY AND THE VIEWING FIGURES FOR 'NEWSNIGHT' WENT **THROUGH THE ROOF!**

GOTCHA, TOM... SO WHO'S THIS CUNT AGAIN?

HE'S YOUR GREAT GRANDFATHER, ROGER...JOSIAH MELLIE

RUFFLE! RUFFLE! RUFFLE!

OKAY...THREE...TWO...ONE...

ACTION!

AH! HERE WE GO...JOSIAH MELLIE...

...DIED OF DYSENTERY... DECEMBER 25TH...1861... FULCHESTER POOR HOUSE

...AGE ....31...

...31... DEAR, DEAR.

31

TUT! TUT!

PHEW!..

...31...

SNIFF!

BLINK! BLINK! BLINK! BLINK!

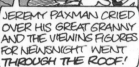
SORRY, TOM, I CAN'T SQUEEZE ONE OUT...CAN YOU SEND A RUNNER TO THE SHOP FOR AN ONION?

CUT!

DON'T WORRY, ROGER...WE'LL SHOOT ROUND IT... WE'LL PUT THE CAMERA BEHIND YOUR HEAD AND DROP SOME WATER ON THE DEATH CERTIFICATE ...LET THE INK RUN A BIT...

...A FEW POIGNANT PIANO CHORDS IN THE BACKGROUND...NOBODY WILL BE ANY THE WISER

I DON'T KNOW, TOM, COME TO THINK OF IT, IS THERE NOBODY MORE INTERESTING IN MY FAMILY TREE THAN THIS TWAT?

I MEAN, WHO WANTS TO HEAR ABOUT SOME VICTORIAN TRAMP SHITTING HIMSELF TO DEATH IN THE WORKHOUSE ON CHRISTMAS DAY?..

NOBODY...

...PEOPLE WANT TO HEAR ABOUT **SUCCESS**, TOM

CAN'T WE FIND SOME OF MY FOLK WITH A BIT MORE PIZZAZZ?

SURELY WE CAN DIG UP SOME LONG LOST TYCOON UNCLE WITH NOBODY TO LEAVE ALL HIS MILLIONS TO, CAN'T WE?

BE TV **GOLD** THAT WOULD TOM...JUST IMAGINE THE EMOTION WHEN WE MEET FOR THE FIRST TIME

HMM!

WELL... I SUPPOSE THIS WHOLE PAUPER ANCESTOR PATH **IS** WELL TRODDEN...

EXACTLY, TOM. IT MIGHT BE NICE TO FIND SOME MORE RECENT, SUCCESSFUL RELATIONS

HEY, SWEET TITS... GET BACK TO LOOKING THROUGH ALL THIS LOT AGAIN, WILL YOU?

GIVE ME A SHOUT WHEN YOU FIND SOME MELLIES WITH A FEW BOB IN THEIR BACK BINS

A WEEK LATER...

WELCOME TO FTV

HI, TOM. ANY LUCK?

AH, ROGER. YES' THE RESEARCHER HAS BEEN DOING SOME DIGGING...

...TURNS OUT YOU'VE GOT QUITE AN EXTENSIVE FAMILY.

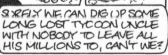
THEY'RE DYING TO MEET YOU, ROGER

REALLY?

YES. YOU'VE GOT RELATIVES YOU NEVER KNEW YOU HAD ALL OVER THE COUNTRY

ARE THEY TALKING MONEY, TOM?

ERM...YES, I THINK THEY ARE, ROGER

GREEN ROOM

GOOD AFTERNOON, MR MELLIE... I'M FROM THE CHILD SUPPORT AGENCY...

C.S.A.

HIGH-WIRE BUILDING SOCIETY

EXCUSE ME - WE'RE LOOKING FOR THE HIGH-WIRE BUILDING SOCIETY AT 28 WOODBRIDGE...?

NAAH, THIS IS NUMBER 26...

...YOU WANT NEXT DOOR.

HERE WE ARE - ONE FLIGHT UP.

↑ 1ST FLOOR
SAVINGS
'STMENTS
MORTGAGES

ERM... WE'VE AN APPOINTMENT.

YES, CAN I HELP YOU?

L DUNBAR MGR.

RECEPTION

THE MACMILLANS AT 11:30.

RIGHT, MISTER DUNBAR IS READY TO SEE YOU. GO STRAIGHT IN.

L DUNBAR MGR.

AH, MR AND MRS MACMILLAN - I SEE HERE YOU'RE APPLYING FOR A HOME PURCHASE MORTGAGE...

I... ER...

PLEASE, HAVE A SEAT!

OOOOH!

AHHHH!

NOW THEN... WHAT AMOUNT WERE YOU LOOKING TO BORROW?

OO - EE - WE NEED £105,000 FOR A £116,000 PROPERTY

BUT WITH HIS WORK WE CAN'T BE - UH! UH! - SURE OF STAYING MORE THAN 5-6 YEARS.

OHHH!

WELL, AS FIRST TIME BUYERS OUR 5-YEAR FIXED RATE MORTGAGE MAY SUIT YOUR NEEDS, AT 4.99% UNTIL JUNE 2011, THEN SWITCHING TO OUR STANDARD VARIABLE RATE (CURRENTLY 6.44%) GIVING YOU MONTHLY REPAYMENTS OF £508.55.

EEP EEP EEP!

WOOOOOO

AAAAH!

THAT'S AN OVERALL COST FOR COMPARISON OF 6.1% APR - PLUS OF COURSE THERE'S ALSO A HIGHER LENDING CHARGE PAYABLE ON LOANS ABOVE 80% OF THE PURCHASE PRICE... HANG ON A SEC —

DEIRDRE, COULD YOU BRING US IN SOME COFFEE PLEASE?

MMMM!

WAH! WAH! WAH!

OOOOO!

HERE YOU ARE MISTER DUNB - WOAH...

TINKLE CLINK

WOAHHHH...

OOOOP!

GASP!!

LAYDEEZ AND GENTLEMENNN — I MUST ASK FOR YOUR **COMPLETE SILENCE**, AS THE MANAGER ATTEMPTS TO FETCH A STANDARD MORTGAGE TAX RELIEF FORM MR311... FROM A **FILING CABINET** SUSPENDED OVER A **CAGE** OF **FEROCIOUS TIGERS**!!

PARDON ME - WON'T BE A TICK, AND THEN WE CAN HAVE A LOOK AT YOUR COMBINED ANNUAL INCOMES AS WELL AS GOING OVER EARLY REPAYMENT CHARGES!

OH, FOR CHRIST'S SAKE...

BADABADABADABADABADABADABADABADABADABADABADABA

NO! NO, I'M SORRY! THIS IS **RIDICULOUS**!

ANNND - HUP!

OOOOHHH!!

FORGET IT - WE'LL JUST GO TO THAT PLACE YOUR BROTHER RECOMMENDED...

SO... WELL NOW, EVERYTHING SEEMS IN ORDER - I'VE GOT YOU TRACKING BASE RATE PLUS .75% FOR 5 YEARS, THEN CHANGING TO SVR FOR THE REMAINING TERM FOR AN OVERALL 6.5 APR. SOUND OK?

YES, THAT'S PERFECT.

GOOD, THEN IF I'LL JUST GET YOU TO SIGN AND PUT THESE ON WE CAN RELEASE THE REQUISITE FUNDS TO YOUR ACCOUNT AND

SSSSSSSSS...

PLAM!!

SSSSS

THE HUMAN CANNONBALL BANK

bizarre

Physician of the year

GOT A STORY? CALL ME OR MY TEAM

SPOTTED leaving a posh London bar – **ABI TITMUSS**, muttering something about a body conjoined by two forces NOT describing the diagonal of a parallelogram in the same time that it would describe those sides, by those forces apart. Stick to the day job, Abi!

biz

COLDPLAY singer **CHRIS MARTIN** has and superwaif **GWYNETH PALTROW**'s daughter **APPLE** had a nasty shock recently when she fell out of a tree. Luckily, little Apple wasn't badly hurt, as she landed on her poor dad's head! Chris says the accident inspired the song 'The Scientist'.

OASIS frontman **LIAM GALLAGHER** has hinted that he might never work again.

"Dunno, might not," he told me during a recent chance meeting at the Royal Observatory. "Might just sit on me arse, like."

Poor Liam. Objects at rest tend to remain at rest unless an outside force acts upon them. Perhaps it's time he got a kick up the *Wonderwall* from brother **NOEL**...

LIAM 'RETIRING'

Messed-up Pete Messes up Again

POTTY PETE DOHERTY was up to his usual tricks last night – making a BABYSHAMBLES of himself by falling flat on his face.

My snapper spotted the 27-year-old singer tripping and falling on the pavement after a private gig at the Royal Society in London's west end.

An onlooker said: "Pete was a bit the worse for wear, and lost his footing when he came down the steps. He managed to laugh it off, though."

Pete – who is back with **KATE MOSS** – should have remembered my law of universal gravitation, which states that every point mass attracts every other point mass by a force directed along a line connecting the two!

And as Kate, around whom The Sun revolves, could have told the wild boy of rock 'n' roll, the force is proportional to the product of the masses and inversely proportional to the square of the distance between them!!

CHRISTINA AQUA-LERA

DIRRTY diva CHRISTINA AGUILERA looks just sizzling as she soaks up the sun between takes on her latest video shoot.

My spies caught the pint-sized pop star spending two hours chilling out in the pool of the Lucasian Hotel in Los Angeles.

The rate of heat loss of a body is proportional to the difference in temperatures between the body and its surroundings.

If T is the temperature of the body,

$$\frac{dT(t)}{dt} = -r(T - Tenv)$$

where r is a positive constant, I can exclusively reveal that:

$$T(t)a = Tenv + (T(0) - Tenv)\ e\text{-}rt!$$

Hope she remembered her towel!

POSH RAPPED BY POSH RAPPER

BAD-BOY rap star J-CLOTH has slammed VICTORIA BECKHAM for not appearing on his new album.

The foul-mouthed toff DJ called Posh "a blithering twiglet" and "nowt but a twopenny ho" after she pulled out of a scheduled recording session.

But Posh, 32, is said to be "jumping mad" at J-Cloth, and has written a song, *You Pig*, about him.

I've said it before and I'll say it again: to every action there is an equal and opposition reaction!

biz

INEXPLICABLE **RUSSELL BRAND** is the latest celeb to back my campaign to bring back the much-missed pound note. "That geezer on the back was right gorgeous, weren't he?" says Happy-Shopper-Keith-Richard Russ.

Queen Takes the Plunge

WELL-KNOWN monarch Her Majesty The Queen is planning to round off her 80th birthday celebrations with a splash this autumn by taking a bath... with former world darts champion Jocky Wilson!

Buckingham Palace says that the Queen, 80, has long harboured the desire to take a bath with the Kirkcaldy-based king-of-the-arrows-turned-recluse.

"Her Majesty likes a bit of darts," said an equerry yesterday. "And if there's one thing she likes more than a bit of bully, it's a nice hot soak in the tub. So taking a bath with Jocky Wilson seems the logical thing to do."

BUT

But plans for the gracious birthday bath have already been branded irresponsible by critics, who say the Defender of the Faith and the twice Embassy World Champion should lead by example and take a shower together instead.

"A bath uses 90 litres of water, whereas a shower only uses 30 litres," said Friends of the Earth chief Jonathan Porrit yesterday as everyone around him yawned and looked at their watches. "With hosepipe bans in place and reservoirs running dry, I'd expect better from the Queen and Jocky Wilson," he added.

BUT

But plans to replace the bath with a more environmentally friendly shower have not gone down well with the people of Peterborough, who recently presented the Queen with a specially commissioned rubber duck to commemorate her Golden Jubilee.

"Everyone knows you can't take toys into a shower," fumed Alderman Alan Alder, Lord Mayor of Peterborough. "We presented Her Majesty with this rubber duck so she could play with it in the bath. If she and Jocky Wilson take a shower, it will be a slap in the face for the people of Peterborough."

BUT

However, manufacturers of shower toys are furious with the Mayor for what they see as a sideswipe at their industry. "We know for a fact that both the Queen and Jocky Wilson have waterproof radios and soaps-on-ropes in their showers," said a spokesman for ShowersCanBeFun.com. "They could easily use those during their celebratory shower."

But safety experts advised caution. "We don't recommend taking a radio into the shower, even a waterproof one," warned a RoSPA spokesman. "Whether you are Head of the Commonwealth or a renowned Embassy World Darts champion from The Lang Toun, it makes no difference.

Shampoo and conditioner are fine, but nothing electrical."

BUT

But the cosmetics industry rejected the safety watchdog's advice, declaring it unnecessary to take shampoo and conditioner separately to the bathroom. "Take two bottles into the shower?" it laughed yesterday. "The Queen and Jocky Wilson should just wash 'n' go."

But Palace insiders say that a combined shampoo and conditioner would be inappropriate for the joyous occasion, and insisted that there were no plans for either Elizabeth II or John Thomas 'Jocky' Wilson to wash their hair during the birthday celebrations. "This will be a relaxed, informal occasion," said a spokesman-in-waiting. "Not an opportunity for a good scrub-up."

BUT

But hair experts yesterday said the bath would send out the wrong message if Liz and Jocky keep their tresses dry. But other hair experts maintained they should not wash their hair in the bath because the soapy water won't rinse it sufficiently. "Nonsense. They could rinse the suds out with a shower head," countered some other hair experts. But bald celebrity swimmer Duncan Goodhew said he considered the whole hair debate highly offensive. "This is a gross insult to my culture," he stormed. But hirsute mahogany model Fabio slammed Goodhew's remarks, calling them insensitive and crass. But ants, who have a chitinous outer carapace and no hair, have lodged a formal complaint about Fabio's remarks with the European Court of Human Rights.

34-YEAR-OLD OBSESSIVE WAR WORKSHOP ASSISTANT

NOW THEN, SON... ARE YOU SURE YOU WANT WARMALLET SOLDIERS? WOULDN'T YOU RATHER GET A FOOTBALL?

NO. DEFINITELY WANT SOME CHAOS SPACE MARINES.

WELL, IT'S YOUR POCKET MONEY.

I'LL HAVE THESE KRONE BERZERKERS AND A BOX OF THESE WOOD ELVES... THEY'RE MINT!

COME ON. LET'S TAKE THEM TO THE TILL.

AH! NOW... YOU DON'T WANT WOOD ELVES. PUT THESE BACK AND GET A BOX OF PLAGUE BEARERS...

OH... ERM... NO. IT WAS WOOD ELVES YOU WANTED, WASN'T IT, SON...?

OOH, YES!

YOU SEE, WOOD ELF ARCHERS ARE FROM WARMALLET, WHEREAS THESE KRONE BERZERKERS ARE FROM THE WARMALLET 40,000 SERIES.

DADDY—I WANT THE WOOD ELVES.

...WARMALLET IS A MEDIEVAL-BASED FANTASY RÔLE-PLAY GAME, WHEREAS WARMALLET 40,000 IS A FUTURISTIC-SET SCIENCE FANTASY WARGAME ENVIRONMENT.

YES, BUT...

...IT'S JUST IMPOSSIBLE THAT WOOD ELVES AND CHAOS SPACE MARINES OF ANY SORT COULD KNOW OF EACH OTHER'S EXISTENCE, LET ALONE MEET EACH OTHER IN ANY SORT OF COMBAT SCENARIO.

I'LL JUST PUT THESE BACK FOR YOU. NOW, THESE KRONE BERZERKERS ARE JUST ONE TROOP, SO YOU'LL BE WANTING A CHAOS LORD COMMANDER AND A HEADQUARTERS PLATOON...

NO. I THINK HE JUST WANTS...

...KRONE BERZERKERS ARE EXCELLENT COMBATANTS, BUT THEY CAN'T FUNCTION AS A UNIT WITHOUT A CHAOS SPACE LORD AS LEADER...

BUT HE DOESN'T WANT A CHAOS SPACE LORD..! HE WANTS THE WOOD ELVES!

...YOU WANT THE WOOD ELVES?

YES.

RIGHT... SO LET'S PUT THE SPACE MARINES BACK, THEN...

NO! YOU DON'T UNDERSTAND. HE WANTS BO...

NOW... PAINTS.

FOR WOOD ELVES YOU'LL NEED COMMANDO KHAKI, SNOT GREEN, BESTIAL BROWN, BLEACHED BONE, ELF FLESH, BOLTGUN METAL, MITHRAL SILVER AND GRAVEYARD EARTH...

LOOK—HE WANTS THESE... AND THOSE! WOOD ELVES AND SPACE MARINES!

I'M SORRY. I CAN'T BE MAKING MYSELF CLEAR. YOU SEE, THOSE ARE WARMALLET... AND THESE ARE WARMALLET 40,000.

I KNOW THAT. YOU SAID. AND THANK-YOU.

...BUT MY SON WOULD LIKE TO BUY BOTH OF THEM, PLEASE.

...WELL HE CAN'T. IT WOULDN'T BE RIGHT. THEY COULDN'T MEET IN BATTLE. THEY CAN'T... THEY WOULDN'T... NEVER.

NO... THEY'RE NOT FOR SALE.

JUST TELL ME HOW MUCH THEY ARE.

OH, FOR CRYING OUT LOUD. I WANT TO TALK TO THE MANAGER. THIS IS RIDICULOUS.

IS EVERYTHING ALRIGHT, SIR?

NO IT IS NOT. MY SON WANTS THIS BOX AND THIS BOX... BUT HE'S REFUSING TO SELL THEM TO US.

AH, WELL THAT'S BECAUSE THEY ARE WARMALLET AND THEY ARE WARMALLET 40,000. THEY INHABIT DIFFERENT IMAGINARY BATTLESCAPES THAT DO NOT...

OH, FOR FUCK'S SAKE.

JUST SELL THEM TO ME, WILL YOU?!

...BUT THE KRONE BERZERKERS ARE ARMED WITH BOLT PISTOLS, CHAIN SWORDS AND PERCUSSION FRAG GRENADES... AND THEY DRIVE AROUND IN LAND RAIDERS.

THE WOOD ELVES HAVE GOT BOWS AND ARROWS... IT WILL BE A MASSACRE.

...A MASSACRE.

I DON'T CARE.

SELL THEM TO ME.

NO.

SELL THEM TO ME NOW.

NO.

Panel 1:
LOOK - HERE'S TWENTY POUNDS. SELL THEM TO ME NOW.
NO.
WHY NOT?
IT'S A SCOTTISH NOTE.
SCOTTISH NOTES ARE LEGAL TENDER.
...BUT IT MIGHT BE FORGED.

Panel 2:
IT'S NOT FORGED. LOOK - YOU CAN SEE THE WATERMARK.
THE TILL'S BROKEN.
YES.
...WE CAN'T GIVE YOU A RECEIPT.

Panel 3:
I...DON'T...WANT...A... RECEIPT.
YOU HAVE TO HAVE A RECEIPT. IT PROVES YOU HAVEN'T STOLEN THEM.

Panel 4:
SO... WHAT WITH THE TILL BEING BROKEN AND EVERYTHING, I'LL JUST... PUT THESE BACK... SHALL I..?

Panel 5:
COME ON SON. LET'S GO AND BUY A FOOTBALL, EH..?

Panel 6:
SHORTLY...
... I'LL HAVE THESE SKAVEN OGRE RATS AND THESE TYRANID GENE STEALERS, PLEASE.
HMMM.....

Panel 7:
AH, YOU SEE WHAT YOU'VE DONE HERE? YOU'VE MIXED UP YOUR IMAGINARY COMBATSCAPE ARENAS. THESE CRITTERS ARE WARMALLET, WHILST THESE LITTLE FELLAS ARE FROM WARMALLET 40,000...
≥ CHUCKLE ≤

Panel 8:
SIX MONTHS LATER...
WAR WORKSHOP
GONE OUT OF BUSINESS

TERRY FUCKWITT

THE UNINTELLIGENT CARTOON CHARACTER

Panel:
I'M VISITING THE ARSE DOCTOR TODAY, READERS
PROCTOLOGY DIPLOMA
I KEEP GETTING THIS SHARP STABBING PAIN IN MY BOTTOM, AND I'M AFRAID THAT I MIGHT HAVE PILES.

Panel:
SO WHAT'S YOUR DIAGNOSIS, DOCTOR? HAVE I GOT PILES, OR WHAT?
WELL TERRY, I'VE MADE A THOROUGH EXAMINATION OF THE AFFLICTED AREA...

Panel:
...AND IF I'M NOT MISTAKEN, THE PROBLEM YOU'VE GOT THERE IS A BURST WATER MAIN.
HUNH?!

Panel:
BUGGER ME. I REALISE I'M A COMPLETE IGNORAMUS, BUT SURELY I HAVEN'T GOT A WATER MAIN UP MY ARSE
THAT'S TRUE, YOU HAVEN'T

Panel:
..BUT THEN, THIS ISN'T YOUR ARSE, IS IT TERRY? THIS IS A HOLE IN THE GROUND.
EEEH I AM A CLOT! I CAN'T TELL ONE FROM T'OTHER

Panel:
NOW KINDLY REMOVE THAT HOLE FROM MY SURGERY BEFORE IT CAUSES AN ACCIDENT.
RIGHTO. OOYAH! THERE'S THAT SHARP STABBING PAIN AGAIN.

Panel:
MEANWHILE
HMM. THIS PICK ISN'T MUCH USE.
ROAD WORKS
BETTER PASS ME THE DRILL.

JURASSIC PARP

Boffins Plan to Clone T-Rex from Dino Guff

DNA EXTRACTED from a fossilised fart could be the key to creating the world's first dinosaur in 65 million years. That's according to a Scottish scientist whose pioneering research is set to shake the world of palaeoentology to its foundations.

In an echo of the blockbuster film *Jurassic Park* Professor Frank Duckworth, Head of Genetics at the University of Auchtermuchty, plans to extract Tyrannosaurus DNA from prehistoric flies trapped within amber before implanting it in modern reptile eggs. But unlike his movie counterpart, Duckworth won't be looking in the flies' blood for his samples, he'll be looking in their lungs.

He explained: "These flies died millions of years ago when they became caught in sticky amber whilst flying round the primeval forest. In the last moments of their lives as they struggled to get free, there is every chance that they could have breathed in a beefy eggo dropped by a passing dinosaur."

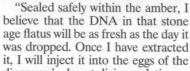

T-REXCLUSIVE!

"Sealed safely within the amber, I believe that the DNA in that stone age flatus will be as fresh as the day it was dropped. Once I have extracted it, I will inject it into the eggs of the dinosaurs' closest living relatives - crocodiles, aligators and frogs. If my cloning plans are successful, I see no reason why marauding, blood-thirsty lizards weighing upwards of a hundred tons each should not be roaming the Fife countryside in the very near future," he added.

PLANS

But Professor Duckworth's plans to begin a large-scale dinosaur breeding and release programme from his college campus fifty miles north of Edinburgh have been met with horror by local groups. Auchtermuchty Parish Councillor Morag McTavish told us: "We are very concerned about these plans. If the

NO T-REX PLEASE WE'RE BRITISH: Dinos like this one could become a familiar sight on Fife streets, tomorrow.

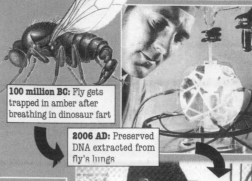

HOW THE PLAN WILL WORK

100 million BC: Fly gets trapped in amber after breathing in dinosaur fart

2006 AD: Preserved DNA extracted from fly's lungs

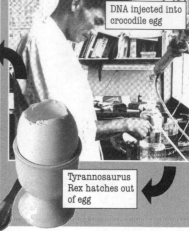

DNA injected into crocodile egg

Giant dinosaur released into Auchtermuchty

Tyrannosaurus Rex hatches out of egg

professor gets his way, the countryside round here will be full of hungry dinosaurs, and that's bound to impact on the local economy. These things are very large - some of them are as big as five double decker buses."

FORMULA

Professor Duckworth is unimpressed by the arguments, however. "People always attack things they don't understand," he explained. "Auchtermuchty Parish Council is behaving just like the villagers in horror films, who burn down the castle just because Dr Frankenstein has created an uncontrollable monster from parts of dead bodies stolen from the local graveyard." And he had this

warning for anyone tempted to try to disrupt his research. "If they come anywhere near my laboratory, I'll kill them," he told us.

SQUIRREL

But there is still hope for the objectors. Duckworth says he is having difficulty extracting the genetic material he needs from his samples. "I bought some amber on eBay, but when I sawed it open and got to the fly, I couldn't smell dinosaur shit," he told us. "I suppose I'll just have to keep looking until I find one that breathed in a T-Rex cupcake at just the right moment."

Cottage loaf

Oh yeah...

WHITE SLICED

LETTERBOCKS

Letterbocks
Viz Comic
PO Box 656
North Shields
NE30 4XX

E-mail
letters@
viz.co.uk

Could I just say a quick thank you to the person who owned my house in the early 80s and decided to glue woodchip wallpaper to the entire house? Also a thank-you to the 2 owners since who glossed over it several times. I hope you all enjoyed your Easter as much as I did.

Andy Bryant
e-mail

According to the BBC website, Heather Mills has blamed the breakdown of her marriage to Sir Paul McCartney on 'constant intrusion' into the couple's private life. It seems a shame that Heather objects so much to the public taking an interest in her personal business. If only she had mentioned it in one of her two published autobiographies, *A Single Step* and *Out On A Limb*, or the 'About Heather' section of her website *www.heathermillsmccartney.com*, or perhaps when she sold her life story to the *News of the World* in 1993. Perhaps then the public would have got the message and left her to live her life out of the constant glare of publicity.

A Cherry
Leeds

I am currently serving my third tour of duty in Iraq. I would just like to thank the two gentlemen who were kind enough to fire a 105mm rocket at me and my colleagues the other morning. Had the nearby explosion not thrown me out of bed, I may have overslept and missed part of my day staring death in the face in the middle of a dusty shit hole.

Johnny Jihad
Iraq

Our office joker Dave used to love endlessly repeating catchphrases from telly shows, such as "I'm not bovvered" and "I want that one" until our boss joined in by saying "Dave - you're fired."

Nick Pettigrew
London

Perusing the letters page of *Old Science* magazine, I was surprised to see John McIntyre of Stoke remark that "the weight of a fully grown lobster is about seven kilos". I wrote in to point out that a lobster carries on growing throughout its life and that, before it became standard practice to harvest them so aggressively, it wasn't uncommon to find specimens of ten or even more kilos. After conducting some light research, Mr McIntyre conceded the point, but I feel the message needs to reach a larger audience and am writing to you accordingly.

Stuart Lavin
e-mail

Hats off to Tory toff Boris Johnson for having the guts to do what we all would love to do and headbutt a German in the cock during a celebrity football match. If his Conservative predecessor Neville Chamberlain had should shown half Boris's spunk and nutted Herr Hitler in the knacker when he met him in 1939, how different the world would have been.

J Giles
Leeds

At some traffic lights earlier today in Stratford upon Avon, I saw Matthew Kelly standing there with his arm in a sling. He turned away at the wrong moment, but he looked like he'd been trying to swallow a wasp when he realised I was trying to take a photo. I wonder if any other readers have got some equally poor photos of injured minor celebrities.

Shaun Garrod
Ashby de la Soul

Well, readers. Have you managed to take a picture of Tony Blackburn with his leg in plaster? Or perhaps you've managed to snap Bernie Clifton with a pan stuck on his head. Send us your shots of minor injured celebs. There's a crisp tenner for any we print.

year old woman, no crime has been committed.

T Hennesey
London

What a disappointment Live 8 turned out to be. Twenty years earlier during Live Aid I got a blow job off Emma Whitmore. During the last one, the most I got was a cup of tea off the wife. I mean, come on, Geldof.

Mansh
e-mail

The downloading of pornographic images by paedophiles seems to be on the increase. As a service to the public, could I suggest that Jeanette Krankie post several naked pictures of herself on the internet. Anyone who is turned on by schoolboys could then satisfy their sick desires, and since she is a 60-year old woman, no crime has been committed.

How long do you think it took the Germans to find Pele in his disguise at the end of *Escape to Victory*? I have a feeling he may have stood out a bit in wartime occupied France.

A Hunter
e-mail

"What'choo talkin' 'bout, Willis?"

Each week, Diff'rent Strokes's shortarse *Gary Coleman* asks three famous Willises to talk 'bout an unspecified subject which we ask YOU to identify.

Bruce Willis
"*The thing I'm talkin' 'bout is a British motorcycle manufactured from 1948 to 1971, and which was available with three engine capacities; 123, 148 and 172cc. Its design was based on the pre-war German DKW RT125. The original engine had a 58mm stroke, a 52mm bore, and a 6.5:1 compression ratio.*"

What'choo talkin' 'bout, Willis?

Wincey Willis
"*The thing I'm talkin' 'bout is a special place of interment, usually reserved for the remains of the members of royal, or otherwise distinguished, families. It takes its name from that of the tomb of an ancient King of Halicarnassus, erected in 352 BC, which was one of the seven wonders of the world.*"

What'choo talkin' 'bout, Willis?

Bob Willis
"*The thing I'm talkin' 'bout is an anaemia-causing disease carried by a tiny worm which enters the victim's body through the feet and passes through the bloodstream into the lungs, eats through into the bronchial tubes, climbs the windpipe and passes down the throat into the stomach, eventually ending up in the duodenum.*"

What'choo talkin' 'bout, Willis?

ANSWERS

Bruce Willis is talkin' 'bout the BSA Bantam.
Wincey Willis is talkin' 'bout a mausoleum.
Bob Willis is talkin' 'bout Hookworm disease

Next week: The same three famous Willises talk 'bout things.

If you turn this picture of John Prescott upside down, he looks remarkably like Kenneth Clarke. It doesn't bear thinking about, but if during her affair Tracey Temple did a 69 with the deputy Prime Minister, it would have appered to her that she was noshing off the former Tory chancellor and MP for Rushcliffe. Once again, it seems that sleaze follows the Conservatives wherever they go.

J Charlton, Leeds

With reference to the above letter. Just think of the distaste that Ken Clarke's wife must feel each time time she has a 69 with her husband, having to look at John Prescott's adulterous mug noshing away at her fadge.

T Plasterboard, London

I was interested to hear that one of these so-called lesbian marriages has ended in divorce. Well I am a church goer, and divorces are meant to put asunder Adam and Eve, not Madam and Eve. They are not divorced in my eyes, I can tell you.

Dave Holloway
Newcastle

I used to live in Beirut in the flat next door to where Terry Waite was being held hostage. The clanking of his handcuffs went on all day and night for five years, but I never reported it to the police because I thought it was a problem with the header tank stopcock, or an air lock in the system. How I laughed when I realised what it was.

T Barnstaple
Beirut

Why is it old people who die alone in their house always do it at Christmas? When they are found three years later with the telly still on, there is invariably a Christmas tree in the corner of the room. They are never surrounded by Easter eggs or with an unopened box of fireworks in the kitchen. Come on lonely old folk, show some imagination and try dying at a different time of year.

P Lorimer
Leeds

I have followed with interest your recent spate of letters about feeble soap opera punches. However, your examples look like Mike Tyson's mightiest right hook when compared to this ineffectual sock on the jaw on the cover of this 1950s Australian comic.

Mr T Lectern
Holy Island

To the zookeeper in 1978 who replied "I'll tell you when you're older" when I asked him why one of the monkeys stuck its tongue up another one's arse: I'm 36 now and still waiting for that explanation.

Joe McKeown
e-mail

They say that being the manager of the England football team is the loneliest job in the world. Well, I work in a lighthouse on a rock in the middle of the Pacific Ocean, 8000 miles from land. However, it's quite a large lighthouse and I am part of a team of eight people. So maybe they are right.

T Cherry
Leeds

VICTORIA NEWTON'S upside-down bizarre

SEEN SOMEONE UPSIDE DOWN? CALL ME OR MY TEAM Tel: 0999 782 4036

THIS WAY UP

GIRLS ALOUD have finally gone over the top, if their latest publicity photo is anything to go by... Hold onto your hats, fellas, the girls are UPSIDE DOWN!

The sexy fivesome - **SARAH HARDING, NADINE COYLE, CHERYL TWEEDY,** and **THE OTHER TWO OUT OF GIRLS ALOUD** - seem to be head-over-heels in love with being the wrong way up, and let's face it, it's ALL OVER for the girl group if they have to resort to attention-grabbing gymnastics to get thesmelves noticed.

GIRLS ALOUD? Girls Upside Down, more like!

Is it just me or is outrageous Radio 1 ladette **SARA COX** looking increasingly UPSIDE DOWN these days? I've checked every photo on my desk, and she's arse-over-tit in every one. What's up, **COXY**?

Hunky beast **DERMOT O'LEARY** doesn't usually fall for the latest celebrity crazes, but even he can't resist the new trend for being UPSIDE DOWN, judging by this latest snap. After spending a long morning rearranging my chair to the other side of the desk, I was looking forward to flipping through the latest press shots, but oh no! Not you as well, **DERMOT**! Where will it end?

Drunken bakers

This is very pleasant.

Yeah...

Actually, no.

It's bloody shite.

But the sun is so nice. And the flowers...

Oh. Right.

I thought you was on about the beer.

Naah.

That ain't bloody pleasant.

I know.

It's shite.

Gone warm in the sodding sun.

Sickly.

Special are best cold.

Yeah. Proper bastard ice...

Goes like malty glue.

We need some snow.

It isn't going to snow.

No. Never bloody does.

When your specials are warm...

We should dump it in the pond.

Good idea. Then nip back the shop and get that White Horse.

I mean to cool it.

Good idea.

Not too far.

There might be an undertow.

This is still warm.

Give us a pull.

You're right.

Maybe another two minutes...

Stand up too fast?

A Walk On The Tired Side!

THE ORGANISERS OF the London Marathon are threatening to disqualify one of the top 100 finishers after it was revealed that he ran the race in his sleep.

Bolton shopkeeper Gideon Tadpole, who came 67th and raised thousands of pounds for charity over the 26.2-mile course, says he is baffled by the decision.

"There's nothing in the rules about being awake during the race," he says, "and it's not as if I was aware I was running it. The first I knew about it was when I woke up from a vivid dream where I was doing my maths 'O' level and I hadn't done any revision, and found my bedclothes strewn with sponsorship forms and empty isotonic drink bottles.

"I was a bit stunned, but it turned out that I'd raised over £10,000 for the PDSA," adds Tadpole. "I had no recollection of it at all, but my feet were sore and the cuffs of my pyjama bottoms were filthy."

RAMBLE

This isn't the first time that Tadpole has suffered from disturbed sleep, but

By our Charity Mouse
MIDGE URE

he is taken aback by the scale of his nocturnal ramble. "My ex-wife used to occasionally catch me on the landing with a messy sort of sandwich I'd made with my eyes closed," he says. "But I'd never get further than the front door. The Marathon is the most arduous sleepwalk I've ever done. But it's nice to find out it was all in a good cause. I just hope my record time stands."

RUMPTY

Amazingly just three nights after completing the gruelling run, Gideon unconsciously pushed himself to the limit in aid of the Sue Ryder Appeal. Sponsorship forms in his dressing gown pockets the next morning showed he'd sleepwalked from Land's End to John O'Groats, raising nearly £8,500.

"Sometimes it's every night. No sooner do I nod off than I'm making a difference for worthy causes," says the 48-year-old ironmonger. "One night I'll be lying in a bath of baked beans, snoring. The next, I'll be bungee jumping in a sleeping bag. It seems every time I go to sleep, I end up raising money for where it's needed most."

Last summer Gideon awoke to discover he had organised a global pop concert in aid of Oxfam. "Apparently, Coldplay and Madonna headlined, and David Bowie and The Sugababes joined The Kaiser Chiefs for a medley of songs by the Who," he says. "It was televised all over the world. My sister told me I sang an Al Green song in my t-shirt and pants with my hair all sticking up at the back at both the London and Chicago venues. Apparently I'd flown between them on a specially chartered plane. The show raised over £4m. It's just a shame I slept right through it."

RITTLE TED

While he anxiously waits for the London Marathon's organisers to recognise his result, Gideon says he hopes his fundraising snoozes continue. "Who knows what I'll be up to tomorrow night!" he smiles as he stirs his Horlicks.

In the meantime, top charities around the worldwide are reportedly rushing to cash Gideon's cheques before the bubble bursts. Michelle Reasonable, Oxfam's Chief Fund Raising Organiser, told reporters: "We never hang around when we get a donation from Mr Tadpoles. It goes straight in the bank. You know, just in case he wakes up and discovers it's all been a dream."

THE BRAZEN HUSSY!

AYE. SHE'S ONLY AFTER HIM FOR HIS BLOOD SAUSAGE AND FAGGOTS, YOU KNOW DOLLY.

WELL SHE'S ALWAYS BEEN LIKE THAT, MAUDE KERBISHLY. NEVER WANTED FOR STOCKINGS OR CHEWING GUM IN THE WAR, DID SHE? ALWAYS HAD A G.I. JOE ON HER ARM.

ANYBODY'S IN THE ANDERSON SHELTER, SHE WAS, AS LONG AS THEY HAD COUPONS.

SHE ONCE DID BELGIAN BISCUIT WITH A B19 BOMBER CREW FOR A GALLON OF RED PETROL, TWENTY CORK-TIPPED DU MAURIER AND HALF A WOOLTON PIE, YOU KNOW.

EEEH, DOLLY.

THE MORE I HEAR, THE MORE DISGUSTED I GET.

WELL MR. PLAXTON'S MINE THIS WEEK, DOLLY, I TELL YOU.

HOW'S THAT THEN, ADA?

I'M GOING TO CATCH HIS EYE WITH SOME NEW SHOES. HE'S ALWAYS HAD A PENCHANT FOR A SHAPELY ROOT, HAS MR. PLAXTON. HE'S WELL KNOWN FOR IT.

IS HE?

OH AYE. HE'S GOT ONE OF THESE FEET FOOTISHES.

IN FACT, HE'S BEEN TO PRISON FOR IT, ACTUALLY.

EEEH, NO!

OH YES.

HE GOT CAUGHT MASTURBATING OVER A RACK OF HIGH-HEELED SLINGBACKS IN FREEMAN HARDY AND WILLIS.

BY. HE'S A DARK HORSE, THAT MR. PLAXTON.

WELL, I'M GOING TO WOW HIM THIS WEEK, DOLLY. I'VE BOUGHT MESELF A NEW PAIR OF SHOES.

LET'S HAVE A LOOK AT 'EM, ADA.

EEH, ADA! THEY'RE SMASHING, THEM. THEY'RE THE MOST BEAUTIFUL THINGS I'VE EVER SEEN!

THEY'RE SPEEDY DUCKS, DOLLY.

I GOT 'EM IN THE SALE. TWENTY POUND OFF, THEY WERE.

SPEEDY DUCKS!? TWENTY POUND OFF!? EEH! IT'S A MIRACLE!

ARE THEY COMFY?

NOT REALLY, NO. YOU SEE, WHAT WITH ME CORNS AND ME HAMMER TOES, I CAN'T GET SHOES TO FIT, BUT THEY WERE TOO MUCH OF A BARGAIN TO PASS UP.

WELL, YOU'D HAVE BEEN A FOOL TO, ADA, AT THAT PRICE.

AYE, DOLLY! MAUDE KERBISHLY WON'T GET A LOOK-IN WHEN MR. PLAXTON SEES ME TRIPPING THE LIGHT FANTASTIC IN THESE!

EEH — LOOK AT THE TIME, ADA. WE'D BEST GET DOWN THE TOP RANK SO YOU CAN STAKE YOUR CLAIM ON HIM, EH...!

SO...

...HERE WE ARE, DOLLY. I HOPE SHE HASN'T GOT HER MITTS ON HIM YET, 'COS I'M SPITTING FOR A FIGHT.

TONIGHT IN CONCERT... SLIPKNOT PLUS SUPPORT

SHORTLY...

...MY TURN TO LEAD, ADA.

RIGHT YOU ARE, DOLLY...

...DOLLY...

YES, ADA?

CAN YOU SEE MR. PLAXTON YET?

NO.

...C'MON MOTHERFUCKERS!! ...PEOPLE = SHIT!! PEOPLE = SHIT!! PEOPLE = SHIT!! WHATCHA GONNA DO...!?

I HOPE HE GETS HERE SOON. THESE RUDDY SHOES ARE PLAYING MERRY HELL WITH ME BUNIONS.

CROWN F

Palace Chiefs Cock Up Again

ALARMING lapses in royal security have been highlighted after yet ANOTHER undercover reporter tricked his way into a job at Buckingham Palace. *Daily Star* journalist Nick Lazenby used forged references to secure a post as Second Breakfast Underfootman, a position which brought him into daily contact with the Queen. Lazenby played the part of the faithful royal servant for the best part of a morning before his cover was blown when he was caught in the Queen's dressing room, going through her underwear drawer.

But during his near 4 hours in the midst of the Royal family, Lazenby was able to compile a terrifying dossier highlighting over a dozen opportunities when he could have put Her Majesty's life in danger. His appointment has proved a great embarrassment to members of the royal household and his explosive story will make uncomfortable reading for palace security chiefs.

PALACE

Lazenby, 38, found out about the palace vacancy after speaking to a fellow reporter in a pub one evening. "He told me he had just been working undercover at the palace himself, but had been exposed and sacked. So I knew there would be a job going," he told us. "I called the Comptroller of the Queen's Household and asked for the job and he told me to come down straight away. At the interview, I just had to sign a bit of paper saying I wasn't a terrorist or a reporter. He then asked me for some identification, and I showed him a fake gas meter reader ID card that I'd bought from the small ads in the back of a disreputable comic."

To his amazement, Lazenby was given the job on the spot and sent to be fitted for his footman's uniform. Ten minutes later, the undercover reporter was given his first task, making a pot of tea for the Queen.

Come on in and kill our Queen: Lazenby found Palace gates flung open to terrorists, nutters and crackpots.

" "I couldn't believe how easy it was. Nobody knew me from Adam, yet here I was, entrusted with making a cuppa for the Monarch of England. There was nobody else in the kitchen and I could have done anything I wanted to it. On this occasion, I merely wiped the teabags up and down the cleft between my buttocks. But had I been a terrorist, I could have filled the teabags with rat poison, or even worse. It doesn't bear thinking about."

MAZE

Lazenby took the tea into the royal bedroom and handed it to

"Thankfully on this occasion it was only my anal perspiration the Queen was drinking."

the Queen, who was sitting up in bed.

"I watched as she drank it, and it sent a shiver down my spine," he said. "Thankfully on this occasion it was only my anal perspiration the

Queen was drinking. Had I been a member of Al Q'aeda, Her Majesty might not have been so lucky."

However, Lazenby's chilling reflections were cut short when the Queen herself barked out an order for a slice of toast and marmalade. Once again he found himself unsupervised in the kitchen, preparing food for her Majesty.

...ercover Cereal Killer

...OOLS

"Unlike most people, the Queen doesn't eat marmalade from the jar, it has to be placed into a special silver dish. I'm sure any self respecting assassin would have taken the opportunity to mix lethal anthrax spores into the marmalade before decanting it. Just thinking about it made my blood run cold, and I was furious with the staff for putting her in such danger," said Lazenby. "It was sheer luck that I was not an assassin, and had merely urinated in her marmalade. And pushed the toast down the back of my pants and farted on it."

TIPPS & ALISTAIR

However, as Lazenby put the tray on the royal bedside table, he received an unexpectedly frosty reception. Contrary to what many people may think, the Queen is a very independent woman and likes to perform many everyday tasks for herself. One such is spreading her own marmalade onto her toast at breakfast. On this morning, she pointed out that Lazenby had forgotten the knife, and furiously tore a strip off her hapless servant.

"I pushed the toast down the back of my pants and farted on it."

"She gave me a roasting and sent me to the kitchen to fetch a knife, " he continued. "Little did she realise she could have been signing her own death warrant. I was a harmless undercover reporter, but no one asked questions about my mental state when I was given the job. I could just as easily have been a murderous pyschopath or serial killing cannibal. And here I was, walking into the Queen's bedroom carrying a knife. Fortunately for her I had just scraped it underneath my farmer's hat, but for all anyone knew or cared, I could have been about to disembowel our head of state and tuck into her organs. I shudder now to think about it.

Shortly afterwards, Lazenby was arrested by members of the Royal Protection Squad when Her Majesty caught him performing an obscene act into her open underwear drawer and raised the alarm.

"I explained to the police that I was a reporter and was just trying to highlight how easy it would be for a determined Fathers For Justice campaigner to slip a small venomous snake into the Queen's dressing table, but they wouldn't listen," he told us.

Earlier this week at Bow Street Magistrates Court, Lazenby was found gulity of obtaining employment by deception, an act of gross indecency, and four counts under the Health and Hygiene Act 1982. Sentence was deferred pending psychiatric reports.

Lazenby hit the headlines ten years ago when he used a forged passport to get a job as a postman in Gloucestershire. On that occasion, in order to highlight the risks posed to the Royal family by letter bombers, he delivered more than 20 packages containing excrement and obscene polaroid photographs of his genitals to the home of the late Princess of Wales.

At risk: The Queen yesterday.

What The Butler Saw

DURING his few hours in the palace, Lazenby witnessed some shocking lapses in security. Here are some of the worst, snapped with a concealed disposable camera.

Royal Wee: Tangy taste of marmalade could disguise anthrax spores.

Pot Shot: The Queen's cuppa. One lump of cyanide or two?

Knife to See You: Monarch could find blade turned on herself.

The Butler Did it: For reasons best known to himself, Lazenby broke wind on Queen's toast.

circle of shame!

CIRCLE OF SHAME! CIRCLE OF SHAME! CIRCLE OF SHAME! CIRCLE OF SHAME! CIRCLE OF SHAME! CIRCLE OF SHAME! CIRCLE OF SHAME!

WE SHOW YOU THE STUFF THE STARS WANT TO HIDE!

A fine mess!

LGV DRIVERS HANDBOOK 1998
HARDCOVER
REFERENCE / TRANSPORT

FEB 21 1999
JUL 04 1999
JUL 1

Screen siren Uma Thurman looks a million dollars at this charity gala at the Beijing Opera, but uh oh! What's that under her arm? She certainly wouldn't want her fans spotting that those library books are horribly overdue, and there'll be a big fine to pay when she takes them back.

Miller mishap!

Even fashion icons can make basic style howlers. Slinky Siena Miller has perfected the just-got-out-of-bed look, but check out her chic Dolce & Gabbana nightdress-inspired outfit. There's all shit up the front of it.

Gee whiz!

It-Girl Paris Hilton has the world at her shoes, but a bare-shouldered outfit reveals she's really put her foot in it – with this ill-advised drunken tattoo of Les Dennis' late comedy partner, *Laughter Show* star Dustin Gee! Oh no!

What a boob!

Scarlett Johanssen probably hoped a dose of Hollywood glamour would knock 'em dead at this West End premiere, but anyone hoping to check out her dynamite curves would be left cold by the old Gregg's pasty bag she's left stuffed into her cleavage. Clang!

Hair apparent!

Gorgeous Charlize Theron dazzled at the Oscars with this stylishly cut white suit, but what's that make-up hiding? Sure enough, an unflinching close up reveals that her thick foundation is concealing a big 1970s IRA moustache. Probably.

Carry On Behind

Ex-Hear'Say stunner Myleene Klass may look as pretty as a picture at the opening of Gordon Ramsay's new restaurant, but take a closer look. Inside her mind is the opinion that the best Carry On film is *Carry On Behind*. Whoops!

We hate you! We hate you!

GILBERT RATCHET

IT'S CHRISTMAS EVE, READERS. I CAN HARDLY WAIT TO OPEN MY PRESENTS TOMORROW.

SANTA'S COMING!

BLUURGH!

—SPROING—

SO I'VE BUILT THIS LABOUR-SAVING **FESTIVE ANTICIPATOR** WHICH LEAPS UP AND DOWN ON THE SOFA, SHRIEKING AND THROWING UP OVER DAD IN A FRENZY OF OVER-EXCITEMENT.

SORRY GILBERT ~ I'M AFRAID ALL YOUR PRESENTS WILL HAVE TO BE THROWN OUT.

HUNH? WHY'S THAT, MUM?

APPARENTLY SCIENTISTS HAVE DISCOVERED THAT THE GIVING AND RECEIVING OF WRAPPED SEASONAL GIFTS CAN CAUSE CANCER.

SO I'M CHUCKING THEM ALL IN THE BIN

PRESSIES LINKED TO PLONKER

HRUMPH! NO PRESENTS FOR ME.

CLONK

SOME CHRISTMAS THIS IS GOING TO BE.

TUT TUT, GILBERT! CHRISTMAS ISN'T JUST ABOUT GETTING PRESENTS: OUR THOUGHTS SHOULD BE OF MORE SPIRITUAL MATTERS.

STEP INTO MY CHURCH ~ I'M ABOUT TO OFFER UP MY YULETIDE PRAYERS TO THE LORD.

SEE, FOR MY MAIN BIG PRAYER I'M ASKING FOR ETERNAL SALVATION.

THEN FOR MY LITTLE PRAYERS I'VE PUT DOWN A CURE FOR MY BAD FEET, AND A BOP-IT.

NOW WE'LL SEND MY CHRIMBO PRAYER LIST OFF TO GOD.

THAT'S RIGHT GILBERT, JUST POST IT IN THE FONT

AND I'LL LEAVE A GLASS OF SHERRY OUT FOR THE LORD, AND A CARROT FOR HIS CHERUBIMS AND SERAPHIMS.

HULLO ~ THIS FONT IS FULL OF GLOSSY MAGAZINES...

OH NO! THAT'S MY STASH OF EROTIC LINGERIE CATALOGUES. I'D FORGOT ALL ABOUT THEM.

GOD'S BOUND TO HAVE SPOTTED ME OGLING THE BRA PICTURES ~ HE'LL NOT ANSWER MY PRAYERS NOW.

DON'T WORRY VICAR ~ A BIT OF REPENTANCE WILL SET YOU RIGHT WITH THE ALMIGHTY.

MY GUILT-POWERED REMORSE-O-TRON WILL TEARFULLY RIP UP YOUR LINGERIE CATALOGUES AND THROW THEM IN A BUSH FOR YOU

SHRED SNIP

THAT SHOULD DO THE TRICK

UH-OH! A PARTICULARLY HEAVY SNOWFLAKE HAS KNOCKED THE CONTROL LEVER

CLICK

THE REMORSE-O-TRON'S GUILT LEVELS ARE SET TO **FULL POWER**!

WOW! YOUR MACHINE IS SO CONSUMED WITH GUILT AND SELF-DISGUST, IT'S TAKEN TO RIPPING UP PROSTITUTES...

CHOP

SMASH-O HACK

...STARTING WITH MY STATUE OF THE FABLED BIBLICAL PROSSIE MARY MAGDALENE.

SMASH CHIP HACK MUTILATE

WHAT'S ALL THIS NOISE?

FULCHESTER PALACE

COO! HER MAJESTY THE QUEEN IS IN RESIDENCE AT FULCHESTER PALACE, NEXT DOOR.

OH DRAT!

THAT'S TORN IT!

WHAT'S WRONG, YOUR MAJESTY?

I'VE LOOKED OUT ON THE FEAST OF STEPHEN, AND CAUGHT SIGHT OF THIS OLD MAN GATHERING WINTER FU-EL.

AS QUEEN, I AM NOW CONTRACTUALLY OBLIGED TO GIVE HIM A MINCE PIE.

IT'S NOT FAIR! I WANT ALL THESE MINCE PIES FOR MYSELF!

WHY SHOULD I HAVE TO SHARE THEM WITH SOME REEKING PROLETARIAN TWIG-SCAVENGER?

NEVER FEAR, YOUR MAJESTY.

I'LL INVENT A DEVICE WHICH WILL ENABLE YOU TO SHOW GOODWILL TO THAT PEASANT WITHOUT GIVING AWAY A SINGLE ONE OF YOUR OWN PRECIOUS PIES.

THERE ~ THIS **QUEEN AID™ CHARITY-O-MATIC** WILL USE YOUR ROYAL CELEBRITY STATUS TO PERSUADE THE **PUBLIC** TO PAY FOR A PIE FOR THAT POOR OLD MAN

...FE-E-ED THE PAUPER...

HM QUEEN SEZ:

COUGH UP

CLINK

..DOES HE KNOW IT'S FEAST OF STEPHEN TIME AT ALL...

AND SHORTLY

HERE'S A PIE FOR YOU MR PEASANT.

THANK YOU. BUT ACTUALLY, I'M NOT **REALLY** A POOR OLD MAN....

...I AM IN FACT **GOD** IN DISGUISE!

VICAR

QUEEN

GILBERT

AND AS A REWARD FOR YOUR CHARITY, PLEASE ACCEPT THESE PRESENTS WHICH COST A MILLION POUND EACH.

ACE! MERRY XMAS READERS!

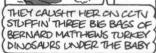

A **BRONCO BULL?** WHERE THE FUCK DID HE GET ONE OF THEM FROM?

BORROWED IT OFF OF DIRTY RON... Y'KNOW... HIS MATE ON THE BINS...

TURNED HIS GARAGE INTO A RITZY LAP DANCIN' CLUB, HE HAS – THE VELVET OYSTER

IT'S A CLASS JOINT... BULL MACHINE, MIRROR BALL, HOME BREW ON TAP, DANCIN' POLE... HIS MISSUS AN' HIS ELDEST DAUGHTER DO THE DANCIN'!

SOUNDS TOP, BAZ

OH, AYE...IT'S A PROPER SET UP IT IS, SAN

THERE'S NO TOUCHIN' OR WANKIN' OR NOWT... PRIVATE MEMBERS ONLY

ALRIGHT, Y' COTTON' PICKIN' VARMINTS!

HEY, I LIKE THE HOLSTER, DAVE... SMASHIN' THAT... IS IT REAL, IS IT?

NAH! IT'S JUST A TOY ONE... THE MISSUS PICKED IT UP IN ASDA.

THE GUN'S REAL, MIND

FUCK ME! COLT 45?

NAH!... IT'S A LUGER, THIS...

FEEL THE WEIGHT OF THAT FUCKER, BAZ

FUCK ME!

ME GRANDAD USED IT IN WWII... COOSHED A GUARD WITH IT, HE DID

I DIDN'T KNOW YOUR GRANDAD WAS A P.O.W DAVE

HE WASN'T

HE GOT CAUGHT NICKIN' A BARREL OF BITTER FROM THE NAAFI STORES IN CATTERICK

CAREFUL, BAZ... THAT MIGHT GO OFF

NAH
SPIN!
SPIN!

...BEEN JAMMED FOR YEARS, TRAY

ANYWAY... WHERE SHALL I PUT THIS BULL, BAZ

ER... I DUNNO, DAVE...

HOW BIG ARE THE CRASH MATS THAT GO ROUND IT?

I DIDN'T BOTHER BRINGIN' 'EM, BAZ... THEY WOULDN'T FIT IN ME VAN

WOT ABOUT OVER BY THE FRUIT MACHINE?

SHORTLY...

RIGHT, WHO FANCIES FIRST SHOT?

ME! ME! ME FIRST!

NOW, IF YOU CAN LAST FOR MORE THAN TEN SECONDS, YOU'RE DOIN' WELL, SAN

THAT'S WOT I SAY TO BAZ WHEN HE'S ON THE NEST

WOOOOO-OOOOOH!

HEY! THIS IS HARDER THAN IT LOOKS, THIS... WOOO!

WA-HOOOOH!

I'M ALL OVER THE FUCKIN' SHOP!

SAN... I'VE NOT SWITCHED THE FUCKER ON, YET...

CLICK!

MENTAL
FAST
MEDIUM
SLOW
OFF

BUCK!

CRASH!

OOF!

SPLATT!

77

Charity Begins at Frome

A FROME MAN known to locals as 'Mr Charity' was yesterday honoured by the Queen for his latest efforts to raise money for worthy causes.

Big-hearted Brian Neatsfoot, who changed his surname by deed poll to Charity in recognition of his many good deeds, became interested in fundraising after watching the annual BBC Children in Need telethon in 2001. He remembers to this day the powerful effect the show had on him. He told us: "I was enraged by the whole debacle. All I could see was a load of D-list celebrities cavorting around in stupid costumes going 'look at me everyone, aren't I great. Look at all the money I'm raising for my stupid charity'. I just thought, 'I'll show them!'"

Brian quickly organised his first charity stunt, a sponsored holiday to Crete with his wife Doris in aid of Save the Children. Although he managed to raise over £2000 from kindhearted locals, the event wasn't quite the success he had hoped for.

"The problem was that people weren't generous enough," he explained. "Once I'd covered my overheads, flights, hotel bills, spending money etc., I was left with about 50 quid. Children In Need made a lot more than that, unfortunately."

However, all was not lost as Mr Charity was able to spend the remaining money on an award for himself in recognition of his efforts. "Of course to me it's not about accolades, it's about helping people," he

OBE for Somerset Fundraiser

told us. "But the award was a lovely gesture and it made me realise that I must be doing something right It made all my hard work worth while."

Brian decided to base his next stunt a little closer to home in order to capture the public's imagination.

"I came up with the idea for a Jacuzzi-a-thon," he said. "I was pretty proud of that one!" The Jacuzzi-a-thon saw Brian and his wife spend over an hour relaxing in a luxury whirlpool bath in their back garden whilst drinking champagne and eating caviar, in aid of Guide Dogs for the Blind. And it was a huge success.

"The public really seemed to get behind this appeal and the donations flooded in," Mr Charity said. "Even after the cost of a top of the range Jacuzzi and the specially imported champagne and caviar had been deducted from the totaliser, I was left with a whopping 500 pounds!"

Brian decided that such a suc-

Mr Charity' Yesterday

cess warranted an equally impressive award and used the leftover funds to splash out on a lavish trophy which Doris presented to him at private ceremony in the couple's lounge.

"You should have seen it," Charity told us. "It really was an award fit for a King - the King of Charity."

At this point, many fundraisers would have sat back and taken it easy. But not Brian Charity. Buoyed by his successes, he embarked on his most ambitious fundraising project to date.

"I decided I was going to raise enough money to pay off my mort-

gage for spina bifida," he said.

Such is Brian's charisma that once again the generous public dug deep into their pockets.

"Although I launched the appeal over Christmas when people are feeling the pinch, the donations rolled in," he told us. "By February, I had raised enough money for spina bifida to pay off my mortgage.

"Not only that, but there was enough left over for me and Doris to buy ourselves a villa in Puerto de Pollenca in aid of Mencap," he added.

And Charity insists that he doesn't want any thanks for his tireless work for good causes. "I'm not in this game for recognition or honours," he said. "It's enough for me to know that I have done my bit for others less fortunate than myself. I never expected to receive an OBE from the Queen, but now that it's happened there's really nothing else I could wish for. Except a statue of me in Trafalgar Square."

Shelley's Bean Dilemma ~ Day 58

Shelley and Dave love each other. But they just can't see eye to eye about kidney beans...

Shelley is having an afternoon shower...

I love Dave, but his dislike of kidney beans is threatening our relationship

Later...

I'm making a chilli tonight, Dave. How about I put just a few kidney beans in it?

No thanks, Shelley. I really dislike them

That night, Shelley has a dream about Dave's mate Steve...

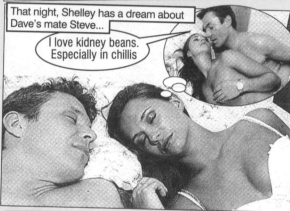

I love kidney beans. Especially in chillis

Next morning, Shelley is confused...

I wish Dave loved kidney beans like Steve

Zzzzzz Zzzzzz

CONTINUES TOMORROW...

Dr Miriam's Bean Advice

The pulse advice lines you can trust

Husband hiding beans under knife & fork	01 811 8055
Worried about cooking times for broad beans	018 118 055
Green beans - steam them or boil them?	0 181 18055
Tempted to eat beans straight out the tin	01811 80 55
Rimming tips to drive your man wild	0 1811805 5

Calls cost 60p/min and terminate on a small scrollwork table at the bottom of Miriam's stairs.

Beans Talk

Britain's best-loved Bean Forum

with TVs Morrison's ad voiceover man **Sean Bean**

WELL WHAT a week it's been, (and that's 'been' as in the past participle of the verb 'to be', not a small leguminous seed). The Met Office tells us that it's been one of the hottest summers on record, so in between doing ads for Morrison's and some of my many other projects, I decided to do a bit of sunbathing in the garden. When I came in the house my wife, it I've got one, quipped "Oh, look. A baked Bean!" And talking of beans, here's a selection of the best bean letters that have 'been' sent in this week...

Star Bean Letter

My husband sent me to the greengrocers to get some beans for his tea. "You'll have to be quick," he said. "Why?" I asked. "Because I want runner beans," he replied. How I eventually laughed after he had explained this hilarious beans-based wordplay.

Mrs Ethyl Acetate Rochdale

* £5 goes to Mrs Acetate

WHAT A swizz these so-called baked beans are. I opened a tin of them the other day and they were cold.

T Power, London

HEINZ BEANZ FACTZ

57 Amazing Facts about Beans, brought to you by Professor Heinz Wolf

1. THE MOST dangerous bean in the world was Wild West hanging judge Roy Bean. In a thirty year career working at Dodge City Magistrates' Court, Bean sentenced 2,463 outlaws to death. By an eerie coincidence, 2,463 is exactly the number of baked beans in a 4oz tin!

Don't miss Heinz's Fact no. 2 on the next page!

WHAT'S THE deal with beans? With some beans, like kidney beans and baked beans you just eat the beans. But with others, for example string beans and runner beans, you eat the pod as well. What's all that about?

Jay Leno, California

MY SON emigrated to Australia over ten years ago. As a boy he used to love baked beans, so to stop him feeling homesick I started posting him a parcel containing four tins of them each week. Over the years it must have cost me a small fortune in stamps, but he's worth it. He never writes to thank me... he's probably too busy tucking into his favourite beans!

Ada Golightly, Sunderland

WHAT'S the deal with coffee beans? They're not beans at all. For a start, they don't come in a pod. And you don't eat them, you cover them with boiling water and you drink them. What's all that about?

D Letterman, New York

IN THE 1980s I was taken hostage in Beirut by Hesbollah. For five years I was chained to a radiator and given only beans to eat. Luckilly they are my favourite food so it was a lovely treat each day that kept me smiling through my ordeal.

Brian Keenan, Dublin

IT ALWAYS makes me laugh when a lively person is referred to as being 'full of beans'. I was once 'full of beans' after eating 18 catering-size tins of them for a bet. I didn't feel in the slightest bit lively. I spent the next four days lying on the sofa farting, clutching at my swollen belly and belching into my cheeks every few seconds.

K Turnpike, Leicester

AS BEAN enthusiasts, my wife and I were very excited to see that our local theatre was putting on a play called 'Jack and the Beanstalk', and immediately bought front row tickets. However, although the beanstalk referred to in the title was featured in the production, we were disappointed that beans themselves did not make an appearance. We left after two hours feeling very short-changed indeed, and needless to say we haven't 'bean' back to that theatre again.

Dr H Trubshaw, Cheshire

DURING my incarceration at the hands of terrorists, I spent two years in a windowless room with Brian Keenan. He spent all day everyday going on about how much he liked beans whilst farting incessantly. What a miserable experience that was. The day my captors put a bag over my head and dragged me off to solitary confinement was the happiest day of my life.

John McCarthy, Cornwall

WHILST in the greengrocers the other day I was amused to notice a sign reading 'Bean's 45p/lb'. I immediately pointed out to the shopkeeper that he had put an apostrophe where none was necessary. However,

Has Beans

Celebrities from the Past who still enjoy Beans

No. 38 ~ Russ Abbott

"I used to be the drummer in The Black Abbotts, so I suppose you'd expect me to like black beans. But they bring me out in a rash on my scrotum. It's broad beans for me every time."

Next week: John Inman

Kids Say the Beaniest Things!

I TOOK my 5-year-old grandson into a fast food restaurant the other day, and saw that they were selling bean burgers. "They must be made from runner beans," he said!

Mrs Ethyl Acetate
Rochdale

* Mrs Acetate wins £5

imagine my embarrassment when he explained that he hadn't made a mistake, and that the beans in question had been reserved earlier in the day by rubber-faced funnyman Rowan Atkinson aka Mr Bean. The apostrophe was there to turn his characters name into the possessive noun!

Lynn Truss,
London

I'M AN Australian, and packages containing tins of beans keep arriving at my house addressed to the previous occupant. He left six years ago without leaving a forwarding address. The thing is, I can't stand beans so I end up throwing them in the bin. I always open the parcels first, though, because they sometimes have money in.

Bruce Hogan,
Melbourne

HEINZ BEANZ FACTZ

57 Amazing Facts about Beans, brought to you by Professor Heinz Wolf

2. THE MOST widely-travelled bean in the world is former astronaut Al Bean. As commander of the Apollo 16 mission, Bean flew 516,274,309 miles to the moon and back. By an eerie coincidence, 516,274,309 is exactly the same number of baked beans in one of them really big catering tins that they use in schools!

Don't miss Heinz's Factz nos. 3 to 57 next week!

MANY YEARS ago whilst working as an envoy for the Archbishop of Canterbury, I was taken hostage in Beirut. For five years my kidnappers fed me on nothing but fish fingers, chips and beans. I absolutely hate beans, but I didn't want to hurt my captors' feelings in case they killed me. So I used to slip the beans into my pockets when they weren't looking. By the time I was released and flown into RAF Brize Norton, I had over four tons of beans in my pockets.

Terry Waite,
Canterbury

Bean Texts

☐ I LUV PS! BNS R 4 LOO-ZRS! GET A LYF U SADOS! **hairy al, lvpl**

☐ bnz r gr8 ps r gay! **rod scott, bath**

☐ plz prnt more lush pix of mung bnz 4 the ladz on hms invincible. **the beanster**

☐ P EATIN SCUM SHUD B STRNG UP. WIV STRING BEENZ! **angry coppa, nott'm**

Bean Jokes

Q. What bean isn't very slow when it moves?
A. A runner bean.

Mrs Ethyl Acetate
Rochdale

* Mrs Acetate wins £5

Knock knock!
Who's there?
Ivor
Ivor who?
Ivor liking for beans.
Mr Ian Likingforbeans
Cardiff

Q. What sort of bean would you find half way down a child's leg?
A. A 'kid knee' (kidney) bean.
Stephen Fry, Norfolk

Q. What sort of bean would you find half way down a young goat's leg?
A. A 'kid knee' (kidney) bean.
John Sessions,
London

EMERGENCY MASTURBATORY INTEREST

81

PETER Bowles has been a fixture on Britain's TV screens for over thirty years. His perfectly judged performances in shows as diverse as *To the Manor Born*, *Executive Stress* and *The Bounder* have made his face into a household word from Land's End to John O'Groats.

Throughout his career he has played many parts in many stories, but none has been as strange as the story of his own life. It is a life which has seen him on the brink of sporting superstardom one day, to nearly taking a job in the world's most famous rock group the next; from almost becoming supreme leader of the world's largest religion to just about being offered the opportunity to go into outer space. Now, in this exclusive extract from his autobiography '*To the Manor Bowles*', (PanMacmillan £12.99) he lifts the lid on one of the most extraordinary careers in showbusiness.

I have played many parts in many stories, but none have been as strange as the story of my own life

MOP-TOP OFFER NEARLY HAD ME BEAT

'I had wanted to be an actor all my life, so it came as quite a surprise when, out of the blue, I was offered the chance to become a pop star,' says Bowles.

'One day back in the sixties I was in my kitchen, making myself a bite to eat, when the phone rang. Picking it up, I immediately recognised the Liverpudlian voice at the other end of the line. It was Paul McCartney out of the Beatles. "Mr Bowles," he said. "It's such a privilege to speak to you. I've enjoyed your work in shows such as *Nanny Knows Best* for many years. In fact, I think you are the best actor in the whole world."

'He went on to explain that his group was busy recording their seminal Sergeant Pepper's Lonely Hearts Club album at Abbey Road Studios, just a stone's throw from my flat. He said that Ringo Starr had been taken ill and asked me if I would be interested in taking over as the Beatles' drummer. He told me that only someone with my impeccable timing would be suitable for the job. As you can imagine, I didn't need asking twice! But I told him I couldn't get round there for a few minutes, as I was just about to eat quite a large cheese sandwich.

'As it turned out, by the time I had finished my sarnie and got round to Abbey Road studios, Starr had recovered from his illness so I never did become a member of the world's greatest rock band. *But I often stop to think how different my life would have been as one of the Fab Four... John, Paul, George and Peter Bowles!*'

'THRONE' BY MISSED HOLIDAY JOB OPPORTUNITY

'As an actor, work opportunities happen all the time, often at the most unexpected moments. But even I found it hard to believe the job offer I received once whilst I was on holiday in Rome.

'I was sitting in a cafe, about to have my lunch, when I was approached by an elderly priest. He explained that he worked at the Vatican as the Pope's personal assistant. "The holy father is a great fan of yours," he told me. "In fact, he spends many hours every day sitting in his private apartments watching tapes of your programmes, such as the second and third series of *Executive Stress*, when you replaced Geoffrey Palmer in the role of Donald Fairchild."

'The man told me that his boss was thinking of retiring soon, and had started looking around for someone to take over after him as head of the Catholic church. "The Pontiff has been very impressed with the way you have made that role your own," he explained. "His holiness would be greatly honoured if you would come to the Vatican and become Pope Peter Bowles the First."

'Just at that moment, the waiter arrived with a mozzarella and tomato sandwich I had ordered, so we were unable to continue our conversation. But I often wonder what would have happened if I had followed up that job offer and become the infallible figurehead of the billion-strong Roman Catholic faith.

'I know one thing for sure, I couldn't have starred as Hilary, Rigsby's camp playwright tennant in *Rising Damp*, if I'd been the Pope. The show was always recorded at Yorkshire TV's Leeds studios on a Sunday evening, when I would have had to be a thousand miles away in Rome, *taking Mass from my balcony overlooking St Peter Bowles's Square!*'

MY FOOTBALL NEAR MISS WAS THE FINAL STRAW

'I was standing at a snack bar near Wembley Stadium when a bald man in a red tracksuit walked up to me. I recognised him as Sir Alf Ramsey, the England football coach. "I can't believe it's really you," he gushed. "You're my favourite actor of all time. I just can't get enough of your work in shows like *The Bounder*," he added. He explained that he needed a quintessential Englishman like me to spearhead the national team's attack in a game which was just about to kick off over the road.

'I sadly explained that I couldn't accept his offer as I had just that moment bought a bacon, lettuce and tomato sandwich which I was about to eat. "That's a shame," said Sir Alf. "I'll have to find another centre forward."

'In the last forty years, I have often wished I had foregone that sandwich and turned out to represent my country in that match. For the man that replaced me in the England team was none other than Geoff Hurst, and it was his third goal in the last second of the match that secured the 1966 World Cup for England. During breaks in filming on some of the many hit shows I have starred in, I sometimes imagine how that famous commentary would have sounded with my name instead of Hurst's. *"And here comes Peter Bowles out of To the Manor Born! Some people are on the pitch, they think it's all over! It is now!"*

© *Peter Bowles 2006*

Next Week:
One Small Step for Man, One Giant Leap for Peter Bowles!
The time I met Buzz Aldrin in the BBC canteen and narrowly missed a chance to go to the moon. Because of a sandwich.

...SO, MR ACE - ARE YOU STILL GETTING THOSE BAD HEADACHES EVERY DAY? AYE DOCTOR. I SEE.

NOW I EXPLAINED TO YOU LAST WEEK THAT MIGRAINES CAN BE TRIGGERED BY SENSITIVITY TO ITEMS IN THE DIET... AYE.

...AND I GAVE YOU A NUTRITIONAL DIARY TO KEEP. DID YOU REMEMBER TO FILL IT IN, MR.ACE? AYE... EXCELLENT. A'VE GORRIT 'ERE.

HMM...LET ME SEE... A PATTERN IS EMERGING... I'M GETTING AN IDEA OF WHAT MIGHT BE CAUSING YOUR HEADACHES, MR.ACE...

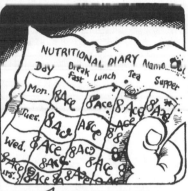
NUTRITIONAL DIARY Name. Ace
Day Breakfast Lunch Tea Supper
Mon. 8 Ace / 8 Ace / 8 Ace / 8 Ace
Tues. 8 Ace / 8 Ace / 8 Ace
Wed. 8 Ace / 8 Ace / 8
8 Ace / 8 Ace / 8
8 Ace / 8 Ace

NOW I'M REFERRING YOU TO A LOCAL SPECIALIST CONVALESCENT UNIT. A MONTH OR SO IN THERE SHOULD SORT YOU OUT. CHAMPION.

SO... SECURE HIGH DEPENDENCY & REHABILITATION UNIT

A MONTH LATER... ...CONGRATULATIONS, MR ACE! YOU'VE SUCCESSFULLY COMPLETED THE TREATMENT PROGRAMME! HERE IS YOUR CERTIFICATE. THANK-YOU.

SHORTLY... ...I'M HOME DEAR! AND YOU WON'T BELIEVE THE CHANGE IN ME!

PLEASE... OPEN THE DOOR, MY LOVE. I'M DIFFERENT...! I'VE KICKED THE ACE ONCE AND FOR ALL! KNOCK KNOCK

COME ON... GIVE ME ANOTHER CHANCE. I'LL NOT LET YOU DOWN. IT'S TIME TO DRAW A LINE UNDER THE PAST AND MOVE ON...! LET ME IN THE HOUSE...!

BLAM! BLAM!

JUST OPEN THE DOOR...! OPEN THIS FUCKING DOOR NOW!...YOU IGNORANT FUCKING......COW!

LET ME IN! LOOK...I'VE GOT A CERSTIFICATE TO SAY I'M OFF THE ACE! A FUCKING CERSTIFICATE IN BLACK AN' FUCKING WHITE...!

BLAM! BLAM! BLAM! BLAM! BOOT!

YOU FF-FFUCKING B-BB-BBITCH! LOOK WOT YER'VE DRIVEN ME TER...

THIS IS ALL YOUR FAULT, YER ROTTON OWLD F-FF FFUCKIN' CUNT!

MUTTER...GRUMBLE... A'LL SHOW 'ER... THE F-FF... FFRIGGIN'!...

SLAM!

PULL FIZZ...GLUG-GLUG
PULL FIZZ...GLUG-GLUG
PULL FIZZ...GLUG-GLUG
PULL FIZZ...GLUG-GLUG
PULL FIZZ...GLUG-GLUG
PULL FIZZ...GLUG-GLUG
PULL FIZZ...GLUG-GLUG

SLAM! OOH... ME FFUCKIN' 'EAD.

ROGER MELLIE
THE MAN ON THE TELLY

Panel 1: GREAT IDEA FOR A SHOW, TOM... '**WHO'S THE DADDY?**' YOU GET THIS COUPLE WHO WANT A SPROG, BUT THE HUSBAND'S FIRING BLANKS... ROGER, MAY I INTRODUCE...

Panel 2: SO YOU GET SIX BLOKES ALL COMPETING TO DONATE THEIR SPUNK... ROGER, MAY I... AND THEY DO MENTAL AND PHYSICAL AGILITY TESTS... A BIT LIKE THE KRYPTON FACTOR...

Panel 3: ...THE WINNER GETS TO BANG THE WIFE LIVE ON TELLY... PAY PER VIEW... WE COULD GET LORD ROBERT WINSTON TO HOST IT OR **RAY** WINSTON ...MAY I INTRODUCE ALEX DOVE

Panel 4: ALEX IS THE FOUNDER OF 'GODBOX TV' THE CHRISTIAN BROADCASTING CHANNEL HI, ROGER OH, LOOK, I'M SORRY, PAL, BUT I'M A BIT SHORT AT THE MO...

Panel 5: NO, ROGER... I'M NOT AFTER YOUR MONEY... I WANT YOUR SERVICES! OH? WE'RE HAVING A FUNDRAISING EVENING ON GODBOX TOMORROW. WE NEED TO RAISE £1 MILLION FOR OUR MISSION AROUND THE WORLD...

Panel 6: AND WE'D LIKE **YOU** TO HOST THE EVENING... ME!? WELL, I DON'T WANT TO TURN DOWN WORK, BUT WHY ME?... I'M HARDLY CLIFF FUCKIN' RICHARDS

Panel 7: YOU KNOW, ROGER... THAT'S WHAT **I** THOUGHT... BUT **GOD** LED ME TO YOU... HE TOLD ME THAT **YOU** WERE THE MAN TO DO **HIS** WORK TOMORROW EVENING

Panel 8: YEAH!?... AND DID **HE** TELL YOU HOW MUCH **HE** WAS PAYING? £50,000... UP FRONT

Panel 9: **50 GRAND!?** HALLELUJAH! PRAISE THE LORD... TELL HIM IT'S A DEAL THAT'S GREAT NEWS, ROGER PAY FOR MY NEW SWIMMING POOL, THAT I'M GLAD **HIS** SPIRIT FOUND YOU... PERHAPS WE SHOULD OFFER A PRAYER OF THANKS

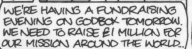

Panel 10: 'OH, LORD' WE THANK YOU FOR GIVING ROGER THE COURAGE TO USE HIS GIFTS TO DO THY WORK TOMORROW NIGHT...

Panel 11: ...AND WE ASK THAT YOU ENTER HIS HEART AND FILL IT WITH YOUR LOVE GIVING HIM THE STRENGTH OF YOUR...

Panel 12: NEXT EVENING... I WONDER WHERE ROGER IS... WE'RE ON AIR IN TWO MINUTES MISSION NIGHT 01 811 80

Panel 13: OH, HERE HE IS NOW 'PRAISE THE LORD, TOM'

Panel 14: EVENING EVERYONE ROGER... WHAT ON **EARTH** DO YOU THINK YOU LOOK LIKE?

Panel 15: HOLD ON, TOM... WAIT 'TILL YOU SEE IT WITH THE TEETH IN... FUCKIN' HILAR-IOUS.

Panel 16: BLEFF EE-U, MY FFUN...BLEFF EE-U. FFPECTACLES, TEFFTIC-LES, WALLET AND WATCH...FFPECTACLES, TEFFTICLES... ROGER...WHAT ARE YOU DOING?...**NO**

Panel 17: YOU'RE RIGHT, TOM...THE PUNTERS WON'T UNDERSTAND A FUCKIN' WORD I SAY IN THESE... MISS CAN WE SEND A RUNNER OUT TO GET A SMALLER SET?

Panel 18: ROGER...THIS ISN'T A **JOKE**! WE'RE TRYING TO RAISE **MONEY** FOR OUR **MISSION**! WELL YOU'VE COME TO THE RIGHT MAN... I HOSTED FTV'S 'KIDDIES IN NEED' TELETHON SIX YEARS ON THE TROT

Panel 19: HOW ABOUT WE KICK OFF BY GETTING A COUPLE OF BIRDS DRESSED UP AS NURSES TO SHAVE MY BOLLOCKS LIVE ON THE SHOW...? THE PLEDGE LINES WILL GO ABSOLUTELY MENTAL, ALEX, YOU MARK MY WORDS

Panel 20: NO...NO, IT'S NOT THAT SORT OF THING, ROGER. IT'S A RELIGEOUS SHOW AFTER ALL... EH?...WELL YOU'RE THE BOSS, ALEX

Panel 21: SORRY, GIRLS... WE WON'T BE NEEDING YOU AFTER ALL. STU

Panel 22: HOW ABOUT SOME NUNS DOING A STRIP, EH!?... THEY DON'T TAKE THE NEXT LAYER OFF TILL THE MONEY GOES UP

Panel 23: NO, ROGER. WE'VE GOT TO RAISE £1 MILLION BY APPEALING TO PEOPLE'S LOVE OF JESUS CHRIST NOW GET THAT STUPID COSTUME OFF WE'RE ON AIR IN 30 SECONDS... TAKE YOUR LEAD FROM ME.

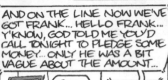

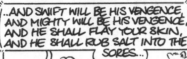

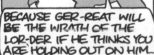

EVERY SECOND COUNTS

Scientists Warn of Bleak Future as Time Runs Out

EVERY DAY, newspaper scare stories warn that we're exhausting the world's natural resources. Whether it's oil, gas, ozone, rain forests or fish, chances are we're using our dwindling supplies up like there's no tomorrow. But now, says a report from a leading university, there may not even BE a tomorrow. For if the boffins' calculations are correct, we are wasting TIME at such an alarming rate that by the year 2040 we will have run out of it altogether and everything will stop.

"People simply don't seem to realise that time is a finite resource," the report author Arthur Author told us. "Unless we start saving it, and quickly, there will be none left for future generations to enjoy."

Cambridge professor Author lays the blame squarely at the door of our modern lifestyles. "Britons are using time faster than ever before," he said. "The average person now wastes time at over twice the rate he did he did twenty years ago. These days, adults come home from work and fritter away hours on end doing Sudoku puzzles and watching repeats of My Family on UKTV, whereas their 1980s equivalents would have done something useful with their time, such as putting up some shelves, reading an encyclopedia or doing a paint-by-numbers."

END OF THE TIMELINE
As the Sands of Time Run Out, Here's a Brief History of the Life and Times of Time Itself

13 BILLION BC	Our Solar System forms	200 MILLION BC	Age of the Dinosaurs	3 MILLION BC	Stonehenge built by cavemen	2005 AD	Time runs out
The Big Bang	2 BILLION BC	First single-celled life appears on Earth	65 MILLION BC	Man evolves out of some monkeys	100,000 BC	Louis Walsh quits ITV's 'X-Factor'	2040 AD

NO TIME LIKE THE FUTURE

Computerised time egghead Stephen Hawking looks into the future to describe the Britain of 2040, when time has run out

" *The first thing that will strike a visitor to the timeless world of tomorrow will be how very dark it is, even in the middle of the day. That's because light travels to the earth from the Sun at a speed of 186,000 miles per second. Without seconds to travel in, the light will simply stay up in space, casting our world into a state of constant gloom. As a result, we will have to carry torches everywhere we go.*

Ordinary activities which we take for granted now will become impossible when time runs out. Our boiled eggs will always come out wrong, either too hard or too soft, as there will be no way to judge how long they've been in the pan, and setting the video to record our favourite programmes while we are out will be a nightmare.

On the plus side, our journeys will become much shorter, as trains, buses and planes will arrive at their destinations at exactly the same moment they set off. Unfortunately, you will have no way of knowing this as your watch will have stopped working.

And you won't be safe on the streets. With no time for them to "do", prison authorities will be forced to release thousands of murderers and rapists back into society. Gangs of leather-clad mutants, some of them with only one eye, will drive round our town centres in Scrapheap Challenge-style vehicles, killing and maiming indiscriminately in their never-ending search for torch batteries. In such a dark and dangerous Mad Max-style society, life expectancy will plunge. A child born in 2040 will be lucky to see its thirtieth birthday. "

© 2006 Professor Stephen Hawking

"I'll Waste as Much Time as I Like"

Says TV Motorhead Petrolmouth **JEREMY CLARKSON**

SO WHAT if time is going to run out in 35 years? My grandfathers fought in two world wars for my right to waste as much time as I like, thank-you very much. And no hairy-chinned lesbian carpet munching lefty environmentalists are going to stop me.

From now on I intend to put my socks on each morning using chopsticks. And on my daily commute to work I'm going to take the long way round. Via Timbuktu.

Not only that, but I'm going to continue wasting time when I get to work, by making endless television programmes in which I drive unbelievably impractical and expensive motor cars round an airfield. With all smoke coming off the tyres.

And children are no better. "The average child wastes more than four hours each day playing online games such as Runescape or Habbo Hotel," said author. "His pre-internet counterpart could have used this spare time more constructively, perhaps making a kite, oiling his bicycle or learning to play the trumpet," he added.

Even senior citizens do not escape the professor's censure. "Old people are living longer than ever before, but they are spending the last twenty years of their lives complaining about the size of coins or writing doggerel poems about their cats for the Weekly News," he continued. "It all adds up to a colossal amount of wasted time which the world can ill afford."

Author believes that we are squandering one of our most precious natural resources at a frightening rate, and warns of a bleak future if we don't mend our ways. He told us: "We have to act now if we don't want our clocks to simply stop. If we keep on treating time like we have an endless supply of it, I estimate that our supply of months, weeks, days, hours and seconds will dry up some time in the next thirty-five years."

The professor says there are many ways we can all do our bit to conserve time. Something as simple as drinking instant coffee instead of tea can save several minutes per cup, as you don't have to wait for the bag to mash," he told us. "And concrete your garden over. Countless valuable hours are wasted each year by people mowing their lawns, trimming their hedges and weeding their flowerbeds."

S.O.S.
SAVE OUR SECONDS
Timelords Declaring War on Waste

THERE ought to be enough time left to last us for ever, but thanks to our wasteful lifestyles we're in danger of running out of it within a generation. Nobody knows more about the value of time than the Timelords. So we asked the surviving Dr Whos to take time out from saving the universe to offer some advice about how we can save time itself.

"I think we should all stop buying Filet-o-fishes at McDonald's," booms former Dr Who Tom Baker. "Think about it. With a four-minute wait whilst each of the sixty-million filets sold annually is prepared, Britons spend nearly two million days each year hanging round the counter or sitting in the grill order parking space. That time is lost. We can never get it back."

"Think how much time we waste watching daytime television," adds former Dr Who Colin Baker. "When watching Noel Edmonds' new show 'Deal or No Deal', just tune in for the last couple of minutes. That way you'll save the twenty-eight minutes it takes for the programme to grind its way through its interminable format and reach the vaguely interesting bit at the end. Better still, save the whole half hour by not watching it at all."

"The time we all waste sitting on the toilet could be put to much better use," suggests former Dr Who Sylvester McCoy. "Having a shit and preparing a stew are both things that take about half an hour, so keep a chopping board and selection of vegetables in the bathroom. Next time you're paying a 'sit-down-visit', you can prepare a nice salad or a stew on your lap whilst you're on the toilet. Don't forget to wash your hands before you wipe your arse, especially if you've been cutting chillies."

"Ironing clothes that people are never going to see is a complete waste of time," says former Dr Who Peter Davison. "So I never bother ironing my underpants or vest. And I only iron the bit of sock which will be visible between the top of my shoe and the bottom of my trouser leg."

"Millions of us waste hours each Christmas putting up decorations, only to take them down a few days later," moans only just former Dr Who Christopher Eccleston. "If we all became jewish and threw out our trees and fairy lights, just imagine how much precious time we'd save."

FIFA Blows Whistle on Timewasters

FOOTBALL CHIEFS LAST night announced that they were joining in the battle to prevent time running out with a series of sweeping rule changes.

With effect from the start of next season:

- *Half time will be cut from 15 to 5 minutes*
- *Referees will clamp down on time-wasting, making it a red card offence*
- *Post-goal celebrations will be limited to 10 seconds*
- *Referees will be issued with dictaphones to shorten the time needed when taking players' details*
- *Pitches will be shortened to a new length of 20 feet to speed up the game*

FIFA president Sepp Blatter introduced the new rules at a press conference, demonstrating his dedication to the cause of saving time by breathing from a tank of helium so he could speak faster.

Meanwhile Serie A chiefs in Rome have vowed to limit their players' dramatic rolling around in agony after each tackle to 3 minutes instead of the customary 10.

TEN Things You Never Knew About Time

IT FILLS up our past, present and future; busy people don't have enough of it, yet today's youths seem to have far too much of it on their hands. It's neither big or small but it's all around us every minute of the day. It's time. But how much do we really know about it? Let's spend a few minutes looking at ten things you never knew about this fundamental part of our abstract conceptual framework.

Even though we can't see, smell, taste or touch time, we can hear it. That's because watches tick audibly once per second, whilst churches make a loud clanging sound every hour.

Although you can't smell or taste time, you CAN smell or taste thyme small, perfumed stuff like posh salt that comes from the supermarket in plastic pots and little glass jars.

Just like a bus driver when you're running to catch his bus, time waits for no man.

'Time' was also the name of a shit musical written by the drummer out of the Dave Clark Five which starred Cliff Richard and a giant hologram of the late Laurence Olivier. That particular 'Time' would have waited for you, especially if you phoned the theatre and told them you were coming with a party of four or more people.

If you want to know what the time is, ask a policeman, or so the saying goes. However, unless your local bobby has a degree in theoretical physics or a working knowledge of the writings of Leibniz and Nietsche, you'd be better off approaching someone slightly better qualified.

Time is divided into intervals to make it easier to understand. Three of the main ones are dinnertime, teatime and bedtime.

The first people to record time were the Greeks, but the first people to record time and a half were the ancient Egyptians, who came up with the idea when they were doing the pyramids.

In the olden days time was measured using an egg timer, an hourglass shaped vessel half-filled with sand which could only go for three minutes. However, a modern quartz watch is much more accurate and can go for six months before its battery goes flat and it gets put in the drawer.

Although a coffee table is a table for putting coffee on, a timetable isn't a table for putting time on. It's a piece of paper pinned up in a railway station on which is printed a sequence of numbers that bear little or no relation to the movements of trains.

The world's smallest man, Calvin Philips, was also the possessor of the world's smallest wristwatch. It was so tiny that an hour lasted just a minute, and each second just two nanoseconds.

A DAY IN THE LIFE OF A
FIREMAN

THE Fire Brigade. Dial 999 and they'll be there in seconds, with sirens wailing and blue lights flashing. Each day they might tackle anything from a chip pan fire in an old folks' home to a raging inferno at a petrochemical refinery. No two shifts in the job are alike, but let's take a look behind the doors of a busy city centre Fire Station and see what happens during a typical day in the front line of the fight against man's deadliest enemy.

07.30 Green Watch are clocking out after a quiet night on duty, but who knows what may lie in store for Blue Watch who are about to begin their 12-hour shift. Because fires can break out at any time, firefighters are no strangers to missed meals, so it is important that they eat whenever they get the chance. That's why the day starts with a good breakfast of sausages, bacon, beans, fried eggs, fried bread and black pudding.

08.00 Breakfast is over, and tension is high as the men of Blue Watch retire to the day room to await the first call of the day. All seems quiet for now, but everyone knows that at any second they could be called away to rescue hundreds of people from a skyscraper which is being consumed by flames. The firefighters relax in many ways; reading books, listening to classical music, playing chess or watching hardcore pornographic videos.

10.38 It's been a quiet shift so far, but everyone is only too aware that all that could change in the blink of an eye. With a second's notice the alarm bell could sound, sending Blue Watch off to put their lives on the line once more, perhaps battling a massive blaze at a gasworks. To ensure that they have the energy to cope with whatever the day may throw at them, they relax with tea and biscuits whilst watching *European Cum Bath Volume 4.*

11.15 The alarm bell rings and it's action stations. Within seconds, the day room is a whirl of activity. The video is paused as the men of Blue Watch prepare to set out on their first job of the day. As they pull on their uniforms and leap aboard the shiny red tender, they have no idea what lies in store. It could be a simple domestic house fire, or it might turn out to be two fully-loaded jumbo jets that have collided mid air over the town centre.

11.23 After tearing through the streets with their siren wailing and lights flashing, the firefighters arrive to find a tearful old lady whose cat is stuck up a tree. At this point, their many hours of training come into play as they go into action like a well-oiled machine. Within seconds the cat is brought safely down and the grateful old lady serves up a well-earned tray of tea and biscuits. She will be sent an invoice for £850 later in the week.

11.58 After the excitement of the morning, the men wind down with a few snacks whilst watching the rest of *European Cum Bath*, followed by *Bukakke Babes* volumes 6 and 7. It is important for them to be mentally and physically relaxed as at any moment they could find themselves back in the engine, speeding towards a plastics plant which is uncontrollably ablaze, belching out a massive plume of thick, black, toxic smoke.

12.32 It is lunchtime, and once again the tender is back on the road, siren screaming. Hitting speeds of 60mph or more it hurtles through the narrow streets, ignoring red lights and stop signs in a desperate bid to get its precious cargo of fish and chips back to the station before they get cold. Keeping the brave firemen of Blue Watch well fed is vitally important as at any moment they could be called away to battle a forest fire threatening to engulf entire villages.

13.20 Firefighters have to keep themselves in peak physical condition since they know that any moment they could be clambering up a 200-foot ladder and carrying an unconscious, fully-grown man down to safety from a towering inferno. That's why, when they are not eating fried food or relaxing in front of *Cum Stained Casting Couch*, the members of Blue Watch keep themselves in tip-top shape playing volleyball, basketball or snooker.

14.09 The alarm rings for the second time that day and once again it's action stations. *Fucktruck Volume 14* is paused as the men of Blue Watch take to the tender. As in any emergency situation time is of the essence, so it is not until they are on the road that they find out what lies in store for them at their destination. It could be a simple bonfire which has got out of control, or it may be a blaze in a furniture warehouse billowing clouds of deadly cyanide gas.

14.19 Happily, there's no need for the breathing apparatus on this occasion, as the emergency turns out to be a young woman who has got her toe stuck in the bathtap. It is a routine job of the sort that firefighters are called out to all the time. But the chief officer knows that things could go wrong, so he decides to call in Yellow and Red Watches from a neighbouring station. With all these firefighters on hand, the woman's rescue is assured.

15.03 With thanks all round the men return to the station to finish watching *Fucktruck Facials 3*. Then it's time for bacon sandwiches all round while they take it easy watching *Cum on My Tiny Tits Volume 4*. It's been a hectic day, but no matter how tired the men of Blue Watch feel, they have to remain alert. They know that at any time they could be called out to a fire on the seventh floor of a 25-storey block of flats with 200 people stuck on the roof.

18.30 Firemen are an essential part of the community, and one of the men of Blue Watch takes an hour off his busy schedule to partake in a little community service. Firefighters regularly give talks about fire prevention to the public, or take their fire engine along to school fetes to press home their safety message. On this occasion he is demonstrating how a fireman takes off his uniform to a group of young women on a hen night.

19.24 All hands are back at the station and everyone is taking a well-earned breather watching *Anal Angels Volume 2*. There may only be a few minutes left of their shift but, like coiled springs, the men of Blue Watch remain constantly on the alert. At any time they could be called out to a motorway pile-up where a water tanker has collided with a lorry carrying enormous lumps of sodium, which has then been hit by a tanker carrying oxyacetylene.

19.30 It's the end of the shift, and for the first time in 12 hours the men of Blue Watch can switch off, both mentally and physically. For one or two, it is straight home to catch up on some long overdue sleep, but for the majority it's straight back to work in the petrol station, driving a mini cab or stacking shelves at the local supermarket. Meanwhile, for the men of Red Watch the night begins with the first showing of *Two Cocks Up One Cunt*.

Letterbocks

Letterbocks
Viz Comic
PO Box 656
North Shields
NE30 4XX

letters@viz.co.uk

Star Letter

LISTENING to a local radio station at work recently, a bloke in an advert for a large car dealership proclaimed "There's a branch near YOU!" To my amazement, I looked out of the window and saw several large birch trees next to the cabin.

Big Al, e-mail

I BET Wayne Rooney wouldn't have recovered so fucking quickly from his broken ankle if he had been a scouse council worker. That would have been a straight six monther.

Nobby Chinker e-mail

IT SEEMS to me that cartographers have been doing a bad and incomplete job of late. The amount of places that people say they want to 'put on the map' which really should have been there. It's shocking.

Ian Durrant e-mail

LAST week on the cover of the woman's magazine *Love It,* they offered a 'Free paternity test for every reader.' They seem to have drawn some unsavoury conclusions about their readership.

Andy Sands e-mail

HE Ain't Heavy, He's My Brother, sang The Hollies. Well that's not true in my case seeing as my brother is roly poly *Pop Idol* reject Rick Waller.

Tony Waller e-mail

THIS morning I saw a robin pecking frantically at some dogshit. You don't usually see that scene depicted on Christmas cards.

Fat Al White Wrenthorpe

THIS new police knife amnesty is a bloody nightmare. I dutifully handed all my knives in and now I've got nothing to eat my dinner with.

Richard Karslake Oxfordshire

IF only Henri Paul had put a 'Caution. Princess On Board' sticker in the back window of his car. How different things may have turned out.

J Thorn, Hexham

MY wife was delighted recently when given two toilet roll tubes covered in glitter that our two young children had made for her. So I decided to fashion her a lovely necklace out of paperclips rather than waste money on the expensive gold one she wanted for her birthday. Imagine my confusion when she burst into tears. Women, eh?

Mark, Upminster

IN reply to your plea for candid snaps of injured minor celebrities (*Letterbocks p.64*), I was lucky enough to catch Bernie Clifton coming out of a ladies bog at the Grimethorpe Plater's and Gobbler's club with a saucepan firmly affixed to his nut. Do I get a tenner?

Bobby Knutt, Barnsley

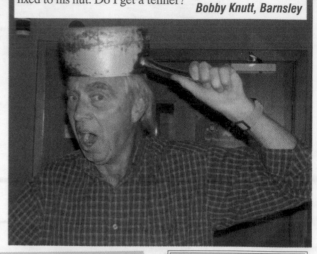

Top Tips

POST offices. Put up a notice saying 'Travel Money Available Instantly Here', let people queue up for ten minutes and then advise them that they need to give 3 days notice to order Euros for the holiday they are going on the next day.

Loz, e-mail

CONVINCE your friends that you play the trombone by standing behind a screen and farting into a watering can.

Peter Hall, e-mail

MOTORISTS. Always have a hot pie in your hands in heavy traffic. Each time the traffic grinds to a halt, just reach for the pie. The instant you place it to your lips the traffic begins to move. This works especially well with the molten lava apple turnovers from KFC.

Pat Jackson, e-mail

PARENTS. Each week count the contents of your cutlery drawer. This way you can quickly identify if any spoons or knives have gone missing that could potentially be used to administer illegal drugs or commit violent crime.

J Dolphin, Northampton

HAS anyone honestly say they have ever seen a less erotic lingerie advert than this one I found in the Sommerfield catalogue. It's the faint *Last of the Summer Wine* overtones that got me.

Cal Brighton

LINGERIE
www.amplebosom.com

Beautiful affordable lingerie by first class post.
All Sizes Great And Small

I SAW a man with a tattoo that said 'There's No Black in the Union Jack'. My friend thought that he might be racist, but I think that is jumping to conclusions. He might just be interested in flags and their colours.

Ian Durrant e-mail

LAST night I saw a woman driving a police car. Whatever next?

Tim Sutcliffe, e-mail

ROAD RAGE POSTBAG

TO THE BLOKE in the silver Astra on the A303 who cut in front of my truck then braked sharply: You're not a clever driver, just a twat. If you hadn't looked round and done a half-arsed wanker sign when I sounded my horn, I would have assumed it was a woman driving and said nothing more about it.

Wrigglytin, e-mail

Viz Comic, PO Box 656
North Shields
NE30 4XX

SUICIDE TEXTS

Viz readers have been doing themselves in in droves and sending us their suicide texts. Here are some of the best we've received...

STAR TEXT

☐ i cnt go on n e more. gonna nd it all 2 day. tel th kidz i luv m. **sad mick, nottm**

☐ i h8 my xstnce. wotz th pnt of goin on? i gt nuffin lft 2 lv 4 :(**harold, ldn**

☐ wn u rd ths txt il b ded n gon. hop ur satisfd. u cn all lol now. cnts. **gutted, l'pool**

☐ i m so alone. evbdy h8s me. no 1 wil care wen im ded. fck u all. **baz, gr8er mnchestr**

☐ my lifz gon rong. 2 mne detz not enuf £z. im takin e z way out. pls 4giv me mum. **bil, 10b, n wls**

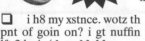

Are you going to kill yourself today? Text in your suicide note to us. The best one we receive wins a £10 wreath, 6 brass coffin handles and a tin of ham for the funeral. All texts cost 25p.

Pear Postbag

We've had thousands of letters this issue on the subject of PEARS. Here's the pick of the crop...

I HATE pears. They're just wonky apples if you ask me.

Eileen Brake, Cork

I SENT my husband to the shops to buy some pears. He came back with 2 of everything! And not even any pears! He's an idiot.

Ethyl Murton, Murton

I ALWAYS get pears and peas mixed up, but I have worked out a way to tell them apart. The spelling. And the fact that one is a fruit and one is a veg. And the fact that they look different.

Lupe Velez, Caracas

I LOVE pears so much I changed my name to Mr Pear and I eat nothing but pears. I really like pears. I hate anything that is not pears.

Frank Pear, Lambeth

I THINK that the children's cartoon *Care Bears* would have been much better if it had been called *Pear Bears* and had been about bears who liked pears. Or maybe it should just have been called *Pears* and been about pears.

Cecil Cunningham, Hull

THESE politically correct people who go around defending pears clearly forget that it is an apple - not a pear - a day which keeps the doctor away. Do these people want us all to die?

Cedric Allingham, Sussex

I **WAS** pleased to hear about the girl who was woken from a coma by James Blunt's song *Beautiful*, but wondered if this was outweighed by the number of people who have slipped into one whilst listening to his tepid drone.

Crystal Tipps, e-mail

AM I the only person who hasn't banged Kate Moss? Everyday the papers are full of stories from blokes claiming to have banged her.

It's something I'm quite keen on doing and I was just wondering if there is some sort of queuing system in place.

Zak Cassidy, e-mail

UP THE ARSE CORNER

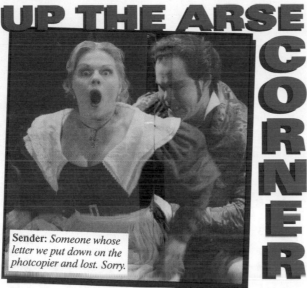

Sender: *Someone whose letter we put down on the photcopier and lost. Sorry.*

Fireman Sham

A feature on pages xx & xx, has got our brave firefighters hot under the collar. 'A Day in the Life of a Fireman' has been slammed by the fire service for its glaring innaccuracies and its stereotypical portrayal of fireman as porn watching layabouts. Here are just some of the complaints we received...

...volleyball is not played on duty due to an increase in ankle injuries. And the fish and chip run would never be undertaken on "lights and bells"; we leave that kind of behaviour to our colleagues in the ambulance service.

Derek Somebody, UK Fire & Rescue Service

we don't have a yellow watch, just red, white, blue and green. And we don't watch porn during the day, only on night shift. And we invite the birds into the station as they walk past from the pubs at night, inviting them in to slide down our poles.

Vic Von Scneider, Rotherham

...in 20 years' service I have never once listened to classical music whilst on duty. I would be grateful if you could print this correction as it could give people the wrong impression of life as a fireman.

Dave, Green Watch, Western-super-Mare

...there was a lack of balance in your article. At least two of the lads on my watch are puddle

jumpers, so we are as likely to be watching *Rugger Buggers*, *Locker Room Cum-Bath 6* or *WWE Spitroasts* as anything with fannies.

Dick Flick, Green watch

State of the Nation

Britain's Brightest Column for people who really like New Order

● The restoration of Wembley Stadium remains mired in chaos after it was announced that the legendary venue will not be ready for action until 2007 at the earliest. All concerts and sporting events scheduled to take place there this year have been rearranged or cancelled, much to the annoyance of thousands of people who have already bought tickets. The news does not affect New Order fans however, as the band had made no arrangements to play at the newly renovated stadium. *Phew!*

● An earthquake in Powhatan, a remote village in India, has left up to 70 people dead and a further 200 seriously injured. Luckily, no members of New Order were hurt in the disaster as they were thousands of miles away in Manchester when the quake hit, working on ideas for a new album which is slated for release next spring. *Watch this space!*

● Controversy in Nigeria where president Olusegun Mathew Okikiola Aremu Obasanjo, who has held power since 1999, is attempting to change Nigeria's constitution in order to allow himself to run for an unprecedented third consecutive term in office. The move has been met with strong resistance from his rival Muhammadu Buhari of the All Nigeria People's Party who is strongly tipped to take power himself in next year's national elections should the more moderate Obasanju be disqualified from running. *State of the Nation* is currently keeping an open mind as to who would be best placed to stabilise the troubled country as neither Obesanjo or Buhari have yet made public their policy on New Order. *Whenever you're ready lads!*

● Sad news as it was announced that June Pointer, the youngest member of the legendary Pointer Sisters, has died aged just 52. The news will be a cruel blow to New Order bass player Peter Hook who revealed in an interview with *Smash Hits* magazine in 1985 that he thought the Sisters' hit *Jump (For My Love)* was "a decent song". Flowers and messages of condolence can be sent to Peter at the usual address. *Remain strong, Pete!*

BIG ARNIE IN MIRACLE ESCAPE

GOVERNOR OF California *Arnold Schwarzenegger* found himself the target of a violent assassination attempt yesterday, yet miraculously escaped without a scratch.

The horrific attack, which lasted a gruelling *THREE HOURS,* came at the end of a routine baby-meeting and constituent-kissing walkabout. As the charismatic statesman made his way back through the crowd, he was *SHOWERED* with gunfire.

One eyewitness, Joseph Schmoseph, described the scene. "One minute the Governor was striding towards his bullet-proof limousine with a huge fixed grin on his face, and the next he was being machine-gunned by a mystery assailant.

"It sounds remarkable, but all the time he kept on walking and smiling. He didn't even break his stride.

EXCLUSIVE!

The bullets were simply bouncing off his chest like they were made out of cork."

Another onlooker, Maude Grape, recalled how the Governor stayed calm in the face of a terrifying hail of ammunition.

torso

"He turned around 180 degrees, legs first followed by upper torso, and broke into a purposeful stride across the street towards the gunman," she said. "Although he was surrounded by high-rise buildings, you could clearly make out a burning desert reflected in his sunglasses."

A large police presence, gathered just minutes after the gunfire broke out, could only sit and watch open-mouthed as the drama unfolded. "We're not trained for anything like this," one cop admitted.

"If we'd walked through that intensity of gunfire, we'd have become human colanders. Literally. I don't know how the Governor managed it in one

Schwarzenegger ~ cool as a cucumber during three-hour assassination attempt, yesterday.

piece, let alone without noticeable injury."

The crowd then witnessed the powerful politician picking up his petrified mystery assailant and tying him in a knot, before throwing him through a shop window and quipping something which onlookers believe sounded like "you're out of shape".

The Governor left the scene seconds later, clinging onto the rail of a passing helicopter and waving. He was unavailable for comment last night, but sources say that the governor remains confident that he will return at some point in the future.

Who Gives You Aggro?

TWO OF THE BIGGEST names in British advertising were involved in a furious bust up outside a London nightclub last night.

Scores of onlookers, including Cilit Bang's Barry Scott, the Yes Car Credit girl and Flash's Jacko out of Brush Strokes were left stunned when bespectacled Howard out of the Halifax Adverts traded punches with the other bloke out of the Halifax adverts outside Chinawhites at 3 am.

FIREWORKS

The hostility between the two singing mortgage advisors had been simmering for some time and there are many in the banking industry who will be far from surprised by last night's fireworks. Only last month, veteran Halifax ad king Howard Brown launched an astonishing attack on the other bloke out of the Halifax adverts, who is believed to be called Trevor or Keith, in a no-holds barred-interview with the Financial Times. "This new bloke has ripped off my act. He's just trying to cash in on my success," fumed the balding building society mouthpiece.

According to revellers at the trendy

EXCLUSIVE

West End venue, the pair had been eye-balling each other all evening. Tensions eventually came to a head when members of the other bloke out of the Halifax adverts's entourage began taunting Brown as he left the club, accusing him of being a 'has been' and 'fanny face'.

THERMOMETERS

Onlookers said Brown responded by branding a recent ad, in which the other bloke out of the Halifax adverts starred as a wild west gunslinger singing a cleverly reworded version of Rhinestone Cowboy, a 'pile of shite'. It was at this point the two disgraced stars briefly came to blows.

ERIC GILL'S COCK

Witnesses reported that the scuffle ended when former eSure Car Insurance ad prostitute Michael Winner intervened. One onlooker told reporters: "I don't know what he said, but it calmed them down immediately."

Two-doku

The World's Most Unewarding Number Puzzle

No. 2,345,945

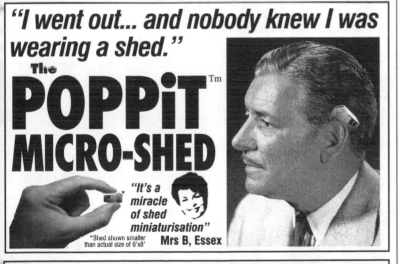

Fill in the grid on the left so that each horizontal and vertical line, and each 3x3 square contains the figure 2 nine times

Last Issue's Solution

NORTH SEA CASH!

BRITAIN'S MONEY CHIEFS were yesterday celebrating the news that fresh reserves of naturally occurring cash have been discovered deep beneath the North Sea.

Offshore exploratory drilling operations have struck vast fields of natural cash, enough to allay recent fears of dwindling supplies. Experts had estimated that, if current patterns of withdrawal continued, cashpoints throughout the UK would run dry within ten years, leaving just moths coming out of the slot.

HIGH PRESSURE

'We're delighted,' said dosh boffin Ollie Lolly of Lloyds Bank. 'On Thursday morning we received the first pictures of a cash gusher off the Northumberland coast. The sight of

By our money, money, money correspondent
BJORN ULVAEUS

those crumpled brown notes pouring into the air was music to my eyes.'

A pipeline is already being built to draw the money from its home beneath the seabed and pump it at high pressure to the thousands of cashpoints nationwide where it is needed most. Meanwhile a huge engineering operation is underway to convert ATMs to accept the new North Sea Cash, which is lighter and spends slightly faster.

MAPPA MONEY — Current British Cash Reserves

NEW FIND HERE

CROMARTY
Discovered 1971
£500m in used fivers. Estimated reserves left £24m. Expected to run out early 2008

FIND...
Disco...
£800m... tens and twenties. Estimated reserves left £100m. Expected to run out 2012.

LABRADOR
Discovered 1980
£50m in pound coins and fifty pees. Estimated reserves left £4m. Expected to run out spring 2007.

DUTCH CAP
Discovered 1974
£2bn in large denomination notes, mainly £50s and £20s. Estimated reserves left £865. Expected to run out 2.45 this afternoon.

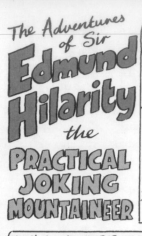

TONY PARSEHOLE

Why Best's death is the worst thing that's ever happened to me

WHEN I heard the terrible news that George Best had passed away I cried and cried and cried. I cried and cried and cried more than I have ever cried and cried and cried in my whole life.

I cried and cried and cried because, more than anyone else I have never met, George Best represented something important and personal to me. Something important. Something personal. To me.

As a schoolboy huddled on the grainy, black and white football terraces of the past, his dazzling football skills opened my young eyes to a Technicolour world that was limitless and free and beautiful. A world that was limitless. A world that was free. And yes, a world that was beautiful.

George Best was all those things and more. He was limitless. He was free. And yes, he was beautiful. Before George, the Saturday afternoon football match was a dismal, grey experience. Drab grey men would pass a lumpy grey leather ball to each other on a cold, churned up, muddy, grey bombsite whilst the crowd of black and white, grey men in dull, flat, lumpy grey caps smoked woodbines, yawned and looked at their feet.

When George appeared on the scene it was like being struck by lightning, sticking your fingers in a socket and being struck by some more lightning all rolled into one. It felt like seeing Jimi Hendrix, the Beatles and Elvis Presley all rolled into one. Every time he touched the ball, he literally defied the laws of gravity. I can still recall the thrill of seeing him on the news yesterday doing things with a football that no-one else on earth would ever have attempted, let alone tried.

With every effortless kick, he taught us more about wisdom than ten Confuciusses. With every graceful swerve around a defender, he taught us more about freedom than a hundred Nelson Mandelas. With every sublime header, he taught us more about artistry than a thousand Michelangelos. With every picturesque indirect free kick, he taught us more about beauty than a million Marilyn Monroes.

By any measure you care to choose, George Best was the most perfect and flawless human being who ever lived.

And yet, he wasn't perfect. Far from it. Like all of us, he had his flaws. And I should know, because for the last ten years of his life I was married to him. And behind closed doors I saw those flaws. I saw the other side of George Best.

I was there to pick up the pieces when he came home legless and knocked my jigsaw on the floor. I took the brunt of his self-pitying drunken rages. It was me who nursed him through his final illness. I alone dug his grave with my bare hands and chopped down a tree to make his coffin. There may have been good times in our marriage, but they were far outweighed by the bad times. And sadly, it is the bad times that I will remember.

But there were good times too, and it is those that I will treasure. The first time we kissed, across a romantic candlelit meal at the Ritz. Walking our Irish setters on the Sussex Downs, feeling the warmth of the sun on our faces, stopping to make love in the bracken. Celebrating our first anniversary with a romantic trip to Paris, where George surprised me with a diamond ring in a trifle. He was an incurable romantic.

And an incurable alcoholic.

So it is that I, more than anyone else, regret his passing with a cocktail of grief, sorrow and distress. A casserole of affliction, woe and bitterness. A smorgasbord of gloom, heartache and infelicity. A porringer of wretchedness, desolation and despair.

Yes. George was the best in the world at kicking a football. But in the end, George Best couldn't kick the most important football of all. The bottle.

Next week: *Why is 'Q' the first letter on my keyboard?*

FRU T. BUNN

THE MASTER BAKER & HIS GINGERBREAD SEX DOLLS

2·30 pm...

JUST IN TIME? JUST IN TIME FOR WHAT?

AH, FRUBERT. YOU'RE BACK JUST IN TIME.

LITTLE CHELSEA'S HAVING A FITTING AT THE ORTHOPAEDIC COBBLERS FOR A NEW BUILT-UP SHOE. YOU SAID YOU'D COME ALONG, THEN TAKE US OUT FOR TEA, REMEMBER?

OH, YEAH. THAT.

...WELL I'M AFRAID I CAN'T COME WITH YOU... I'M SORRY. SOMETHING'S COME UP, YOU SEE...

WHAT?

ERM... ER... ER..., ERM...

VAT RETURNS..! I'VE GOT MY VAT RETURNS TO DO. YES, THAT'S RIGHT... IT'S MY VAT RETURNS... I'VE GOT TO DO THEM NOW...

...BUT FRU...

YOU DID PROMISE...

LOOK. IF I DON'T GET THESE FORMS COMPLETED I'LL GO TO PRISON AND YOU AND CHELSEA WILL END UP IN THE WORKHOUSE..! IS THAT WHAT YOU WANT..?

'COS THAT'S WHAT'LL HAPPEN!

SLAM!

SHOVE.

HEH-HEH! WHAT A PAIR OF SAPS! I'VE GOT THE KITCHEN TO MYSELF THANKS TO THAT BRILLIANT RUSE!

VAT RETURNS INDEED! SOMETHING'S COME UP ALRIGHT..!

...MY COCK-END! §SLURP!§

AND WHEN I SAY SLUTTISH I *MEAN* SLUTTISH..! I'M USING UNREFINED FLOUR.

...IN ANTICIPATION OF A RAMPANT AFTERNOON SEX SESH WITH THE SLUTTISH GINGERBREAD BIRD I'M ABOUT TO COOK MYSELF UP..!

½ AN HOUR LATER...

TING! ♪

AH! SHE'S READY!

GAW! WHAT A SMASHING BIT OF ROUGH! SHE'S COMMON AS MUCK, THIS ONE. SHE LOOKS LIKE SHE'D GO WITH ANYONE..!

I'LL DO HER BETWEEN THE MERINGUE UDDERS TILL I'M ALMOST THERE, THEN FINISH MESELF OFF UP HER DIRTY SLACK DOUGHNUT.

...UH! UH! UH! UH!... ...OOH, YEAH!... OOH! YEAH! THAT'S THE WAY I LIKE IT, YOU CHEAP BISCUIT SLAPPER! TAKE IT..! TAKE ALL 4¼ INCHES OF IT..!

UH..! UH..! UH..! OOOOOUH!!!

A FORTNIGHT LATER...

SKRAT! SKRAT!

...MR BUNN..?

VD CLINIC

WAITING ROOM RULES

SKRAT! SKRAT! SKRAT!

PANT PANT

WELL — YOU'VE DEFINITELY GOT AN S.T.D., MR. BUNN. IT'S AN INFESTATION OF BAKER'S CRABS.

BAKER'S CRABS?

YES. PUBIC LICE CLOSELY RELATED TO THE FLOUR MITE *Chortoglyphus arcuatus*. BUT DON'T WORRY. I'LL GIVE YOU A PRESCRIPTION THAT'LL CLEAR THEM UP IN NO TIME

§PHEW!§

HERE YOU GO... AND IF YOU COULD GIVE ONE OF THESE CARDS TO EACH OF THE SEXUAL PARTNERS YOU'VE HAD IN THE LAST FORTNIGHT...

...SO THEY CAN MAKE AN APPOINTMENT FOR A CHECK-UP...

NEXT MORNING...

OH MY GOD, FRUBERT! YOU'VE GOT VD!... STAY AWAY FROM ME, YOU FILTHY BEAST..!

BUT DEAR...

YOU DISGUST ME, FRUBERT. MY MOTHER WAS RIGHT... YOU'RE AN ANIMAL... ...AN *ANIMAL!* §SOB!§

I... I DON'T KNOW WHAT YOU'RE TALKING ABOUT.

AS A MATTER OF FACT, THE DOCTOR TOLD ME I PROBABLY...ER... CAUGHT IT OFF A TOILET SEAT AT THE BAKERS' CASH & CARRY WHEN I WAS COLLECTING SOME MARZIPAN.

REALLY? IS THAT POSSIBLE?

ABSOLUTELY.

YOU MEAN...YOU'VE NOT... BEEN... WITH SOMEONE ELSE?

OF COURSE NOT DEAR. THERE'S NEVER BEEN ANYONE BUT YOU, I SWEAR IT..!

PROMISE?

...ON LITTLE CHELSEA'S LIFE.

OH, FRUBERT! HOW CAN YOU EVER FORGIVE ME? I'M SORRY I EVER DOUBTED YOU. I KNOW YOU'VE ONLY EVER HAD EYES FOR ME!

MRS. BUNN..?

VD CLINIC

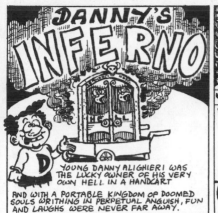

DANNY'S INFERNO

YOUNG DANNY ALIGHIERI WAS THE LUCKY OWNER OF HIS VERY OWN HELL IN A HANDCART

AND WITH A PORTABLE KINGDOM OF DOOMED SOULS WRITHING IN PERPETUAL ANGUISH, FUN AND LAUGHS WERE NEVER FAR AWAY.

I THINK I'LL TAKE MY INFERNAL PIT OF DAMNATION TO THE PARK TODAY, READERS

WHAT'S UP, MATES ~ YOU LOOK A BIT GLUM.

WE WANTED TO PLAY FOOTY IN THE PARK, DANNY

BUT THE QUEEN GOT HERE FIRST AND BAGSIED THE PITCH FOR A POSH GAME OF CROQUET.

IT'S NOT FAIR. SHE'S BEEN HOGGING THAT PITCH FOR HOURS.

WE'LL NEVER GET A GAME AT THIS RATE.

DON'T WORRY, PALS ~ I'LL GET HER MAJESTY OUT OF THE WAY FOR YOU...

..WITH THE AID OF MY DOMAIN OF TORTURED SOULS WHO WAIL AND GNASH THEIR TEETH IN UNENDING SUFFERING, ON WHEELS.

STAND BACK WHILE I OPEN THE GATES AND UNLEASH THE INEXTINGUISHABLE FLAMES OF CEASELESS AGONY

OUR MUCH-LOVED MONARCH WILL BE PLUNGED INTO HER OWN PERSONAL HELL BEFORE YOU CAN SAY JACK ROBINSON.

ROAR

AY SAY, WHAT'S GOING ORN?

HO HO! THERE'LL BE NO MORE GAMES OF CROQUET FOR THE QUEEN...

..SHE NOW HAS TO SPEND THE REST OF ETERNITY SHARING EVERLASTING CUPS OF TEA AND CHIT-CHAT WITH AN INFINITE NUMBER OF ORDINARY WORKING-CLASS HOUSEWIVES FROM GLASGOW.

THAT'LL KEEP HER OCCUPIED UNTIL THE CRACK OF DOOMSDAY

CHEERS DANNY. NOW WE CAN HAVE OUR GAME OF FOOTY.

BUT~ CHALK IT, CRUMB-SNATCHERS! I'M DA BIG DAWG TIM WESTWOOD, AND YOU IS IN MY HOOD.

ME AN' MY HOMIES ARE HAVIN' A BUSTIN' OPEN-AIR PARTY IN DIS PARK ~ SO CLEAR OFF. FACHEEZIE!

DROP DA BOMB ON DAT! LET ME BORROW YOUR DRY-ICE MACHINE, LITTLE BRO'!

HUNH?

IT'S GONNA MAKE MY PARTY GO BANG IN YO' FACE! GET YO' SWIRL ON!

OH, ERM.. CERTAINLY, MR WESTWOOD. YOU CAN BORROW MY.. (AHEM) "DRY-ICE MACHINE"

JUST OPEN THE GATES TO LET THE DRY ICE OUT (SNIGGER)

FO' REAL

ROAR

FEELIN' DAT!

ARF ARP! TIM WESTWOOD IS CONDEMNED TO SIT THERE UNTIL THE END OF TIME WHILE HIS MUM SHOWS ENDLESS PHOTOS OF HIM AS A CHILD TO SNOOP DOGG, 50 CENT AND THE GHOST OF BIGGIE SMALLS

NOW, HERE'S ONE OF TIMOTHY WHEN HE WAS A CHOIRBOY. WASN'T HE SWEET?

HIS FATHER WAS THE BISHOP OF PETERBOROUGH, YOU KNOW.

THREE CHEERS FOR DANNY AND HIS FIREY ABYSS OF ETERNAL TORMENT

HIP HIP HOORAY!

LEADER O
BANG

Firing Squad Execution Set to be Greatest Show on Earth

BOB GELDOF is planning yet another charity spectacular, and the headline act is going to be convicted paedophile Gary Glitter. But the ageing glam-rocker won't be singing a medley of his songs; instead he'll be being shot dead by a firing squad.

In scenes reminiscent of 2005's Live8 extravaganza, Glitter's execution for child sex offences later this year will be a glitzy Wembley Stadium stage show. And Sir Geldof hopes to enlist the help of many of his star friends to ensure that the gig goes with a bang.

A source close to Geldof told us: "After the success of last year's Hyde Park concert, everyone's mad keen to get on board. Bob's already got Coldplay, the Killers, Arctic Monkeys and Elton John confirmed for the afternooon. It's going to be a great atmosphere."

As the climax to a day of top-line entertainment, the disgraced glam rocker will be dragged onto the stage in one of his trademark glitter suits, his eyes will be covered with a flamboyant sequinned blindfold and he'll be tied to a sparkly post before a squad of five Vietnamese soldiers shoot him through the chest and face.

"Live8 saw the reformation of the classic Pink Floyd lineup," the spokesman continued. "But the execution of

EXECLUSIVE

Gary Glitter live on stage is going to top that. It's the event that the rock world has been waiting for. It's literally the holy grail of pop."

"It won't be the longest set Gary's ever done, but it'll certainly be one of the most memorable," the source added. "And if the shooting goes down well with the crowd, the execution squad might bring Glitter's corpse back out on the stage and bayonet it for an encore."

Organisers expect a crowd of over 100,000 to witness the execution, which will be carried live on giant screens in Hyde Park, on Wimbledon's Henman Hill and in the courtyard of Edinburgh Castle. In addition, the event will be beamed round the world to an estimated TV audience of over a billion.

All the stars, including the firing squad, arc giving thcir services for free, and the profits from ticket sales and TV rights will be going to the St Columb Donkey Sanctuary in Cornwall.

Although the line-up is not yet finalised, there are rumours that U2 plan to split up specially for the event. However, organiser Geldof ast night remained tight-lipped about his plans. He told us: "I don't know what you're talking about. This is the first I've heard about any of this."

"Anyway, Wembley Stadium doesn't even fucking exist any more," he added.

Bob Geldof yesterday

Top Himse

NOW languishing in a Vietnamese jail, Gary Glitter faces spectacular showbiz execution when he is found guilty being a nonce later this year. But the ageing 70s pop icon ha vowed to cheat the firing squad by topping himself in priso

However, thanks to the spartan conditions in which Glitter finds himself, carrying out his threat may be a trickier task than it seems. Without any ropes, guns or sharp knives available in his cell, the ageing rocker may find himself being forced to keep his appointment with his rifle-toting executioners.

But chubby survival expert Ray Mears reckons that with a little ingenuity, there are a million-and-one ways for the veteran star to shuffle off his mortal coil. He told us: "Gary is literally spoiled for choice. If he looks hard enough, he will find that his apparently empty cell is an Aladdin's Cave of suicide equipment."

Here Mears takes us through just a few of the ways that Glitter could

pop his platform clogs before the Vietnamese authorities get a chance to tie him to a post and shoot him through the heart.

Ray of hope?: Weed-gobbler Mears ponders Glitter's fate yesterday.

FTHE

Looking through Gary Glitter's eyes: Ageing glam rocker Gary faces death by firing squad at Wembley spectacular.

f of the Pops Glitter Vows to Dodge Bullets

HANGING...................

"The laces from Gary's famous silver platform boots will have been confiscated by canny guards, so throttling himself with those is out of the question. But the sturdy whiskers from his trademark hairy chest could easily be woven into a rope with which the glam-rock king could hang himself from the light fitting in his cell."

POISONING................

"At breakfast time every day, Glitter should pour himself a bowl of Alpen. If he slips the raisins from his cereal into his pocket, he could spread them on the floor of his cell and tell the warders that they are rat droppings. He could then save up the rat poison that they put down until he has set aside a sufficiently large dose to kill himself."

BURNING....................

"As a non-smoker, Gary will not have any matches in his cell. However, by carefully arranging the reflective wing collar and shoulder pads from his glitter suit into a series of parabolic mirrors, he should be able to focus the sun's rays into a powerful white hot beam with which he can burn himself to a crisp, like an ant under a schoolboy's magnifying glass. To sit still whilst such a death ray fries him alive will take quite a bit of willpower, but I have every confidence that the Leader of the Gang is up to the task."

CHOKING....................

"Prisoners often while away their long hours of incarceration by playing table tennis. To choke himself to death, all Glitter has to do is open his mouth wide and swallow the ball as his opponent serves. As luck would have it, the average ping-pong ball is exactly the same diameter as Gary Glitter's trachea. Once his airways are blocked, as long as no-one in the jail knows how to do the Heimlich manoeuvre, I estimate that Gary should be turning up his toes in less than two minutes."

VIOLENT DEATH......

"Pecking order is very important to prison inmates. Anyone who tries to muscle in on Mr Big's action is liable to find themselves the victim of vicious retribution. Accordingly, if Gary makes his way around the exercise yard asking everyone he meets if they want to be in his gang, his gang, his gang, he can confidently expect to be beaten to death with a snooker ball in a sock the moment the guards' backs are turned."

DISEASE...................

"Shiny objects hold an irresistible fascination for many birds, such as ravens and magpies. Like Burt Lancaster the Birdman of Alcatraz, Gary would arouse little suspicion if he used sequins from his stage suit to attract birds into his cell. However since he is in Vietnam, his new feathered friends would almost certainly be riddled with Asian bird flu, and it would be only a matter of hours before Glitter himself succumbed to the killer plague, cheating his executioners of their moment of glory."

TRAUMA..............

"Glitter could enlist the aid of his fellow pop diddler Jonathan King, getting him to bring in a cake with a bar of soap concealed inside. In the shower block, Gary could deliberately drop the soap, and bend over to pick it up whilst singing 'Do you want to touch? Do you want to touch? Do you want to touch me there? Yeah!' In the resulting melee, Glitter would almost certainly perish from a combination of internal injuries and massive rectal haemorrhaging."

What's in a Name?

This week: **CHARLOTTE CHURCH**

CHARLOTTE CHURCH has gone from fresh-faced cherub of the classical music scene to chest-heavy diva of the pop charts in one easy move. We think we know all about her from seeing her every day on TV and in our newspapers. But stop imagining her soaping down your Nissan Primera in a wet vest for one moment and ask yourself: How much do we really know about Charlotte Church? You may be surprised to learn that there is more to her than meets the eye... and once again, *IT'S ALL IN THE NAME.*

...is for CHURCH

THE VOICE of an angel star was actually born Charlotte Reed in 1986, but decided to change her name after watching Songs of Praise one Sunday evening. Captivated by the beautiful hymns and Bible stories, it wasn't long before Charlotte Songsofpraise was wowing audiences at school productions. However, record company bosses decided her name was too long to fit on a CD box and ordered her to change it again. And the rest is history.

...is for HELLRAISING

LIKE ANY **normal teenager, the Welsh wild-child likes to go to parties. But unlike her peers, once there Church likes to drink alcohol, causing her to become mildly intoxicated. On several occasions, the out-of-control star has been photographed walking out of a nightclub not smiling for photographers and with her eyes half shut when the flash went off.**

...is for AGE OF CONSENT

ON THE 21st February 2002, the editors of Britain's tabloid newspapers breathed a sigh of relief as the Welsh warbler finally turned 16. Overnight, their feelings towards Charlotte changed from ones of paternal interest in her career, to ones of priapic, salivating lust over her arse and tits, with the police powerless to intervene.

...is for RUGBY

CHARLOTTE **is currently engaged to Welsh rugby international Gavin Henson, son of the late Muppet magnate Jim. The couple are often referred to in the UK tabloids as the Welsh Posh and Becks (Pwysh y Bylls). Although why the people of Wales would want their own version of the sour-faced, clunk-voiced spendthrift and a Joe Pasquale-soundalike, PA-nudging free kick specialist is anybody's guess.**

...is for LEEKS

IT IT NOT known if the Swansea soprano has ever expressed any particular interest in her native principality's national vegetable. However, if she wanted to grow the world's largest specimen, she'd have to beat the 3 monsters with a combined volume of 537.83 cubic inches grown by John Pearson from Ashington in 2002.

...is for ONIONS

IF CHARLOTTE **decided growing monster onions was more to her taste, then John Sifford's 16lb 8^1/2oz specimen, which won the retired engineer from Romsley a £1500 cash prize at the 2005 Harrogate Autumn Flower Show, would be the one to beat.**

...is for TURNIPS

ONCE BITTEN by the giant vegetable growing bug, the taffy temptress may like to try her hand at cultivating a gargantuan turnip. If she could surpass the whopping 39.2lb leviathan grown by Scott Robb of Alaska in 2004, then she could add yet another world record to her already impressive tally.

...is for TATE

IN DECEMBER **2005, Charlotte appeared on a special Christmas edition of the Catherine Tate Show. Unlike the programme's titular star, Charlotte only made a brief appearance, failed to deliver one of three semi-memorable catch phrases, didn't stretch one minute's worth of material out for six minutes, and generally refused to outstay her welcome on our screens.**

...is for EX-BOYFRIENDS

THE VOICE of an angel vocalist has hit the headlines with a string of far from angelic suitors. Amongst others, the Newport nymphette has been romantically linked with rapper Steven Johnson, DJ Kyle Johnson, great train robber Ronnie Biggs and nazi war criminal Martin Bormann.

...is for CIGARETTES

CHARLOTTE is well known for her love of smoking. She was recently stopped by customs officers at Dover whilst driving a rented Luton van. In the back, officers found almost 1^1/2 million Marlborough Lights, which the Ffestiniog faghound had purchased at a Calais cash & carry. She then proved that they were for her personal use by smoking the lot, there and then, whilst port officials looked on in amazement.

...is for HURTUBISE

CHARLOTTE **has been terrified of bears since falling into the bear pit at the North Wales Mountain Zoo in Colwyn Bay as a child. Should she visit that zoo again, she would be well advised to wear the armoured bear-proof suit, developed by Canadian nut job Troy Hurtubise. The 145lb titanium, chain mail and rubber outfit would provide ample protection should the Llandudno llovely suffer a repeat of her childhood mishap.**

...is for UNSTABLE

ALTHOUGH SHE claims to be a 'Crazy Chick' in the chorus of her chart-topping hit, it is not thought that Charlotte's mind is any more unstable than the average female of her age. But if the Swansea sexbomb were to suffer from any severe form of mental illness in future years, then she is in luck. For Wales has several mental hospitals and residential homes all within driving distance of Cardiff, enabling the Brecon Beacons babe's family to visit her with ease.

...is for REAR

THE SNOWDONIAN **siren was voted Rear of the Year in 2002. And it's lucky that she was, because later that year Charlotte contracted haemorrhoids after sitting on a cold radiator at an Aberystwyth Eisteddfod. With bum-grapes the size of plums, her bottom was declared ineligible for the 2003 competition, which was probably won by Kerry Katona or somebody like that.**

...is for CURSING

WHEN SHE **is singing, the Llanfairpwllgwyngyllgogerychwyrndrobwllllantisiliogogogoch nightingale has the voice of an angel, but after a few drinks it's more like the voice of a Hell's Angel. Charlotte's tendency to turn the air blue is legendary in her native valleys, where she is often heard using language that would make a docker vomit. But ironically, Welsh speaker Charlotte has to slip into English when she wants to curse, as her consonant-heavy native tongue doesn't have have swearwords! Except Cwm.**

...is for HUGE MELONS

SHOULD Charlotte **tire of growing giant leeks, onions or turnips, she could turn her attentions to the biggest challenge in the vegetable world - the melon. But unless she could produce a specimen bigger than the 268lb 12oz monster grown by Lloyd Bright of Hope, Arkansas, the Bangor bombshell would do well not to give up her musical day job.**

NEXT WEEK: MR T

That's Your Lotto!

UNEXCLUSIVE

LOW CLASS vermin are to be barred from winning the lottery after a survey by the *Daily Mail* showed that large wins by scrotes made many of its readers physically sick.

The report found that 108% of Mail readers thought it unfair that while they were mowing their lawns and worrying about their endowment policies, hordes of dole cheats, single mums and immigrants could be lying around at home collecting as much as £1million per hour playing scratch cards and Daily Play games.

Now Camelot bosses are to restrict large lottery wins so that only the middle classes scoop the jackpot. Chief executive Sir Thomas Titt said: "Many people find the sight of a lottery winner in a shell suit collecting his cheque extremely galling. It's never an opera lover who wins. It's always somebody with black teeth and tattoos."

"We are currently introducing measures to restrict the number of lowlifes winning large prizes. For instance, anyone buying a ticket in certain postcodes will be disqualified when their numbers come up,

A lottery Jackpot yesterday and inset, TV scratter Vicky Pollard off of TV's Little Britain

and people who buy tickets from KwikSave will have their numbers automatically thrown in the bin," he added.

The news was greeted with warm approval by decent people all over the country. *Daily Mail* reader Thomas Trevillion said: "It's a victory for common sense. I'm out washing and dry waxing my car at 7.30 every morning. Why should some lazy layabout win my money?"

Daily Mail editor Paul Highblood-Pressure was delighted with Camelot's decision. "This is wonderful news. It's about time these scums found out what it's like to lose," he told reporters. "Now we're going to launch a campaign to prevent homosexuals from matching more than three numbers in the Lotto draw and to stop them being able to choose a Thunderball," he added.

WAIT!

DON'T THROW AWAY THAT STEAM!

- you could be pressing a shirt or opening a railway or something

Without realising it the average housewife throws away 38 miles of steam every year. Good, clean British steam that could be utilised for countless other applications throughout the Commonwealth.

So next time you're doing something in the kitchen, be sure to keep a milk bottle handy to capture any excess steam. You never know, it might come in useful. And then again, it might not.

FRUIT FLY JOKE

DO YOU FANCY GOING ON A DATE?

It's Official!
Bigger IS Better

Top Ghiza: A pyramid is much better than Jack Straw's penis, say boffins.

SCIENTISTS working on a part-time basis at Preston Adult Education Centre have finally solved one of life's great Mysteries - Is Bigger Better? And according to boffins, the answer is *YES IT IS.*

For years, top philosophers have questioned whether size was important, or whether is was what you did with it that made the difference. But now a team led by Professor Basil Brush has come to the conclusion that when it comes to the crunch, bigger things ARE better than smaller things.

"Take elephants and rice, for example," says Professor Brush. "Surely no one can say that a grain of rice is better than an elephant. We've been through hundreds of big things such as lighthouses, Jupiter, the Titanic, Robert Pershing Wadlow - and none of them can be bettered by anything small."

However, Brush's findings were dismissed as 'a load of balls' by fellow scientist Dr Charles Mooncat. He has led a team from Blackpool College of FE working on the theory that good things come in small packages.

"The professor doesn't know what he's talking about," Mooncat told a deserted press conference this morning. "What about diamonds, baby ducks or a tear on the face of a child? He can't tell me that a skyscraper is better than those."

Trinny 'Vile and Ugly'

TRINNY WOODALL, one half of TV shut-up-and-do-what-we-say duo Trinny and Susannah, has been voted The Nation's Least Favourite Shape.

Woodall, of an indeterminate age somewhere between 32 and 71, took the top spot in a magazine poll, beating sausage dogs, junior hacksaws, and the Fiat Multipla

"VILE AND UGLY"

Hippolyta Jameson-Jamieson, editor of *Dahling!* magazine, described the pointy fashionista as "absolutely the winning shape – vile, ugly and with all the seductive curves of a cardboard scarecrow pegged to a fence."

Many of those polled drew

EXCLUSIVE

attention to the way Woodall's obsessively-chosen outfits look like they've been tossed over her to dry, and the enormous distance from her chin to her shoulders broken only by a neck like an index finger.

The award will soften the blow of Woodall's recent loss of title of The Nation's Least Favourite Personality to one of those people from Big Brother who won't stop shouting.

War on Terror "Over"

SECURITY levels all over the world have dropped to amber following the news that US President George Bush has declared the War on Terror "over".

In a statement, Bush reported that on waking up Thursday morning, he no longer felt frightened, and that therefore the terms for winning the war had been met. "I declare this war on terror over," he told his wife. Rubbing his stomach and opening a window, the president then declared war on hunger and war on not being able to find his slippers.

> *Associated Press*

Local Trader Appeals Against Decision

FEZ-WEARING businessman The Shopkeeper off of Mr Benn is on the verge of having his costume hire business shut down by the local council, after failing to obtain planning permission for the various other worlds he keeps at the back of his shop.

"It's only a tiny little portal," says a disappointed The Shopkeeper. "But my livelihood depends on it. My customer's not going to want to put on a cowboy costume or a caveman outfit without being able to step into an adventure where my back yard should be." The Shopkeeper is expected to appear as if by magic before a planning committee later this week to appeal against the decision.

IS HE A GOOD PILOT?

YES. HE REALLY PUSHES THE ENVELOPE.

Letterbocks

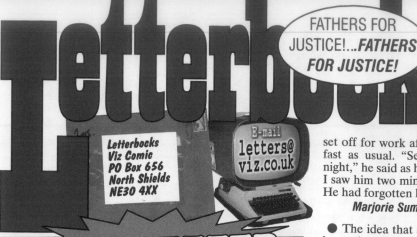

Letterbocks
Viz Comic
PO Box 656
North Shields
NE30 4XX

E-mail
letters@
viz.co.uk

FATHERS FOR JUSTICE!...FATHERS FOR JUSTICE!

STAR LETTER

Last month I was genuinely upset to read that Jim Davison had gone bankrupt, because when I saw his picture on the BBC website I thought he was dead.

J Thorn, Hexham

● They say that if a man wants know what his hair will be like when he's older, he should look not at his father, but at his mother's brother. Well my mum hasn't got a brother, so I'll probably be as bald as a coot.

Max Crumbhorn, Leeds

● The other night I dreamt that I was playing football with Manchester United pretty-boy cry-baby Christiano Ronaldo. The twinkle-toed tart lofted a decent ball to the far post, but I couldn't reach it and it drifted harmlessly wide. Has anyone had a less fulfilling, or more pointlessly self-defeating dream

involving a sports personality than this?

M Bigault, Wimbledon

My husband is so forgetful, it is comical. The other day he

set off for work after breakfast as usual. "See you tonight," he said as he left. But I saw him two minutes later. He had forgotten his keys!

Marjorie Sumpoil, Stoke

● The idea that a man will have the same hair as his mother's brother is frankly ludicrous. My uncle Frank has got a mullet. And a massive moustache.

J. Poultry, Hackney

● I went to a house the other day to fix a lady's washing machine, a Zanussi ZWF 161, which kept stopping halfway through the spin cycle. I took it apart, but couldn't for the life of me see what was causing the problem. I realised why when I suddenly remembered that I was not an electrical engineer, but a pensions and savings advisor with the Cheltenham & Gloucester Building Society. How foolish I felt as I tried to put it back together.

Norman Topsoil, Luton

● Whenever I buy a DVD I have to sit through a trailer telling me not to watch pirate movies. Yet Johnny Depp stars in one and the posters all say 'Must See'. Make your minds up, Hollywood moguls.

John Scone, Bonne

● Rather than relying on laws to discourage people from riding mini-motos, why doesn't everyone simply point and laugh when some twat farts past on one in a cloud of blue smoke with his knees up round his ears?

Eve Pudding, London

● It seems the government are being very short-sighted in crushing confiscated mini-moto bikes. I think they should give them to dwarves so as they could ride them to the pantomine, circus or diamond mine where they work.

Edith Montefiore, Luton

● I just read a block of phot... which says o... ket 'Guaranteed ...e.' Well I should ...ll hope so. Honest... ...er next?

Gra... ...ham, e-mail

● The ...woman sitting nex... ...n the train reading ...book. How innaprop...

Chris... ...artin, e-mail

● Yeste... ...received an e-mail fr... a ...ored housewife look... fo... ome action. Eager to please the young lady I sent her my ironing. That should keep her quiet for a while.

Warren, e-mail

● What is it with celebrities who seem to forget their public as soon as they reach a certain level of fame? A few months ago I wrote to *Dr Who* star Billie Piper asking if she's like to go out to a local restaurant and have a meal with me, and perhaps a coffee back at my house, and I have yet to receive a reply. Admittedly I went into detail about what she might like to do after the coffee, on reflection perhaps a little too graphic. But if she didn't want to, all she had to do was drop me a quick line saying 'No thanks'. Good manners cost nothing.

Hector Charteris, London

● I am surprised to see so many of these Peruvian pipe bands busking in our towns and cities. I'm surprised they make enough for their plane fares home every night. I certainly never give them anything, the ruddy din they make.

Edna Crumble, Tooting

● My husband must be the most absent-minded man on earth. Last week we decided to go out for the day and he packed a picnic. "Are you sure you've remembered everything?" I asked, and he said he had. But when we came to have the picnic, you've guessed it. He'd forgotten the milk for the tea!

Marjorie Sumpoil, Stoke

● I was at a wedding yesterday, and the vicar said - I kid you not - "Don't be embarrassed to touch your rings if it gives you pleasure." No one understood why I laughed out loud.

Dominic Twose, e-mail

● Mel Gibson has certainly blotted his copybook by reportedly making anti-semitic remarks when being arrested for drunk driving. But all may not be lost. He should arrange a photo call, standing hand in hand with the Jewish commu-

● At thirteen months, I suspect I may be your youngest reader. I love the humour in your comic. It's sometimes a little childish for my tastes, but in the main I find it quite amusing. Keep up the good work.

Theo, e-mail

* Have you got a picture of your baby laughing at something else whilst holding a copy of Viz in its hands? Send it to Letterbocks. Actually, don't bother. We have to get permission to use the photo and then double check it and it's just not worth the arseache.

nity at his garden gate, and claim that they are standing by him at this difficult time. It worked for me when I offended my missus by banging that scrawny actress whose name escapes me.

Rt Hon David Mellor MP, London

Double act Tony Blair meets the Governor of California Arnold Schwarzennegger in Los Angeles yesterday.

● Hats off to Tony Blair for being taller than Arnold Swarzennegger. Arnie is perhaps the toughest man on the planet, and seeing him dwarfed by our Tony at the recent Los Angeles summit made me proud to be British.

Jim Turpin, Leeds

● I agree with Mr Turpin's letter *(left)*. It has become fashionable to criticise Tony Blair for his empty promises, disastrous policies and repeated lies. But until the Conservatives can come up with somebody taller than the Terminator, they don't stand a chance of forming a credible government.

T Kavanagh, Wapping

● With reference to the above letters. May I remind your readers that in politics, size is not everything? The best Prime Minister this country has ever had, Winston Churchill, was only 5 foot 6.

T Ramsbottom, Nottingham

● With reference to Mr Ramsbottom's letter *(above)*. Whilst I agree that Churchill at 5 foot 6 was our greatest Prime Minister, his argument is flawed. He must take into account that during Winnie's premiership, the hardest man in Hollywood was James Cagney who stood only 5 foot 4 in his socks.

Tarquin Boils, Hull

● I have to laugh at my husband's forgetfulness. The other day he left the house to go for a walk. Half an hour later the police brought him back home. It turned out he had forgotten not to expose his genitals to a group of young women in the park. Honestly, he'd forget his head if it wasn't screwed on!

Marjorie Sumpoil, Stoke

● So Superman is returning is he, after missing 9/11, a tsunami and countless bombings? He can piss off back to Krypton.

David McIntyre, e-mail

● I haven't seen The Cheeky Girls around lately, and they certainly haven't made any records for a while. But I haven't seen them in any porn films yet. It must be difficult for them in this transitional period.

Matthew John, Northants

Give Our Kids Brain Boost Oil

Mr Hiram J. Pepperworth and his assistant yesterday.

PARENTS in Nottingham are demanding that their children be given free Snake Oil in order to improve their examination results.

Snake Oil, though not scientifically accepted as a 'brain supplement' or 'food', has long been associated with increased brain function in pub conversations and newspaper columns, a fact which parents are keen to see reflected in school spending.

BENEFITS

Supporters of the proposal insist that anecdotal evidence for the benefits of Snake Oil is unarguable. A series of anecdotal trials carried out in 2005 by Dr Hiram J. Pepperworth's Travelling Circus and Health Supplements Laboratory found that children who sat GCSE examinations after taking Snake Oil improved their results by one grade, as well as growing full heads of luxurious hair and gaining the strength of ten men.

By our Science Correspondent
Old Mother Shipton

Hiram J. Pepperworth's marketing director deflected the scientific community's criticism of their methods. "These impressive results came from a full trial," he said while ripping a telephone directory in half. "Not a trial in the scientific sense, but there are other sorts of trial, which are more what this trial was like. Motorbike trials. Sheepdog trials. That sort of thing. Here, punch me in the stomach as hard as you can."

A campaign has been launched by the *Daily Mail* to divert school funding to the purchase of Snake Oil tablets, and away from school dinners, sports equipment or text books.

TOP TIPS

LIGHTEN up worrying trips to the doctors by posing every question with the prefix 'Doctor, Doctor.'

Christina Martin, e-mail

UNDERTAKERS. Put a flashing yellow light on the top hat of the man walking in front of the hearse to warn other road users of the slow procession of cars.

Campbell Moore, e-mail

FOOL your friends into thinking you use expensive butter by simply using cheap margerine and ripping holes in the bread.

Jools B, e-mail

BASEBALL cap manufacturers. Save the wearer the bother of turning your caps round by putting the peak on the other side.

John Davies, Carlisle

HOUSEHOLDERS. Store yellow crayons, broken pencils, dried up biros and highlighters somewhere handy. I keep mine in a jar by the telephone.

Mikey, e-mail

FAT partygoers. Your overloaded plate is more likely to go undetected if you don't sing, whistle or hum with delight at the buffet.

Macker, e-mail

WHAA! ECHOKE GAG COUGH! I REQUIRE AUXILIARY ASSITANCE! I HAVE ENGULFED A HEFTY TOME OF WORDS, THEIR DEFINITIONS AND EQYMOLOGY AND IT IS LODGED WITHIN MY ESOPHAGUS

EH? HAVE YOU SWALLOWED A FUCKIN' DICTIONARY?

WOOLLY MAMMOTH

SIGH!

NOW WHERE ON EARTH DID I LEAVE MY CAR KEYS?

ANYTHING ELSE, MISS?

...ER, YES. CAN I HAVE SOME CHEESE, PLEASE?

CERTAINLY, MISS. WHAT TYPE?

WHAT TYPE?

OH GOSH. I'M NOT SURE. I–

GOSH. THEY ALL LOOK NICE.

...ER...

WHAT P

FATHERS FOR JUSTICE!...*FATHERS FOR JUSTICE!*

ELTON JOHN'S BANDIT BEATER

SIR ELTON IS BEING INTERVIEWED BY 'YOOHOO!' MAGAZINE

...AND FINALLY SIR ELTON, I COULDN'T HELP ADMIRING YOUR VERY ELEGANT WEDDING RING

YES, DAVID AND I HAD THEM SPECIALLY MADE, YOU KNOW

I INSISTED THAT THIS RING MUST BE EXACTLY THE RIGHT SIZE, SHAPE AND WEIGHT. THAT WAS VERY IMPORTANT TO ME.

WELL, I'M AFRAID I HAVE SOME OTHER BUSINESS TO ATTEND TO...

OF COURSE. THANK YOU FOR YOUR TIME, SIR ELTON.

ARF ARF! I DIDN'T MENTION THAT I HAD MY WEDDING RING MADE THE EXACT SIZE, SHAPE AND WEIGHT OF A **TWO QUID COIN**...

...WHICH MEANS I CAN USE IT TO DIDDLE THE FRUIT MACHINE IN FAT MARY'S CAFF.

I JUST TIE A BIT OF THREAD TO THE RING, DROP IT IN THE SLOT ~ AND WHEN THE MACHINE STARTS UP, I PULL IT OUT AGAIN

HEY PRESTO! UNLIMITED FREE GOES ON THE FRUITY.

AND OFF WE GO! HEH HEH. THESE OLD BANDITS HAVE GOT A GLITCH IN THE PROGRAMMING.

IF YOU KEEP YOUR FINGER ON THE CANCEL/COLLECT BUTTON THEN HOLD DOWN THE BONUS ROLL WHILE SPINNING THE REELS, YOU GET FIFTY NUDGES.

THERE, PIECE OF PISS. TEN QUID JACKPOT HERE I COME.

HOY, YOU!

OO-ER! IT'S FAT MARY

I TOLD YOU THAT YOU WERE BANNED FROM THIS CAFF AFTER YOU KEPT EMPTYING THAT MACHINE.

GET OUT AND STAY OUT!

OOYAH! **BOOT**

HMM, I'M BANNED FROM THE ARCADE AS WELL. I'LL HAVE TO ADOPT A CRAFTY DISGUISE IF I'M GOING TO GET IN THERE.

AND SO... AFTERNOON SQUIRE, I'M FROM THE PINBALL WIZARD AMUSEMENTS REPAIR COMPANY

I'VE COME TO CLEAN THE BALL BEARINGS IN YOUR PINBALL MACHINE

GO AHEAD ~ YOU WANT ANY HELP?

NO NEED. EVER SINCE I WAS A YOUNG LAD, I'VE CLEANED THE SILVER BALL ~ FROM SOHO DOWN TO BRIGHTON, I MUST'VE CLEANED THEM ALL.

I'M IN! NOW TO START CLEANING THE MACHINES ~ **CLEANING THEM OUT OF CASH**, THAT IS!

IN GOES THE OLD WEDDING RING...

OH NO! IT'S A NEW MODEL WITH ANTI-CHEAT OPTICAL SENSORS BUILT INTO THE CHUTE.

YANK KER-CHUNK

THE BLOOMIN' THING HAS SWALLOWED UP ME WEDDING RING!

I'VE GOT TO GET THAT RING BACK OR DAVID WILL KILL ME!

PSST! IF YOU WANT TO EMPTY THAT BANDIT, I'LL SELL YOU THIS DEVICE FOR FIFTY QUID

IT'S A HANDHELD MICROWAVE REMOTE JAMMER ~ POINT IT AT THE FRUITY, PRESS THIS BUTTON AND IT'LL JAM THE BANDIT'S MECHANISM ONTO JACKPOT PAYOUT MODE.

GREAT! I'LL BUY IT. HERE'S YOUR FIFTY SQUID

RIGHT, LET'S SEE...

I POINT IT AT THE MACHINE, AND PRESS THIS BUTTON...

ALERT! ALERT!

THIS IS AN ILLEGAL DEVICE! ALERT! ALERT!

GRR! COME BACK HERE, YOU!

YOW! WAIT TILL I FIND OUT WHO THAT BUGGER WAS WHO SOLD ME THAT DEVICE

THAT'LL KEEP THE ATTENDANT BLOKE OCCUPIED FOR A FEW MINUTES. OK, FELLOW SURVIVING MEMBERS OF QUEEN ~ ALL TOGETHER... PUSH!

WEEE WILL, WEEE WILL, ROCK THE TUPPENNY WATERFALLS...

MICHAEL WINNER'S "JUST DESSERTS"

I DON'T WANT ANY MORE MAIN COURSE, MUM ~ **JUST DESSERT** FOR ME, PLEASE.

THAT TRIFLE LOOKS TRULY SCRUMPTIOUS. HMM-MMM!

OH NO, MY LAD. YOU KNOW THE RULES IN THIS HOUSE ~ NO PUDDING TILL YOU'VE FINISHED YOUR DINNER.

LOOK ~ YOU HAVEN'T EVEN TOUCHED YOUR CAULIFLOWER

COME ON, OPEN WIDE. HERE'S THE GOLD-PLATED LIMOUSINE GOING INTO THE TUNNEL

BRUM! BRUM!

FOR GOODNESS SAKE, MOTHER. I'M A HIGHLY SUCCESSFUL 71-YEAR OLD FILMMAKER AND BON VIVEUR. I'M QUITE CAPABLE OF FEEDING MYSELF.

FINE. I'LL LEAVE YOU TO IT.

BAH! CAULIFLOWER IS ABSOLUTELY YUCK!

BUT IF I DON'T CLEAR MY PLATE, I'LL NOT GET ANY OF THAT YUMMY PUD.

I KNOW ~ MY DOG BRONSON CAN HELP ME OUT

CHOMP! WOLF! GUZZLE!

THAT'S IT BRONSON ~ GET IT DOWN YOU!

GOOD BOY BRONSON ~ YOU'VE SCOFFED THE LOT

PAT PAT

BURP!

WHO'S A CLEVER CHAP, THEN?

WAH! LOOKS LIKE BRONSON ISN'T OVERLY KEEN ON CAULIFLOWER EITHER.

BARF!

NOW IT'S EVEN LESS APPETISING THAN IT WAS BEFORE.

HANG ON ~ I'VE JUST REMEMBERED

I'M PRODUCING A FILM IN THE BACK GARDEN GUEST-STARRING MY OLD MATE THE LATE MARLON BRANDO

GOOD OLD MARLON WILL EAT JUST ABOUT ANYTHING.

GRUNT. ACTUALLY, I AM A BIT PECKISH. PASS ME THAT SPEWED-UP CAULIFLOWER.

ARF! ARF! DYING OF LUNG FAILURE IN 2004 CERTAINLY DIDN'T DIMINISH YOUR APPETITE, MARLON.

JUST ONE MORE FLORET TO GO, MARLON.

CHOMP MUNCH

RIGHT. IN THIS SCENE OF THE FILM, THE HERO SHOOTS A MUGGER IN THE HEAD AND BLOWS ALL HIS BRAINS OUT.

IS THE DUMMY MUGGER IN POSITION? OK, AND ACTION!

DIRECTOR

TASTE KNEE-JERK RESPONSE, MOTHEREFFER!

BANG BANG

EXCELLENT! A POUND OR SO OF CAULIFLOWER MAKES VERY CONVINCING "BRAINS".

WHAT THE DEUCE?

MY PLATE IS SUDDENLY FULL OF HORRID CAULI AGAIN!

MICHAEL! WHO GAVE YOU PERMISSION TO GET DOWN FROM THE TABLE?

YOW!

SIT DOWN THERE AND EAT YOUR DINNER PROPERLY BEFORE I GET CROSS.

OOOH! MUM REALLY TWEAKED MY EAR THEN

HANG ON ~ THAT GIVES ME AN IDEA

I'LL JUST STICK THESE BITS OF CAULIFLOWER OVER MY EAR, USING TOMATO KETCHUP AS GLUE...

..LIKE SO!

MUM! MUM! YOU'VE GIVEN ME A TERRIBLE CAULIFLOWER EAR BY TWEAKING TOO HARD!

SOB! SNIFF!

GASP! OH, MY POOR DARLING, I'M SO SORRY!

>SNIFF< DESPITE THE AWFUL PAIN IN MY EAR, I MANAGED TO FINISH MY DINNER

YOU POOR BRAVE BOY. HAVE SOME PUDDING ~ YOU DESERVE IT!

OOPS! THAT TOMATO KETCHUP WASN'T QUITE STICKY ENOUGH

PLOP!

SO! TRYING TO SWINDLE YOUR OLD MUM ARE YOU?

00-ER! BUT MUM I JUST WANTED MY **DESSERT!**

I'LL TEACH YOU A LESSON, MY BOY, JUST YOU WAIT

RUMMAGE

MISC. OLD FILM PROPS

HO HO! CALM DOWN, DEAR ~ IT'S ONLY A HUNDREDWEIGHT OF ROTTEN CAULIFLOWERS

OOYAH

PROP FROM OLD FILM

ROTTEN CAULI

STOCKS

HA HA! NOW MICHAEL REALLY **HAS** RECEIVED HIS DUE COMEUPPANCE

UGGH!

Sting in the Tail

IT SEEMS that every day our newspapers are full of scare stories about meteorites, Al Qaida attacks and tsunamis. But now, as heat levels soar due to global warming, sun-baked Britain could be facing an even more terrifying threat than skin cancer, forest fires and hosepipe bans - an increase in attacks by BEES.

For, according to an old woman on a bus in Newcastle, as temperatures rise the stripy insects become angrier and are liable to sting with greater frequency.

In a press conference held on the No 62 from Byker to the City Centre, 82-year-old Ethel Carstairs said: "Look at that bee buzzing around. It'll be angry that. It's the heat as makes them angry. It's going to sting somebody, that."

Following the announcement, hospitals across the country went on a state of high alert. A spokesman for the North Tyneside General Hospital at Rake Lane told reporters: "In the light of what the old woman has said, we have begun to stockpile antihystamines, tubes of Savlon and sticking plasters. But we urge the public to remain calm if they see a bee. If people simply stand still and don't panic, the chances are the bee will simply fly off and sting someone else."

Meanwhile Mrs Carstairs had this advice for her fellow travellers: "Somebody wants to open a window and shoo it out."

A bus similar to the one Mrs Carstairs was on, and (below) an old lady similar to Mrs Carstairs who was on the bus similar to the one above.

"Don't Get Stung!" says Sting

Arsehole popstar Sting gives his top ten tips to avoid being stung by bees this summer.

" My parents named me after a bee's arse, so it is only natural that from a very early age I have been fascinated by these creatures. I spend my life surrounded by bees, yet in twenty years on the road with the Police I have never once been stang off of one. And if you take these few simple precautions, you too will avoid being a bee sting victim this summer. Here are my top ten things you can de-do-do-do, de-da-da-da to avoid being steng. "

1 TAKE a tip from my fellow arsehole pop star Morrissey out of the Smiths - wear a hearing aid and carry a bunch of flowers around in your back pocket. If you hear a bee approaching you from a distance, simply throw the flowers to one side and the bee, smelling the pollen, will go for them instead.

2 BEES are attracted to movement, so if one comes buzzing around you, keep perfectly still. It will eventually lose interest and move on.

3 ALL bees love honey, so it stands to reason that just as opposite poles of a magnet repel each other, bees will be repelled by the opposite of honey, which is Branston Pickle. A little bit smeared on the back of the neck, forehead and behind each ear will keep bees safely at bay.

4 BEES are attracted to the bright colours of flowers, where they go each day to collect pollen and nectar. In order to avoid being mistaken for a flower, wear dark or muted coloured clothing, such as a bespoke £3000 Armani jacket or a hand-stitched £4000 Alexander McQueen suit.

5 BEES often land on light-coloured surfaces, so if you have pale skin it is a good idea to cultivate a year-round all-over tan by moving to the Seychelles, Mustique or buying a huge villa in Tuscanny. Either that, or do as my fellow arsehole pop star Mick Hucknall out of Simply Red does and 'black-up' like Al Jolson during the summer months.

6 A BEE knows that if it stings you it is signing its own death warrant, so you are ten times more likely to get stang off a depressed or suicidal bee. If you encounter one of these, try to cheer it up by playing it a happy tune on your kazoo.

7 FOR CENTURIES, monks have kept the bees in their hives drowsy and unaggressive using smoke. But few of us carry a smoke canister around with us! So simply use the smoke from a £2000 Cuban Havana cigar available from DuCannard Tobacconists in Knightsbridge.

8 IF A BEE comes towards you, run around quickly in small circles flapping your arms wildly and shouting. The noise and movement will confuse it and it will eventually move on.

9 IT IS A fact that 90% of all stings take place inside cars. Trapped in the car and unable to escape, the bee panics and begins to attack. So avoid becoming one of these statistics by simply driving a convertible car such as a Bentley Continental GT cabriolet or a custom-built Ferrari F50 Bolide.

10 BEES will sting when they are angry or stressed. Over the years I have found that the best way to ease stress is by doing yoga. So if you are attacked by an angry bee, simply fold its legs into the lotus position and fix them there with a small piece of sticky tape. If after ten minutes the bee has not calmed down, simply hit it with a rolled up newspaper.

Be Bee-Free with our Freebie...
BB King Bee-Be-Gone

"Thanks to my Bee-Be-Gone, the only bees in my house are the ones I play on my famous guitar, Lucille."
Mr BBK, New Orleans

"Thanks to BB's Bee-Be-Gone, it's bye-bye bee blues"
Howlin' Mrs B, Essex

"I agree with Howlin' Mrs B, Essex"
Blind Lemon Mrs W, Luton

FOLD

   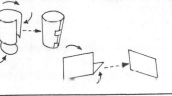 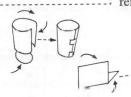 

1131.- COSTA DEL SOL
Vistas diversas
Vues diverses
Various views
Verschiedene Ansichten

PARA BILBAO MADRID
BARCELONA Y VALENCIA
ESPAÑA

Dear Sandra,
I hope you got home okay. At the moment I am with Antonio and he sends his love. Me and Fransico haven't said one word to each other yet. My dad says I can't go to the disco with Pedro and all the other's who have asad. I'll write you a letter when I get home to tell you the rest.
luv Michelle

351, East Road
Bridlington
N. Humberside
YO51 3LH
ENGLAND

DID YOU WOKE UP THIS mornin' and found a bee in your front room? Have you done got the blues because it won't buzz off?

Well don't fret, because King of the Blues BB King can help chase those bee blues away with this fantastic **FREE Bee-Be-Gone.**

It's the answer to the prayers of anyone who is being pestered by a bee in the front room who simply can't be arsed to fetch a glass and a piece of card from the kitchen.

Simply cut out and assemble the revolutionary 2-part patented *Cup'n'Slide*™ bee apprehension device as shown in the diagram. Then follow BB King's four s i m p l e steps to bee removal.

INSTRUCTIONS

1. Wait untill the bee alights on a flat surface, such as a window or Tara Palmer Tomkinson's tits, and place the 'glass' over it.

2. Tilt one edge of the glass slightly and slip the 'card' underneath, making sure not to trap the bee's legs.

3. Walk briskly into the kitchen whilst shouting "Somebody open the door! Somebody oipen the door!"

4. Walk into the garden in your socks, release the bee at arms length and run back into the kitchen before it follows you.

MAJOR MISUNDERSTANDING

ROLL UP! ROLL UP! COME ONE, COME ALL, TO BILLY BUTTON'S CIRCUS, TONIGHT ONLY ON THE VILLAGE GREEN

THERE'S THRILLS AND SPILLS AND FUN FOR ALL THE FAMILY

GASP WITH WONDER AT THE ACROBATS ON THE FLYING TRAPEZE!

ROAR WITH LAUGHTER AT THE ANTICS OF THE CLOWNS!

IT JUST SO HAPPENS THAT WE HAVE A THING CALLED FREEDOM OF SPEECH IN THIS COUNTRY

IF YOU HAVE A PROBLEM WITH THAT, WHY DON'T YOU GO AND LIVE IN IRAN.

I DIDN'T SEE YOU LOT DEMONSTRATING AGAINST THE JULY 7TH BOMBINGS. YOU WEREN'T GOING TO BEHEAD ANYONE FOR THAT, WERE YOU?

WELL I AM A MEMBER OF THE CHURCH OF ENGLAND. AND IF SOMEONE OFFENDS MY BELIEFS, I DON'T RUSH OUT INTO THE STREET SCREAMING AND WAVING PLACARDS AND SETTING FIRE TO EMBASSIES.

THAT'S HOW WE DO THINGS IN THIS COUNTRY. WE TRY TO ACT IN A CIVILISED MANNER.

OH NO, BUT WHEN YOUR PRECIOUS RELIGION GETS SLIGHTED, ALL OF A SUDDEN YOU'RE OUTRAGED.

NO, I REGISTER MY PROTEST BY WAY OF THE LETTERS PAGE OF THE FULCHESTER EVENING CHRONICLE.

IF YOU DON'T ABIDE BY THE RULES, I SUGGEST YOU GO AND LIVE ELSEWHERE.

111

Have Your Say!

This month the whole nation wept as one when it heard that Wilma the Whale had died in the Thames. The massive rescue mission to save this creature ultimately failed, but she left a legacy of joy in our hearts. Or did she? We went on the street to let YOU spout off about Wilma the Whale.

…I DON'T know what all the fuss was about, spending all that money on a rescue. We slaughter cows every day and eat them, and whales are just enormous water cows with no legs.

T Hennesey, Nottingham

…WHEN we were all fish millions of years ago, we crawled out of the water to live on the land and breathe air. Whales chose to go back into the water, nobody forced them. Wilma only has herself to blame that she drowned.

Barry Lyons, Clifton

…I THINK Wilma was an inspiration to everyone. She fought so bravely for her life. I think she should be posthumously made Dame of the British Empire and voted Sports Personality of the Year.

Renton Webb, Leeds

…I DON'T trust whales. They have too many teeth and they grin like paedophiles. If another one comes up the Thames, or any river where children play, it should be castrated or put on the sex offenders register.

M Thrumpton, Treadwell

…I LIVE in a village in Ethiopia. The rains have not come for four years now and we are facing another year without food. It is a terrible situation. But when I heard of the plight of Wilma the whale stuck in the Thames, it put all my problems into perspective. She really is an inspiration to everybody.

Pipi Okwekwe, Addis Ababa

…WITH the Olympic games coming to London in 2012, I think it is important that we keep whales out of the Thames as they could interfere with the rowing events. The last thing we want as Sir Steve Redgrave is about to take his seventh Olympic gold is some great blubbery baffoon coming up to spout and knocking him out of his canoe.

M Trickbury, Leominster

…IT always makes me laugh when people say that whales are intelligent. Bunkum! This thing swims one way up a straight river, and then is too thick to turn round and go back the other way when it's had enough. The thing must of had shit for brains.

E Windsor, Buckingham Palace

…WHAT is it with these do-gooders and whales. Whenever they find one on a beach they all start trying to push the thing back in the water. They may well be trying to evolve back to living on land. Leave them alone, I say.

T Nutkin, London

…WILMA the whale meant so much to so many people, that she truly was the Whale of Hearts. Her death shouldn't go unmarked. I reckon the perfect tribute would be a special park in the middle of the Thames with a memorial fountain and an underwater book of condolence. And Britain should be renamed Whaleland. And our currency should be plankton.

Lucy Pencilbox, Okehampton

…WINNIE the Whale, or whatever her name was, brought joy to everyone who saw her. I don't think I'll ever forget the heart-warming sight, on an otherwise cold and miserable January day, of her on that inflatable dinghy thrashing around, struggling for air.

Rev K Morris, Bucks

…I'M sick to death with Londoners going on about the bloody Thames Whale. The Scots never make this much fuss and they've got a Loch Ness Monster in their water supply.

R Humber, Humberside

…I'M sure it's very nice for whales to know that when they swim into our cities they'll be looked after at the taxpayer's expense. But I wonder how many whales would come to my rescue if I fell off the end of a pier into the sea? It's typical of soft-touch Britain that we bend over backwards for visitors from outside our shores, but can't expect the same treatment in return.

Peter Borough, Peterborough

Drunken bakers

Post's been.

Both for you.
Why me...

This is from my sister-in-law.
I didn't know you had a brother.
I don't.

He dropped dead.
Christ.
Gin?

How come I never met him?
You did.

He popped in here last year.
You duffed him up.

Had I been on the scotch?
We both had -
- then he told you your battenburg was dry.

Sorry 'bout that.
Don't be.
I think I joined in near the end...

You make a moist battenburg.
Mostly, yeah...

What did he look like?
Cos' I recall belting a squat bloke with a ponytail.

Yeah, that was this morning.
The little deaf girl.

He looked a lot like me, only younger.
Although he was six years older.

People used to confuse us.
They'd go, you're Adrian, and I'd go, no I ain't...

He is.
When's the funeral?
Last Monday. The family didn't want me there.

The other one is from my nephew.
Says if he ever sees me again he'll kill me.

Seems to think his dad never recovered...
Ahhhh, tears.
That's gin that.

114

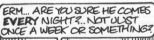

Who is Britain's Best One-eyed Gordon B?

BROWN

BANKS

IS IT Iron Chancellor **Brown**, who suffered a detached retina playing rugby at Kirkcaldy High School, and under whose prudent stewardship the country's economy goes from strength to strength? Or is it goalkeeper **Banks**, who was blinded in one eye after crashing his car into a ditch near Stoke, and who was part of England's 1966 World Cup-winning team? We've put the contenders through their paces to decide once and for all.

BROWN	Score	Category	Score	BANKS
On the face of It, Brown's parliamentary career looks glittering; opposition Spokeman on Trade and Industry, Shadow Chief Secretary to the Treasury and Chancellor of the Exchequer are all posts which he has held. However the keys to 10 Downing Street have always eluded him, and this failure to achieve the highest office in the land is reflected in his mediocre score for this round.	6	**Parliamentary Career**	3	After leaving school, Banks played for Chesterfield's youth team whilst working as a coal bagger. After national service in Germany he finally turned professional, signing for Leicester City in 1959 and becoming England's keeper in 1963. This busy career left him little time to stand for Parliament or indeed for election to any public office, so it's a disappointing kick off for Banks in his match against Gordon Brown.
In October 1997, Brown took charge of this country's plans for membership of the European Single Currency. At that time he set his famous 'Five Economic Tests' in order to decide whether the economic case had been made for Britain to adopt the Euro. In June 2003, he announced that the tests, whatever they were, had not been met. Accordingly he earns a moderate score in this round.	7	**Work on the European Single Currency Issue**	2	The England goalkeeper played 510 games for his teams Colchester Utd, Leicester City and Stoke City between 1959 and1972. Throughout this entire time, Banks didn't set a single economic test to judge whether the fiscal circumstances were suitable for a move over to a pan-European monetary unit. Tragically, before he had a chance to put this right, his goalkeeping career was cut short by a car crash.
Historically, the Chancellor of the Exchequer has been responsible for setting the country's interest rates. However, one of Brown's first actions upon taking office was to cede this power to the Bank of England, effectively giving The Old Lady of Threadneedle Street independence in the conduct of monetary policy, and thus sole responsibility for setting UK interest rates. This reluctance to shoulder responsibility reflects badly on Brown, and consequently results in a low scoring round for the Chancellor.	5	**Setting Interest Rates**	7	In the 90th minute of the 1966 World Cup final, Jack Charlton gave away a free kick 30 yards from goal. It was Banks's job to organise a defensive wall to prevent German soccer ace Lothar Emmerich from scoring. Unlike Brown, Banks did not cede this important responbility to anyone else and organised the wall himself. It follows that had Banks been put in charge of setting interest rates, he would have done so, despite the fact that Wolfgang Weber scored in the ensuing goalmouth scramble, sending the game into extra time.
At the time of going to press, Gordon Brown is Britain's longest serving Chancellor of the Exchequer this century. Since taking office in May 1997, he has held the post continuously, delivering no fewer than 14 budgets before Parliament. However, Victorian Chancellors William Gladstone and Nicholas van Sittart, who served for 12½ and 11 years respectively, knock Brown's paltry 9-year tenure into a cocked hat. Surprisingly, what initially looked like a good scoring round for Brown turns out to be another middling effort.	6	**Length of Time in Office**	8	The ex- Stoke number 1 has never served a single day as Chancellor of the Exchequer, so at first glance one might expect him to score poorly in this round. However, if each one of his 73 England caps were translated into a budget, it would mean that Banks had occupied the footballing equivalent of 11 Downing Street for over half a century, a Parliamentary record that Brown cannot touch... unless he remains in office until the grand old age of 98! Banks's creditable performance in this round reflects this impressive record.
In Labour's 1997 election manisfesto, Brown pledged not to increase the standard or higher rates of income tax. And whilst he hasn't broken that promise he has, by increasing national insurance and cracking down on tax loopholes, raised the UK tax burden from 39.3% of Gross Domestic Product in 1997 to an estimated 42.4% today. A high scoring round for the Chancellor.	8	**Raising the Tax Burden**	3	The erstwhile England netman may not have raised taxes, but he raised England's spirits many times with his spectacular saves. One particular save in the Guadalajara Jalisco Stadium during England's 1970 World Cup clash against Brazil was later described by Pele as the greatest save he had ever seen. However, Brazil went on to win the match 1-0, a fact which is responsible for Banks's low score in this round.
A poor showing for Brown in this section. To the widespread puzzlement of the public, the Chancellor insists on dropping and pulling in his chin for a split second at the end of every sentence. As a result of this downright peculiar and distracting trait, he fails to pick up a single point.	0	**Not Doing That Weird Thing with Their Jaw**	10	Earlier this month, Sheffield-born Banks had the honour of being the first person inducted into a 'Walk of Fame' in front of his home city's Town Hall. Whilst making a thank-you speech afterwards to a crowd of onlookers, Banks's jaw moved in a perfectly normal fashion throughout and did not once drop and get pulled in at the end of a sentence.

HOW DID THEY DO?

32 BROWN

Oh, dear! These results are certain to make Brown feel Blue. Already used to playing second fiddle to Tony Blair on the political stage, the Chancellor must now learn to play number 2 to the former England number 1 in the one-eyed Gordon Bs arena.

33 BANKS

While Brown will be sick as a parrot, Banks is sure to be over the moon with this result! In a victory that will mean more to him that his 1966 World Cup winner's' medal, the ex-England keeper has pulled a convincing win out of the old onion bag.

Next week: The clash of the drugged-up gay Georges: **Boy versus Michael**.

WHOO! WHOO! GOODNESS GRACIOUS I'M OFF TO TAKE PART IN THE LONDON MARATHON IN ORDER TO GET MY PICTURE IN THE PAPERS.

"OWL'S" ABOUT THAT THEN, GUYS 'N' GALS? TU-WHIT, TU-WEEURGH-EEURGH-EELGH.

THERE. THAT'S ANOTHER OBE I'VE JUST MADE.

IT'S STILL RED-HOT FROM THE FORGE, SO I'LL POP IT ON THE WINDOWSILL TO COOL.

BUCKINGHAM PALACE

WHOO! WHOO! NOW THEN, NOW THEN, WHAT 'AVE WE HERE? AN OBE! I LOVE OBES.

AND THAT WOULD LOOK GRAND HANGING ROUND MY NECK WHILE I'M JOGGING THE MARATHON.

I'LL JUST SWAP IT FOR ONE OF MY CRAPPY, WORTHLESS JIM'LL FIX IT BADGES

SEEMS LIKE A FAIR EXCHANGE, EH GUYS 'N' OWLS?

NOW TO FLY OFF TO THE MARATHON...

WHOO! WHOO! UPON MY WORD, THIS OBE IS HEAVY ~ ITS WEIGHING ME DOWN!

BY JOVE! A PROTECTED SPECIES OF WILDFOWL, FLYING AT A TEMPTINGLY LOW RANGE.

PUFF! PANT!

TAKE THAT, Y'USUALLY NOCTURNAL BLIGHTER!

BLAM BLAM BLAM BLAM

TU-WHIT, TU-WODOYAH!

AND THAT'S A NASTY SHOTGUN WOUND IN YOUR LEG, SIR JIM. YOU'D BEST NOT RUN THE MARATHON TODAY

LONDON MARATHON START

BAH. NO PUBLICITY FOR ME.

LATER NEVER MIND ~ I'LL FLY OVER TO THE TELEVISION STUDIOS. THEY'RE FILMING A DOCUMENTARY ABOUT THE HISTORY OF TOP OF THE POPS.

IT'S A PERFECT OPPORTUNITY FOR ME TO APPEAR ON TELLY AND SPOUT ANECDOTES ABOUT THE GOLDEN YEARS OF POP MUSIC.

NEARBY FLUNKEY! FETCH ME ONE OF MY EXPENSIVE CIGARS ~ SHOOTING THAT BIRD HAS GIVEN ME AN APPETITE FOR A SMOKE.

CLICK

AT ONCE, YOUR ROYAL HIGHNESS

WHOO! WHOO! HELLO, HELLO, THAT LOOKS LIKE ONE OF MY FAVORITE HAVANA CIGARS, AS IT 'APPENS.

I'LL FIX IT FOR ME TO SNAFFLE THAT BEFORE THE DOCUMENTARY FILMING STARTS.

FIRST I'LL COUGH UP AN EXTRA-LARGE OWL PELLET MADE OF MOUSE FUR AND BONES

URP! URP!

HURP! THERE ~ A PERFECT CIGAR REPLACEMENT.

BY THE TIME ANYONE REALISES THE REAL ONE IS MISSING, I'LL BE SMOKING IT SAFELY IN THE TV STUDIO.

OH PHILIP ~ YOU'D BETTER NOT LIGHT THAT CIGAR.

EDWARD HAS JUST CONFESSED THAT IT'S A JOKE SHOP EXPLODING CIGAR, WHICH HE PLANTED THERE FOR A HILARIOUS PRANK.

BANG!

YOW! OR SHOULD I SAY ~ Y-OWL! MY POOR BEAK!

AND SORRY, SIR JIM ~ WE CAN'T UNDERSTAND YOUR ANECDOTES WITH YOUR BEAK ALL BANDAGED UP. WE'LL HAVE TO CUT YOU FROM THE DOCUMENTARY.

TV STUDIO DIRECTOR

MMNN NN NN, MNN-NN-NN.

*TRANSLATION: WOULD YOU BELIEVE IT, EEURGH-EEURGH-EELGH.

LATER I'LL NOT BE DISTRACTED FROM MY QUEST FOR PUBLICITY THIS TIME. I'LL FLY OVER TO GUYS HOSPITAL AND MAKE A PERSONAL APPEARANCE.

NOBODY CAN SAY THAT SIR JIMMY SAVILE DOESN'T GIVE A "HOOT" FOR CHARITY

I'VE FINALLY GOT AROUND TO CLEARING OUT MY DEAR OLD MUM'S CLOTHES.

I'D BETTER TAKE THEM TO THE CHARITY SHOP.

NOW THEN, NOW THEN. IF I AM NOT MISTAKEN, THOSE ARE DEAD MOTHER'S CLOTHES.

BUCK PALACE

WHOO! WHOO! I CAN'T RESIST DEAD MOTHER'S CLOTHES.

I MUST TAKE THEM HOME AND WRAP THEM UP IN PLASTIC, SO I CAN LOOK AT THEM EVERY DAY.

SWOOP

NOT FOR MORBIDLY SENTIMENTAL REASONS, OF COURSE ~ SIMPLY OUT OF RESPECT FOR DEAD MOTHERS.

I'LL TAKE THOSE CLOTHES, IF YOU DON'T MIND

OH NO! IT'S PAUL BURRELL THE MAGPIE!

I WANT TO FEATHER MY NEST WITH ROYAL BRIC-A-BRAC

SQUAWK! GIVE ME THOSE CLOTHES!

FLUTTER PECK

TWOO! TWOO! I HAD THEM FIRST!

WHOO! WHOO! LOOK AT THE MESS WE'VE MADE OF THE QUEEN MUM'S CLOTHES

AND HERE COMES THE PALACE GUARD!

I'M ARRESTING THE PAIR OF YOU FOR CAUSING WILFUL DAMAGE TO THE FROCKS OF THE NATION'S FAVORITE DEAD GRANDMOTHER

OO-ER!

AND LATER CROWN COURT

DOWN WITH SIR JIM

TU-WHIT, TU-WEEURGH-EEURGH-EELGH!

I'VE GOT PLENTY OF PUBLICITY NOW ~ BUT IT'S NOT THE SORT I HAD IN MIND!

YOU SOD BBC

BOO! HISS!

HO HO! LOOKS LIKE SIR JIM IS GOING UP BEFORE THE 'BEAK'!

READERS' VOICES

YES. AND THEN HE'LL BE DOING SOME 'BIRD' AND SO FORTH.

The Pleasure I Will Never Know

SOUP-ERNATURAL FORCES: Spooky mentalist Geller being haunted by his inability to eat a bowl of tomato soup yesterday.

HE FIRST burst onto our screens in the seventies with his astonishing spoon-bending powers. His uncanny abilities defied rational explanation and left scientists scratching their heads in bafflement. Thirty years on, his powers are just as strong as ever, and he has achieved fame and fortune beyond his wildest dreams. Amongst his friends he numbers some of the greatest starts in the world - Pop legend Michael Jackson, former BBC royal correspondent Jennie Bond and fat DJ Jono Coleman to name but a few. He appears to have the world at his feet.

But Uri Geller is a man with a secret heartache, one that eats away at him every day of his life. Because he can never know the everyday experience that normal people take for granted; *the simple pleasure of eating soup*. Here in an exclusive extract from his latest book, *'I Can't Eat Soup'*, Uri describes the 40 year living hell that has come close to costing him his mind.

EXCLUSIVE

POWERS

"My paranormal powers have been a great blessing in my life. Thanks to them I have brought much happiness to millions, I have travelled the world, and I have made friends with such influential people as Michael Jackson, Jennie Bond and Jono Coleman. But my spoon-bending abilities have also been a curse, constantly preventing me from tasting the soup I so desperately crave.

"As a boy growing up in Tel Aviv, I used to love soup. Oxtail, leek and potato, farmhouse vegetable. You name it, I loved it. my family nickname was Soupy, so fond was I of my favourite nourishing broths.

"Then on my fourth birthday I was struck by a strange light from space. Scientists cannot agree what it was - perhaps it was a paranormal beam from another universe, or maybe a laser fired from a passing flying saucer. Whatever it was, it changed my life forever. For that night when I sat down to my usual bowl of cream of tomato, the spoon just bent in my hand and the soup fell back in the bowl. My mother gave me another spoon, and the same thing happened. By the end of the evening, every spoon in the house was twisted beyond use, and that soup was still in my bowl. I tried eating it with a fork, but I was soon in despair as it kept slipping through the prongs."

As the years went by, Geller shot to fame, travelling the world demonstrating his unique gifts to credulous scientists and chat show hosts. But his private soup anguish never left him.

"It's hard to believe, but I would have given it all up - the fast cars, the jet set lifestyle, the star studded parties with such luminaries as Michael Jackson, Jennie Bond and Jono Coleman - for just one taste of the soup which my powers denied me."

CAMBRIDGE

Then one night in 1990, Geller was asleep, dreaming of soup, when the phone rang. "It was 3 o'clock in the morning, so I knew it must be an important call. It was Jono Coleman. He sounded pretty excited, and he told me that he had had a dream where I was eating soup through a straw. It was a eureka moment. In my excitement I rushed down the stairs into my kitchen and opened a tin of ministrone. As I smelt it warming up in the pan, my mouth watered. My 30 year wait was almost over. I poured it in the bowl and stuck in a straw. I sucked eagerly, but not a single drop of soup came through. It soon became apparent why - a crouton had become wedged half way up the straw."

HEALEY

In frustration, Geller threw the bowl of soup against the wall. "The bowl, like my dreams of ever tasting soup again, lay shattered in a million pieces. And the soup that ran down the wall echoed the tears that ran down my face, except that they didn't have little bits of pasta in."

Geller was in despair, but a few months later, he received a letter with a California postmark. "It was from my great friend Michael Jackson, the international star. He said he could solve my problem and invited me over to America. Excitedly, I packed my soup bowl, tucked a napkin into my shirtfront and set off for the airport. Wacko Jacko met me at the gate of his Neverland ranch and took me inside. His plan was ingenious. He had trained his chimpanzee Bubbles to spoonfeed him with soup. I watched in amazement as the clever monkey fed Jacko a bowl of delicious-looking carrot and coriander without spilling a drop. He even tilted the bowl to get the last few dregs and held the spoon with his finger crooked."

Jackson heated up another pan of soup, this time for Geller. But it was at this point that things started to go wrong.

"I can only guess at the cause of what happened next. Bubbles was a highly intelligent monkey, almost human in his behaviour. But when he approached me with my first spoonful of soup, a change seemed to come over him. Not only do I have the ability to bend spoons, it seems that I can also bend monkeys' minds. I can only suppose I was giving off some magnetic vibrations at the same frequency as a monkey's brain that made him revert to his wild state. He started to scream, bare his teeth and scratch under his armpits. Then he upturned the soup

JACKO: Not Guilty Megastar

bowl, threw a lump of his excreta at me, and ran into the corner of the room where he began performing an obscene act upon himself.

"As I sat there in Michael Jackson's Neverland Ranch, my tears of despair mixing with the chimp ordure on my cheeks, it seemed like soup was further from my grasp than it had ever been."

MAJOR

Over the years, Geller has tried to eat soup with spoons made from practically every material known to science. "You name it, I've tried to eat soup with a spoon made from it. Titanium, tungsten, carbon fibre, the lot. Every one of them has bent and snapped. The British army even made me a spoon from bullet proof kevlar, but even as I touched it, it curled up like a jester's shoe. I often joked that the only spoon I hadn't tried was one made out of diamond, the hardest substance known to man."

BOND: Former Royal Correspondent

Geller never thought he would get the chance to eat soup with a diamond spoon, indeed he didn't even think that such a spoon existed. But all that changed when one day he bumped into his good friend Jennie Bond at Jono Coleman's birthday party in the BBC Radio London canteen. She told him that just such a diamond spoon existed in the State Rooms at Buckingham Palace. She told Geller that the Queen was on holiday, and she had been asked to pop in once a day to feed the corgis, turn some lights on and run the Union Jack up and down the flagpole to make burglars think someone was in.

CHESTY

"She asked me if I'd like to go round and try the spoon. I didn't need asking twice. Before I knew it, I was inside Buckingham Palace with a steaming bowl of cockaleekie in front of me. Jennie went to the State Room and came back with the glittering crystal spoon, a present to Queen Victoria from Tsar Nikolas the First. As I lifted it from its velvet cushion my heart was in my mouth - if it bent, not only would my lifelong lust for soup not be sated, but I would be looking at a repair bill for a cool £10million.

COLEMAN: Celebrity Fat Cunt

"I picked it up, and to my joy, it remained as straight as an arrow. As I had always suspected, not even my supernatural powers were strong enough to bend diamonds. But how quickly that joy turned to despair. As I dipped it into the soup, I realised that it was a dessert spoon. My ingrained sense of etiquette prevented me from using such an item of cutlery to eat a food for which it was not designed, especially in the grand surrounds of Buckingham Palace. Once again, cruel fate had snatched the soup for which my heart ached from under my very nose."

NEXT WEEK: "The pleasure I will never know ~ Boiled Eggs."

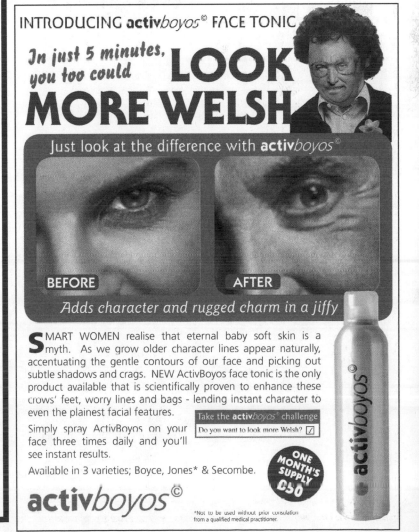

Letterbocks

Viz Comic, PO Box 656
North Shields, NE30 4XX
letters@viz.co.uk

STAR LETTER

■ I WALKED past my local *Big Issue* seller yesterday and was outraged to see him wearing a New York Yankees baseball cap. Now I'm only too willing to help homeless people get back on their feet, but if he's jetting off to the Big Apple, shelling out to take in a baseball game and treating himself to a cap while he's at it, he's not going to do it on my money.

Trevor Cherry, Hartness

■ I watched an orchestra the other night on TV and I was amazed to notice that none of the musicians ever looked up at the conductor, no matter how much he waved his stick about. Perhaps if they had a topless bird with massive jugs standing up there they would pay a bit more attention.

Mark Todd
e-mail

■ Since he appointed Brad Gilbert as his coach, British tennis No.1 Andy Murray has started to develop an awful American accent when he talks. He wants to try to stop it now, or else he'll end up sounding like the former British No.1, Greg Rusedski.

Peter Lorrimer
Hull

■ There's no place like home, they say. Rubbish! I live on a Bovis estate and my neighbour's house is exactly the same as mine. Except with different curtains.

Ben Rodway
e-mail

■ I was shocked to read in the paper that 'Rape Threat Man' was left off the sex offenders' register. How on earth did someone called 'Rape Threat Man' manage to slip through the net?

Christina Martin
e-mail

■ They say that men don't make passes at girls who wear glasses. Well why don't they just take them off before they leave the house?

M Lennard
Hull

■ I paid £1.20 for a bag of chips from my local chippy the other night. Then a friend told me that they were just bits of potatoes fried in oil. I was furious. There could only have been about 20p's worth of potato and the oil must have cost pennies. No wonder the owner drives a G-reg Nissan.

Mick Jones
Liverpool

...UGH! UGH! OOH, YEAH!...UGH!UGH! UGH! UGH!... UGH-UGH-UGH *UUGH!*

I WISH THE MILKMAN WOULD STOP BANGING THAT BLOODY GATE.

■ I am sure that you have had this one before, but this statue at the Vatican Museum is rather familiar.

Guy Abbott
e-mail

■ My so-called permanent marker has just run out. What a rip-off.

Maff Hitchin

■ It's that time of year again when the do-gooders come out of the woodwork to tell us of the injustice that has been done in convicting Barry George of the murder of Jill Dando. But what these people forget is that he may be innocent, but if *he* wasn't in prison for it, then *nobody* would be in prison for it, and where's the justice in that?

T Hennesy
Rutland

■ I saw this Christmas card which was being sold to raise money... *for a children's charity!* Whatever next?

Alex Rayffe
London

■ I never thought I would see the day a woman became Prime Minister of Britain. And I was right. On the eve of Margaret Thatcher's election victory in 1979, I looked at the sun through a pair of binoculars.

Johnny Giles
Tooting

■ Doctors say that you should eat 5 pieces of fruit or veg a day to remain healthy. Last week I ate 5 mouldy plums and that night I shat the bed. What's healthy about that?

Mark J
Barnsley

■ My sides were aching ater I went to see comedian Jimmy Carr recently. Whilst walking out of the theatre half way through the show, I fell down the stairs and cracked two ribs.

Eric Todd
Hull

■ Speaking of Jimmy Carr, please find enclosed the Four of Hearts from a highly dubious pack of playing cards. Is this just a look-a-like, or is the corporate award ceremony work drying up?

Anon
Somewhere

■ As a devout Catholic, I was horrified to read in the *Sunday Times* that premiership footballers are storing their new-born babies' placentas in order to make clone copies of themselves. I've never heard of anything so abhorrent. A team made up of eleven Peter Crouches, for example, may sound like a good idea in theory, but the reality would be the whole team hanging round the six yard box waiting for crosses that never came. The midfield would be non-existent and they would leave themselves wide open at the back.

Monsignor T O'Claherty
Knock

■ T O'Claherty (*Letters, above*) should understand that controversial issues such as stem-cell research and cloning are matters for individual conscience; there are always two sides to every argument. Whilst a team of cloned Crouches would be an abomination, eleven Wayne Rooneys would be a force to be reckoned with. They would have tremendous pace, show flair on and off the ball, and wouldn't be afraid to drop back into defensive positions when they lost possession. It would make the commentator's job a lot easier as well.

J Motson
Grandstand

■ Why doesn't the Speaker of the House of Commons bring a bit of levity to proceedings by dressing up as Elvis and answering 'uh huh! to every question? He could then round off the session with a rendition of *Suspicious Minds*.

Tokio Joe
e-mail

You lot are BONKERS!!

You've been writing in to tell us about your mundane lives and tales of contrived wackiness! Here are some of the best letters we received...

● My friends and I are mad! We went on a hen night recently... *and we all wore hats!*
Maureen Ordinary, Dorset

● I am a mother of 6 and a grandmother of 3.
Edna Average, Trent

● We have a right old laugh in my office. We will sometimes wear casual clothes on a Friday. Once we even dressed up in 1970s clothing for the day to raise money for charity...there has to be more to life than this.
Sally Dreary, Solihull

● I was shattered one Friday and went to bed early. Before I did I told my husband Bob, 56, that I wanted a lie-in in the morning. He only went and tried to fetch me a lion from the zoo!
Mary Frump, Fleet

● My boyfriend and I are getting married this summer.
Michelle Pond, Tewkesbury

● Me and my friends went horse riding recently. We had great fun, horsing around! There was plenty of horseplay! And we nearly laughed ourselves hoarse (horse).
Cheryl Annoying, Dover

● My friends and I are mad! We killed a woman and buried her in a wood.
Jim Carrots, Bexley

■ If you are still looking for pathetic punches, how about this one from the *Irish Post?*

Noel, Reading

■ A really strange thing happened to me at work the other day. However, I am a soldier in the SAS, and so cannot say what it was, as I would then have to kill all your readers. But it really was strange.

*J Charleston
Loughborough*

■ What on earth is the point in toads when there are frogs?

*B Lyons
Nottingham*

■ Pizza Hut's so-called 'unlimited refills' are a joke. You try going back with your glass a week later. They won't serve you.

*Peter Marwood
e-mail*

PS. The same goes for their 'unlimited trips' to the ice-cream factory.

■ According to one newspaper, fan of Columbian produce and enemy of indie bands Richard Bacon was inexplicably

beaten by a gang of youths the other week. What's inexplicable about people beating up Richard Bacon?

*DJ Dave Saunders
London*

■ It is interesting to note that over-excitable Aussie

naturalist Steve Irwin loved animals, and yet died when he got stang off a fish. I on the other hand dislike most animals and yet am still alive. I wonder if the so-called experts could explain that.

*Matt Hindle
e-mai*

■ If these Fathers for Justice activists had been superheroes in the bedroom, perhaps their wives would not have fucked off and left them in the first place.

*Rob 'The Thing' Jones
e-mail*

■ Rush hour? Bollocks. If anything it's the slowest and most difficult bit of the day to travel.

*Peter Marwood
e-mail*

■ French Connection UK might think they are clever with their logos, but I suffer from dyslexia and each time I see someone wearing one of their T-shirts, I recoil in shock.

*P Grummet
Leicester*

TOP TIPS

CITY LINK Couriers. maintain good relations with your account holders by assuring them that their next urgent package sent from Leeds to York doesn't end up in France.

Lee Marks, e-mail

HOMEOWNERS. Avoid losing your house keys during the day by simply leaving them in the door as you leave the house in the morning.

B Sparks, Luton

PEOPLE in lifts. If Bruce Willis gets in wearing a vest and no shoes, exit the lift at the earliest opportunity.

Jason Knight, e-mail

HOSPITAL patients. Arrive for your appointment two hours after the assigned arrival time. That way, you will only have to wait an hour for your doctor to see you.

Dr Grim, e-mail

EXPERIENCE the thrills of a skiing holiday without the expense. Simply sellotape two planks of wood to your feet, sit in your freezer for three hours, then run into a tree as fast as you can.

M Jordan, Wales

CHEFS on *Ready, Steady, Cook*. Impress the audience by looking away when quickly chopping small vegetables. For added entertainment, set fire to a frying pan every now and then.

Grant Warner, New Malden

TREASURERS from social clubs. Rather than take the flack

for bad book-keeping, accuse the bar-steward of theft.

Grant Warner, New Malden

HOMEOWNERS. Avoid coming home to find your video gone, your widescreen TV smashed because it was too heavy to carry and a big steaming turd in the middle of the carpet by not leaving your keys in the door in the morning.

B Sparks, Luton

OLD people. Avoid flu-jab embarassment by not pulling your trousers down whilst the nurse is away getting your jab. It is administered via the arm these days.

Duncan, e-mail

Protester Cornered

A VIZ LETTERBOCKS page was thrown into confusion when a *Fathers 4 Justice* campaigner dressed as Batman scaled the page's fourth column and sat on top of the logo. Frank McHogony somehow managed to slip past security at the printers and clamber up several letters before taking up his position at the top of page 106.

The 45-year-old divorcee from Bedford spent several hours shouting slogans from the top of the magazine's popular letters page. He even-

tually gave himself up and was escorted off the bottom of page 107 by police officers.

routemaster

But Frank, an unemployed greyhound exterminator, was unrepentant. "I just wanted to draw attention to the unfairness of my situation. I am allowed to see my three children for just an hour a week," he told reporters. "And all because my bitch of a missus fucked off with that flash git from the carpet warehouse with his BMW and his 80 grand a year and his timeshare in the Algarve, the

slack-fannied cow," he added.

On the same page, police were called when a bag of purple powder was thrown at the Top Tips. The bottom left hand quarter of the page was sealed off amidst fears that it could have contained anthrax spores. However, tests proved that the powder was flour, and the page was reopened. A man dressed as Spider-man was later found hiding behind a cartoon on page 112, and following a chase through the magazine was arrested at the foot of page 115.

GOD SAVE THE QUEEN!

122

Raffles The Gentleman Thug

I SAY, RAFFLES OLD BEAN. WON'T YOU LOOK AT THAT? IT'S ONE OF THOSE AERIAL CARRIAGES. I READ ABOUT THEM IN THE ILLUSTRATED LONDON NEWS.

INDEED BUNNY. AND A FLIGHT IN IT COSTS A MERE GUINEA.

IT'S BRINGING AIR TRAVEL WITHIN REACH OF THE ARISTOCRAT IN THE STREET.

RECREATIONAL DIRIGIBLE EXCURSIONS 1 GUINEA

WELL, YOU WON'T CATCH ME GOING ALOFT IN ONE OF THOSE INFERNAL CONTRAPTIONS RAFFLES!

COME-COME, BUNNY OLD CHAP. LOOK AT THAT AMPLY-CHARMED ORNITHOLOGICAL SPECIMEN EMBARKING NOW. I FANCY SHE JUST VOUCHSAFED YOU THE GLAD EYE.

ME? ARE YOU CERTAIN?

INDUBITABLY, BUNNY. I AVER THAT YOU'RE IN THERE. THIS COULD BE YOUR OPPORTUNITY TO JOIN THE EIGHT FURLONG HIGH SOCIETY.

I SAY! STEADY ON!

WHAT ARE YOU WAITING FOR? GO AND PLENISH YOUR BESPOKE GALOSHES.

TWO GUINEAS, HUDSON. LORD BUNNINGTON AND I WISH TO TAKE AN AIRBORNE JAUNT.

COME AGAIN?

I REGRET, SIR, THAT WE FIND OURSELVES IN STRAITENED FINANCIAL CIRCUMSTANCES.

IF YOU RECALL, YOUR GRACE BUT LATELY EXPENDED HIS LAST HALF CROWN HAVING "HOORAH FOR THE WOOLWICH ARSENAL ASSOCIATION FOOTBALL TEAM" TATTOOED ON HIS CALF...

HMM...

YOU'RE RIGHT, HUDSON. I DID.

OH, DRAT IT, RAFFLES! WHAT A DAMNABLE INCONVENIENCE!

KEEP YOUR FUCKING COIFFURE ENSCONCED, BUNNY. JUST LEAVE THE FINANCE TO ME.

GOOD DAY TO YOU, SIR. I'M SORRY TO TROUBLE YOU, BUT I APPEAR TO HAVE INADVERTENTLY LEFT MY TURNIP WATCH ON THE WASH-STAND. COULD I TROUBLE YOU TO ADVISE ME OF THE HOUR..?

WHY, OF COURSE!

LET ME SEE NOW... IT IS PRECISELY FIVE-AND-TWENTY MINUTES PAST...

SCREAM!

EADWEARD! HE'S GOT A STANLEY KNIFE!

CAPITAL. NOW DON'T PERFORM ANY ILL-ADVISED ACTIONS OR PEREMPTORY MOTIONS.

DASH M'WIG!!

HAND YOUR POCKET-BOOK TO MY ERSTWHILE COLLEAGUE OR THE TART GETS IT IN THE FUCKING OSCULATOR.

D-D-DO AS HE SAYS, DEAR!

HERE... TAKE IT!

VERY GOOD, SIR.

PORTION OF URINE, BUNNY. LIKE RELIEVING A NEONATE OF ITS CONFECTIONERY.

NOW LET'S GO AND BUY OUR TICKETS FOR THE DIRIGIBLE EXCURSION.

SHORTLY... ...WELCOME ABOARD, LADIES AND GENTLEMEN. PLEASE TAKE YOUR SEATS AS WE ARE ABOUT TO TAKE OFF. GLASSES OF COMPLIMENTARY SHERRY WILL BE SERVED AS SOON AS THE AIRSHIP IS AIRBORNE...

DID YOU HEAR THAT, RAFFLES? THAT'LL BE A WELCOME WARMING BEVERAGE. I HEAR IT IS PERISHING COLD UP ABOVE THE CLOUDS.

SHERRY? FORNICATE THAT EXCRETA.

I'VE SMUGGLED A PARTY JEREBOAM OF SPESH ABOARD.

KRUG CHAMPAGNE

10 MINUTES LATER...

=BARP!=

BY GEORGE, RAFFLES! COME AND LOOK!

HEY! FUCKING GET IN! =HIC!=

ONE CAN SEE HAMPTON COURT FROM HERE! AND THE STRAND!

I SAY SIR! DO YOU MIND? THERE ARE LADIES PRESENT!

KINDLY MODERATE YOUR LANGUAGE!

I TRUST, SIR, THAT YOU EXHIBIT A PREDILECTION FOR THE PROVENDER FURNISHED AT THE MUNICIPAL INFIRMARY..?

I...ER...

POSH!

...BECAUSE HENCEFORTH YOU'RE GOING TO BE EATING AN ELEGANT SUFFICIENCY OF THE FUCKER...

GLASS!

GAAAAAA!!

ANYONE ELSE FANCY A MODICUM? COME AND MAKE AN ATTEMPT IF YOU BELIEVE YOURSELF SUFFICIENTLY RESILIENT.

BIFF! BANG! BANG! BASH!

AAARGH!

OOF! OUCH!

YOW!

OOYAH!

A WEEK LATER AT THE GARRICK CLUB...

TUT-TUT. I SEE LORD RAFFLES RECEIVED TWO YEARS PENAL SERVITUDE, BUNNINGTON. BAD SHOW, BAD SHOW.

THE TIMES
LORD RAFFLES IMPRISONED FOLLOWING AERIAL CARRIAGE ENGLAMENT INCIDENT

INDEED.

I DON'T KNOW HOW HE'S GOING TO COPE WITH HIS INCARCERATION. A FINE FIGURE OF A MAN LIKE RAFFLES IS BOUND TO ATTRACT THE WRONG SORT OF ATTENTION, IF YOU KNOW WHAT I MEAN, LORD BROCKENBURY.

MEANWHILE, AT READING JAIL...

...OH DEAR, LORD RAFFLES. I APPEAR TO HAVE DROPPED THE SOAP, SO I HAVE...

Shower Room

I DON'T SUPPOSE YOU'D BE AN ABSOLUTE DARLING AND RETRIEVE IT FOR ME, WOULD YOU, BEGORRAH, BEGORRAH?

OF COURSE, OSCAR.

HUDSON - BEND OVER AND PICK UP THAT BAR OF SOAP FOR MR. WILDE, WILL YOU?..THERE'S A CHAP.

IMMEDIATELY, SIR.

OUCH!

123

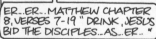

Flippering Heck!

PARIS Hilton last night wowed the crowds at a New York movie premiere when she turned up with her latest accessory, a 3-ton walrus called Fifi. Until recently Hilton was never seen without a pair of shivering, teacup-sized chihuahuas in her $10,000 Prada handbag. But yesterday there were no dogs in sight when the blonde socialite and her stinking grey tusker arrived for the glitzy opening of the new Cannon and Ball film 'Boys in Blue II'.

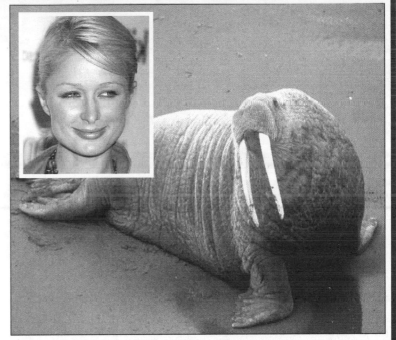

After walking up the red carpet and posing for photographers, Hilton entertained Times Square onlookers by throwing her whiskery companion, who was decked out in a $15,000 swarovski-encrusted collar, several $1,000-a-time Beluga sturgeons from a $50,000 Louis Vuitton bucket.

Amphibious mammals are the latest craze to hit fashion-conscious Big Apple A-listers, and the larger they are the better, says Vanity Fair celebrity pets editor Christopher Hitchens. "Giant, fin-footed pinnipeds are to die for," he gushed. "Anyone who is anyone is desperate to get their

From our Los Angeles Walrus Correspondant

hands on a giant seal of some sort."

"Sex & the City's Sarah Jessica Parker has three matching sealions called Daphne, Mitzy and Lulu who are too darling for words, divorcee property magnate Ivana Trump has a bull manatee whilst it-girl Nicole Ritchie never goes anywhere without a simply divine dugong in tow," he added.

However, US animal charities have been quick to condemn the new trend. "New York dog shelters are full to the rafters with abandoned chihuahuas," says ASPCA spokesman Harvey Wallbanger.

"They turn their snooty little noses up at regular dogfood because they've been spoilt rotten."

"They're used to eating caviar and drinking vintage champagne at $1000 a bottle. It's costing us a goddam fortune," he added. *(Reuters)*

WAYNE ROONEY SLIPS AWAY

HELLRAISING football legend Wayne Rooney is "slipping away," say doctors, and will almost certainly not live to see the next century.

Pandemic Pandemomium Predicted

EXPERTS warned that another flu pandemic could be predicted within the nest five years.

Many predictionists warned that the next prediction could be even worse than the recent prediction with as many as twice the number of people predicted to die. "It's not a case of if there will be another prediction but when," an expert predicted.

On the Wayne: Rooney in happier times.

Hotshot goalscorer Rooney is one of football's brightest young talents, dazzling crowds with standout performances at both club and national level, but the superstar striker is on borrowed time according to health experts, who warn that every passing day brings Rooney closer to a tragic and inevitable death.

BOWEL

Although the cause of the Rooney's death is not likely to be known until it starts happening, doctors predict that, amongst thousands of other possibilities, the star could be finished off by bowel cancer, lung disease, or drowning in his own swimming pool. "It's a matter of when, not if," says Dr Barry Evans of the Royal Hospital, Whitechapel. "It makes us all feel so powerless."

By our slowly circling overhead correspondent **BIG BUZZARD**

PIEPE

News of the Old Trafford hero's sad plight has attracted unprecedented media interest, and a small army of news crews this week began an open-ended vigil outside his home and around the Manchester United training ground, patiently prepared to sit it out, however long it takes.

FIDDLERS THREE

Martine Standaround of Sky News, who had been under an umbrella in Rooney's driveway for three straight days told other reporters: "There's no knowing how long he's got, or when the news will break – it could be any time in the next 70 years. But we're going to be covering either his sad decline or tragic sudden exit every step of the way."

THE KILLER PISSED HIS TROUSERS LEAVING WET FOOTPRINTS AT THE SCENE AND THEIR PATTERN INDICATES A STAGGER-TWO PACES FORWARD, RIGHT FOOT ONE PACE BACK, STEP TO THE LEFT. AND THERE ARE ALSO THE PAWPRINTS OF A DOG, TWO REAR PAW PRINTS BUT ONLY ONE FRONT. QED!

HA! HA! HA! YOU NEVER CEASE TO AMAZE ME, HOMELESS.

SO, HAVING TOLD YOU A LITTLE ABOUT HIM, I SHALL NOW GO AND FIND YOUR KILLER, INSPECTOR.

COME ALONG, SCOTSMAN, THE GAME IS AFOOT.

THANKS TO HOMELESS'S FANTASTIC POWERS OF DEDUCTION WE WERE SOON ON THE TRAIL OF THE VAGRANT RIPPER. IN NO TIME AT ALL WE FOUND OURSELVES ON THE OLD KENT ROAD.

OCH, HOMELESS. THAT FELLOW FITS THE BILL. OOTSIDE OSBERT'S... STAGGERING GAIT...THREE LEGGED HOOND.

YES. IF ONLY WE COULD SEE THE TOOTH...TO BE CERTAIN.

BUT HOW? WE CANNAE JUST GO UP AND ASK HIM TAE OPEN WIDE.

NO, WE COULDN'T. BUT SOMEBODY ELSE COULD. I THINK IT'S TIME FOR ONE OF MY FAMOUS DISGUISES, SCOTSMAN.

AND SHORTLY.

FARTHING FOR A CUP OF TEA, GUV?

CERTAINLY NOT!

FARTHING FOR A CUP OF TEA, GUV?

FARTHING, EH? WELL, WHY NOT... OH DEAR! I'VE ONLY GOT A SOVEREIGN. WILL THAT DO?

A SOVEREIGN!?! GAWD BLESS YAH, GUV!

TAKE THAT, YOU MURDERING SWINE!

SCOTSMAN! FETCH LESTRADE!

RIGH AWA', HOMELESS.

I RAN PELL MELL TO SCOTLAND YARD AND TOLD LESTRADE OF THE ARREST THAT HOMELESS HAD MADE. WHEN HE ARRIVED ON THE SCENE, HIS GRATITUDE WAS SOMEWHAT LESS THAN IT OUGHT TO HAVE BEEN.

YES, WELL WE WOULD HAVE GOT HIM. SOONER OR LATER.

OF THAT I HAVE NO DOUBT, INSPECTOR. AND I HAVE NO DOUBT ALSO, THAT IT WOULD HAVE BEEN LATER RATHER THAN SOONER.

WELL SAID, HOMELESS. AND HOO MANY OTHER TRAMPS WOULD HAE DIED WHILE YOU AND YOUR FORCE RAN AROOND CHASING YOUR TAILS?

ANYWAY, THAT'S THE END OF THIS LITTLE EPISODE.

THERE IS THE SMALL MATTER OF THE REWARD FOR THE APPREHENSION OF THE VAGRANT RIPPER PUT UP BY THE LONDON EVENING STANDARD. TWO SHILLINGS AND SIX PENCE WAS THE SUM MENTIONED, I BELIEVE.

OH YES...WELL... COME TO SCOTLAND YARD TOMORROW. I'LL HAVE IT BY THEN.

THE NEXT MORNING, HOMELESS AND I WALKED TO SCOTLAND YARD WHERE LESTRADE PROMPTLY PAID UP.

EXTRA! EXTRA! READ ALL ABOUT IT!

LOOKS LIKE WE'LL BE DININ' IN THE BINS OOT THE BACK O' THE RITZ THIS EVENING, EH?

TRAMP KILLER CAUGHT

OCH, I THINK NOT, SCOTSMAN. I HAVE A BETTER IDEA.

AAAAGH, FUCKIN' SCOTSMAN YA FUCKIN' BASSAH!

AYE, HOMELESS, YER ME FUCKIN' BESS MATE, YA FUCKIN' BASSAH YE.

LIES on E

IN AN illustrious career spanning more than half a century, Sir David Attenborough's wildlife documentaries have opened the public's eyes to the wonders of nature. His TV shows such as Life on Earth, the Blue Planet and Life in the Freezer have regularly pulled in huge audiences with their spectacular views of the animal kingdom. In his latest blockbusting series, Life in the Undergrowth, the 78-year-old naturalist's cameras have given us a mind-bogglingly close-up look at the microscopic world of insects and creepy-crawlies.

Or so he would have you believe.

For, if the claims of a Bristol-based former children's entertainer are correct, every single shot in every one of Attenborough's documentaries, from cuddling gorillas in the Congo to crawling through an ants' nest in the Kalahari, is a FAKE! And now, following an explosive bust-up with the veteran film-maker, Harry Oliphant says he's set to reveal the on-set secrets he has kept for fifty years.

In these exclusive extracts from his new book Lies, Camera, Action! (Kedgeree Books, £2.99), Harry lifts the lid to give us a behind-the-scenes view of the deceitful world of David Attenborough. A world the BBC would prefer us not see.

" I'd been working as a professional children's entertainer for about ten years when I got a call from the BBC, asking me if I'd like to do a bit of work on a new series they were filming in Bristol. I thought this could be my big break into kids' TV, so I was a little bit puzzled when I arrived and was directed to the nature documentaries department.

I was shown into a room with David Attenborough, who told me they were shooting a documentary about ostriches and emus for Wildlife on One, and he wanted to use Oswald, my puppet ostrich, for some of the shots in the film. I was outraged and told him that faking shots was immoral, but he just laughed and told me not to be so naive. He pushed a twenty-pound into my top pocket and winked. 'And there's more where that f***er came from, if you play your cards right,' he smiled.

EXCLUSIVE FLASH

He explained that the BBC gave him thousands of pounds of licence-payers' money each year to travel the globe filming wildlife, but that he made all his shows in Bristol, using trick photography. 'I just pocket all the cash and none of the stupid f***ers is any the wiser,' he laughed. 'If you don't believe me, just look in the f***ing car park,' he told me. I looked out of the window and there were eight brand new Rolls-Royces, with the number-plates DA 1 to DA 8.

To cut a long story short, I eventually agreed to take part in the film. Twenty minutes later I was up a ladder in Studio 3, pulling the strings to make Oswald walk about, lay an egg and then bury his head in some sand, whilst Attenborough delivered his commentary."

Once filming was over, Oliphant returned home to his digs and thought he'd heard the last of Attenborough. But the next morning, the phone rang again.

"It was David. He told me to be at the BBC that afternoon, and to bring Colin, my Punch and Judy crocodile, with me. Something told me I wouldn't need to bring Mr Punch, Judy or the policeman - this wasn't going to be a children's show.

After lunch I found myself back in Studio 3, where Attenborough was making another documentary, this time about the world of predators. When the programmme went out on telly that night, all you could see was the brave presenter almost los-

MONKEY BUSINESS: Oliphant (left, in monkey suit) and Attenborough (right, in anorak) pose in Bristol Park.

Attenborough's Creepy-crawly Heeby-jeebies

WORKING AT THE BBC, Oliphant got to see a side of the apparently fearless Attenborough that was kept firmly hidden from the public's view.

"Once, while we were filming an episode of Life in the Undergrowth, there was a terrible scream from David's dressing room. Everyone rushed in to see what the matter was. He was standing on a chair with his knees knocking, pointing at his bathroom door. 'Spider!' he sobbed. 'There's an absolutely huge spider in there.' When we went in, we couldn't believe our eyes; there in the bath was a tiny little money spider, no bigger than the head of a pin.

SINKING FEELING: Attenborough screamed when he saw spider in bath.

I couldn't help thinking of the scene we'd shot the previous day of David, supposedly standing in a Venezuelan cave whilst a couple of giant South American bird eating tarantulas crawled all over him. Of course, as usual it was filmed in Studio 3, and it was just me in a black bodystocking with a couple of spider puppets I'd made out of a pair of wooly gloves, some pipe cleaners and a few old ping-pong balls for eyes.

Attenborough may be nearly 80 years old, but he'd run a four minute mile in three minutes if a real tarantula came anywhere near him."

ing his arm to a ravenous crocodile. But what the cameras didn't show was my arm up Colin's green cloth backside, operating his harmless wooden mouth.

I got thirty quid for that one, which was a lot of cash in those days. Back then in the sixties, I would have had to do twenty kids' parties to make the same amount. Working for Attenborough was easy money; I may not have liked deliberately deceiving the public, but before long it had become a way of life. "

rth!

Over the years, Harry was called upon to disguise himself as many different animals; most famously of all when he had to don an ape suit during the filming of the landmark Life on Earth series.

"I'll never forget the uncomfortable day I spent dressed in a gorilla suit, cuddling up to David in a bush in the local park. The script called for him to deliver his lines whilst I sat on his lap peeling and eating a banana.

Well I don't know what was the matter with Attenborough that day, but he just couldn't get his words right. Take after take he kept fluffing his lines, whilst I of course ended up eating banana after banana.

I know that scene has become a classic which has been replayed endlessly, but I can't watch it without getting indigestion!"

In Attenborough's latest series, Life in the Undergrowth, Oliphant was asked to pretend to be a maggot.

"The fruit fly larva is one of the simplest organisms in the world, but faking it for the cameras was one of the biggest challenges of my career. In the scene as it appeared onscreen, the maggot writhes around on a grape whilst David points out its reproductive organs.

We tried all sorts of ways to get the shot but nothing seemed to work, until I had the idea of making a costume out of an old sleeping bag. I zipped myself in and started wriggling about - it looked perfect!

For the final scene, a couple of stagehands operated a giant polystyrene pointing hand which was left over from the Kenny Everett Show, whilst I squirmed about on a spacehopper which had been painted green. The viewers were fooled, but if you look very carefully, you can see a Milletts label sticking out of the larva's mouth!"

Over the years, Oliphant has often been called upon to use his skills as a children's entertainer in the production of Attenborough's wildlife films.

"In the kids' party business, you have to be able to turn your hand to anything; a bit of juggling, some plate spinning, a few conjuring tricks - you've got to be a jack of all trades. One of the most basic skills is balloon modelling. This came in particularly when we were filming a show about poisonous snakes.

There was obviously no way that David was going to go anywhere near a real snake, but none of the alternatives we thought of worked on camera. A sock puppet and a length of hosepipe just didn't look convincing through the lens.

One of the researchers had seen me making balloon animals at an IKEA store opening, and he suggested we try that as a last resort; the show was going out in less than an hour.

I blew up a balloon and drew some eyes and a mouth on it with a marker pen - the efffect was startling and the cameras started to roll. Unfortunately, every time Attenborough picked the 'snake' up and started pretending to struggle with it, it popped.

After a dozen or so takes (and snakes!), I was down to my last balloon and everyone was pretty tense. Luckily, just at that moment, someone noticed that Attenborough was wearing a Remembrance Day poppy, held onto his safari suit with a pin.

With the pin safely removed, and with just seconds to spare before the programme went out, we got the shot in the can. And only just in time - as the director shouted 'cut', the knot in the balloon came undone and the 'boa constrictor' shot across the studio, making a rude raspberry sound! Everybody fell about laughing."

After so many years helping Attenborough fake his films, why has Oliphant chosen now to blow the lid on

"I'll never forget the uncomfortable day I spent dressed in a gorilla suit, cuddling up to David in a bush in the local park."

his secret career? He insists he is not driven by money.

"Admitttedly, things are tight at the moment," he told us. "I've had to give up working as a children's entertainer, following a party where I was doing a trick involving some sweets changing pockets and I got a little lad up to help. There was a bit of a misunderstanding and I ended up being put on the sex offender's register. After all the publicity over the court case, bookings started to dry up, but money is not my motivation for deciding to speak out now.

The reason I've decided to expose Attenborough now is that we've had a bit of a bust-up. I saw him a few weeks ago through the window of a restaurant, so I went in to get his autograph on my UB40.

First he pretended not to know me, then he said he didn't have a pen handy. I couldn't believe the way I was being treated after all I had done for him through the years. To cut a long story short, I threw his dinner on the floor and gave him a piece of my mind in front of everybody. The restaurant manager called the police, I was arrested, bound over pending psychiatric reports and ordered not to go within five hundred yards of David Attenborough.

Over the years I've helped David make films about every animal under the sun, but the truth is that there's only ever been one real animal on the shows - and that's the lying weasel that presents them."

Next Week: *In a further exclusive extract from his book, Harry Oliphant reveals how he had to make life-size glove puppets of two sperm whales mating so Attenborough could fake a scene from the Blue Planet at Bristol Boating Pond.*

The MODERN PARENTS

...Yes, this year we're taking Tarquin and Guinevere on a *non-commercial*, ethically aware, environmentally sustainable holiday... Well, more of an *expedition* than a holiday; obviously, we're going to be *travellers*-rather than tourists.

Of course. Where are you going?

To a little village in Crete. Apparently there are still some places that haven't been ruined by tourism. Tarquin and Guinevere are really looking forward to it, aren't you boys?

Hmm.

Two weeks later...

Good morning, everyone, and welcome on board this flight to Crete. We're currently flying over the English Channel, climbing to our cruising altitude of...

Look, Guin. You can see boats and ships down there... And that's the coast of France, and...

Tarquin, stop encouraging Guinevere to enjoy flying! This plane trip is causing untold damage to the environment.

But you chose to go on this plane!

Yes, well, George Bush and his cronies have organised things so that travellers like us are *forced* to use planes. To counteract the ecological impact we're going to insist that everyone on the plane sponsors our nature reserve charity.

Your nature reserve charity? You mean that patch of nettles by our back door?

Tarquin, small grassroots projects like our back garden nature reserve are the most important factor in saving the planet.

So it's a proper registered charity with a proper licence, is it?

Tarquin, ethical people like us don't need fascist licences and regulations.

Shortly...

Come on, we're expecting substantial contributions from everyone... Your air tickets have been kept artificially low by the government refusing to tax aviation fuel properly, so you should all feel *morally obliged* to give at least £50 to our charity.

Sir, I'm afraid you're not allowed to make charity collections on our aircraft without prior permission. Could I ask you to return to your seat?

Don't you tell me to return to my seat, you eco-murderer!

Your employer is responsible for causing global warming that will end up killing more people than the holocaust, so that makes airline employees like you more evil than concentration camp guards!

Sir, sit down, or I'll have you restrained for the rest of the flight.

Nazi... If I were a Mauritian islander whose country was about to be flooded beneath the rising sea level, I'd be morally justified in strapping a bomb to myself and blowing this plane up.

Later...

EU Passport Holders

Welcome to Crete. Just go straight through.

Trk... There wouldn't have been all this passport control bureaucracy before American globalization. The whole world's becoming one big police state.

Come on. Let's pick up our hire car and get to the village where our holiday apartment is.

BWES   CAR HIRE

Oh dear. Look at all the modern cars and holiday apartments. This village has been completely *spoiled*.

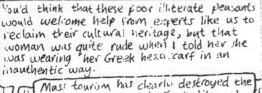

Letterbocks

viz Comic, PO Box 656
North Shields, NE30 4XX
e-mail letters@viz.co.uk

I was watching Vince Voyeur's classic film *Cum Swapping Sluts 3* the other day and was touched to see the video began with a message telling us that they would always remember 9/11. The next thing seen after the patriotic stars and stripes faded out was a woman swallowing jizz. I'm sure the families of the dead who watched this movie thank Vince Voyeur for his support in such a tough time for them.

**Piggarro
e-mail**

What is it with Arsenal football players? They all seem desperate for me to fly Emirates. They wear it on their shirts, their training tops and it's plastered all over the stadium. The whole thing stinks of an advertising deal if you ask me.

**Peter Marwood
e-mail**

It's all very well for Australians to start organising reprisals against the stingray community after the murder of Steve Irwin, but where were they when Rod Hull was pushed off a roof by an emu?

**Charles Pooter
e-mail**

I work at Cambridge University developing recievers for radio telescopes. They operate at temperatures of 0.05° above absolute zero and use state of the art materials and technology. It was while I was cooling down one such device with a dilution fridge (which uses an isotope of helium to achieve these amazing temperatures) that it occured to me that an anagram of TopMan is tampon. Have any of your other readers had such a discrepancy in their highbrow actions/lowbrow thoughts?

**Naich
e-mail**

I recently went to see the pyramids in Egypt. Seventh Wonder of the World my arse! They were rubbish - just loads of stones all piled up. They may have been standing for four thousand years, but if it was up to me I'd pull them down tomorrow.

**T Lightfoot
Oxford**

Ouch! Neville sends Rhys reeling

Here is yet another example of a shite pagga that are frequently seen in soaps these days. Do I win £5? No? Thought not.

**R Evans
Wales**

I have just watched Oliver Stone's new flick *World Trade Centre*, and I have to say I was a little disappointed by the storyline. Two planes crashing into the Twin Towers... on the same day. It's a bit far-fetched.

**Lee Lyons
e-mail**

I travelled to America recently, and I was happy to fill in visa forms, go through extended airport checks and answer questions which helped profile me as a potential terrorist risk. Imagine my surprise when a couple of days later I was shot in the street because the US government hadn't closed a loophole which allows anyone to buy a gun. I've booked a holiday in Iraq next year.

**Colin
e-mail**

ROAD RAGE POSTBAG

Crash! Bang! Wallop!

Not since the death of Princess Diana has a high-speed car crash captured the nation's hearts like that involving *Top Gear* presenter **RICHARD HAMMOND**. His 300 mph rocket dragster crash catapulted him not only into intensive care, but also into the prayers of the nation. His life or death struggle has prompted readers to write in in their droves with best wishes for the *Top Gear* Presenter of Hearts. Here are a few of the ones we received...

...My dad always looks forward to celebrity deaths before Christmas so as he can trot out his favourite joke; Q. What is (dead celebrity's wife) getting for Christmas? A. A smaller turkey. He then tells us that the dead celebrity would have laughed at that. Thanks a lot for spoiling my dad's Christmas, Richard Hammond.

Laurence Tlt, e-mail

...If Richard Hammond had died in his crash and had been carrying a donor, then several people could have become the owner of a genuine Hammond organ. I'm sure Richard would have laughed at this pun in heaven, if, like I say, he had died.

Jeremy Tasteless, Barnett

...With *Top Gear* presenter Richard Hammond making a 'remarkable recovery' after a 300mph car crash, I think it's about time the government removed those road signs that say 'Speed Kills' as this is clearly not the case.

Jonathan Richardson, e-mail

...It was nice to know that Jeremy Clarkson and James May raced to Hamster's bedside after his crash. In true *Top Gear* style, they should have gone, one on a stretcher the other in a wheelchair to see which was the quicker.

Stig, Notts

...My wife fell off a horse and got straight back on. Richard Hammond should have taken a leaf out of her book.

Instead of going to hospital after his 300 mph crash, he should have got straight back in the car and driven it again so as not to lose his nerve.

T Parceltape, Oxford

...The BBC say that they took every safety precaution before Richard hammond attempted to break the land speed record. I beg to differ. In addition to all the safety equipment, training and predrive checks, I would have taken the added precaution of not getting into a jet powered car.

M Molesworth, Leeds

I was disgusted to hear during the recent Davis Cup, the commentator announce 'that was Roddick's eighth ace of the match'. How he can play tennis in that condition is a mystery to me.

T Henman
Wimbledon

DIETERS. Buy only Russian Alphabetti Spaghetti as there are only 22 letters in the Cyrillic alphabet. Just watch the pounds fall off.

Sergei Atkinsov, e-mail

BONO. Take the piss by spending thousands of pounds on pink tinted sunglasses then ask the working class to give to charity.

Ryan P, e-mail

IMAGINE you are small by sitting in a big tree and pretending it's a bonsai tree. And eating a king-size Mars bar.

Doug, e-mail

NORTHERNERS. On hot summer nights go to bed wearing a shower cap full of frozen peas to cool your head. And when you wake up you'll have a tasty mushy pea snack ready for breakfast.

Gary Parslow, e-mail

COMMUTERS. Give away the sad fact that your life consists of nothing but grinding routine by standing in the exact spot on the platform where the train doors will be when the service arrives.

Christina Martin, e-mail

ESTATE agents. Please look up the words *luxurious, stunning* and *spacious* in a dictionary so as I don't have to spend my weekends being shown around badly-built shoeboxes.

Simon Saladcream, e-mail

MUMS. After your kids have mastered spelling with Alphabetti Spaghetti, buy a tin of the normal stuff so as they can practise joined-up writing.

Jay, e-mail

Am I to believe that the *Readers' Wives' Woollen Tits (page 121)* were sent in by different readers? I deduce this is not the case as if you look closely they all have the same worktops! You are either pulling the woollen tits over our eyes or it is just an amazing coincidence for which I apologise.

Sidney Cook
e-mail

Why is it always people who say 'bring back hanging' who also say 'hanging's too good for them'? make your right wing minds up.

Christina Martin
e-mail

With reference to Eric Todd's letter *(Letterbocks page 120).* I was at the same Jimmy Carr show and my sides were splitting. I was stabbed during the interval.

Ross Craig
e-mail

With reference to Mr Craig's letter *(above).* I was there too and I wish it was me who was stabbed. At least Mr Craig got to leave in an ambulance. I had to sit through the second half.

T Breadboard
Luton

I recently had sex with a French girl, and throughout the experience I could not for the life of me get *Oxygene* by Jean-Michelle Jarre out of my head. Have any of your readers slept with someone from a foreign country and thought about that country's most successful music artist throughout?

Steve
e-mail

I was in Canada recently and whilst I was there I went to visit Niagara Falls as I had heard that they were spectacular. When I got there they were absolute rubbish - just a load of water going over a cliff. If it hadn't been free to see them I would have demanded my money back.

T Lightfoot
Oxford

'The Luck of The Irish' they say. Well my mate's uncle was Irish and he died of bowel cancer after a long and painful illness.

Iain Sinclair
Cheshire

I was recently chucked off a building site for not wearing a high-visibility vest. If I was so invisible without it, how come 15 people correctly identified me as the one that chucked a rock at the gaffer's BMW afterwards? I swear that these rules are just there for their own sake.

Captain Cockrol
Dundee

I wouldn't say boo to a goose. I'm not a coward, I just realise that it would be largely pointless.

Mike Potts
e-mail

MAJOR MISUNDERSTANDING

OLD FOLKS HOME

WHITE WASH

PULLING SCOUT TROOP

I SUPPOSE YOU THINK YOU'RE BEING "COOL"

OLD FOLKS HOME

WELL I HOPE YOU'RE PROUD OF YOUR HANDIWORK.

YOU HAVEN'T EVEN GOT THE WIT TO DAUB SOMETHING CLEVER OR AMUSING, HAVE YOU?

NO, IT'S ALL JUST "EFF THIS" AND "EFF THAT", "SUCH AND SUCH FOOTBALL CLUB ARE A LOAD OF EFFING B'S".

EITHER THAT OR YOU'RE SPRAYING THOSE MEANINGLESS SQUIGGLES EVERYWHERE. "TAGS", YOU CALL THEM.

WELL I CALL THEM AN EYESORE AND A BLIGHT ON THE COMMUNITY.

A COUPLE OF YEARS NATIONAL SERVICE WOULD SHARP SORT YOU LOT OUT. GIVE YOU A SENSE OF CIVIC PRIDE AND RESPONSIBILITY.

PERHAPS THEN YOU'D CONTRIBUTE SOMETHING POSITIVE TO SOCIETY INSTEAD OF JUST DEFACING OTHER PEOPLES PROPERTY.

OLD FOLKS HOME

PULLING SCOUT TROOP

DON'T BE RIDICULOUS...

...IT'S A TRANSGENDER TREE. I'VE SPENT ALL DAY UP A LADDER PULLING ALL THE ANTHERS OUT OF ITS FLOWERS, SYMBOLICALLY CASTRATING IT.

WELL, IT SOUNDS LOVELY, MILLIE, AND YOU SEEM TO HAVE THOUGHT OF EVERYTHING.

YES. THIS GYNAEMATROMONY WILL BE A TURNING POINT IN LESBIAN HISTORY...

...! MEAN HERSTORY.

DING! DONG! DING! DONG! DING! DONG!

THIS IS IT, JANE. THIS IS IT...

...ALL THOSE YEARS OF SUFFRAGE AND STRUGGLE FOR LESBIANKIND... FIGHTING... FIGHTING FOR NOTHING GREATER THAN THE RIGHT TO BE CONSIDERED EQUAL TO THE INFERIOR HETEROSEXUAL MALE...

...THE RIGHT TO HAVE LESBIAN LOVE RECOGNISED BY LAW.

THIS UNION WILL SHOW ALL THOSE CLAUSE 28-LOVING WOMEN-HATERS WHO LAUGH AT THE IDEA THAT TWO LESBIANS MAY DECLARE THEIR LOVE FOR ONE ANOTHER...

...THEY'LL LAUGH ON THE OTHER SIDE OF THEIR FACES WHEN I EXERCISE MY HARD FOUGHT RIGHT TO LEGALLY TAKE ANOTHER LESBIAN AS MY LIFE-PARTNER.

SPEAKING OF WHICH, SHE'S LEAVING IT A LITTLE LATE, ISN'T SHE?

WHO?

ERIM... YOUR FIANCE... YOUR LIFE PARTNER-TO-BE.

SHIT!

I KNEW I'D FORGOTTEN SOMETHING.

AHEM!

PP VIZ 06

BIG VERN

ERNIE IS VISITING THE ART GALLERY...

...VERN! FANCY SEEING YOU HERE!

JESUS CHRIST!

SHAT IT YOU PONCE! D'YA WANNA BLOW THE WHOLE FACKIN' TICKLE?

ER...SORRY. I DIDN'T REALISE...

DO WOT!?

I'M WARNIN' YOU, ERNIE. IF YOU'RE PISSIN' ME ABAHT, I'LL CUT YER BLEEDIN' JACOBS OFF.

BUT VERN...

I WAS JUST SURPRISED TO SEE YOU HERE. I DIDN'T KNOW YOU LIKED ART.

I DON'T LIKE IT, ERNIE. I DON'T LIKE IT ONE FACKIN' BIT. IT'S NOT MY GAME. I'M PLAYIN' AWAY, SEE?

THERE'S TOO MANY FACES IN THIS GAFF, ERNIE...IT'S MAKIN' ME NERVOUS, KNOW WOT I MEAN?

YES, VERN. I PREFER LANDSCAPES TOO.

IN FACT...

...THERE'S A COUPLE OF LARGE CONSTABLES BEHIND THAT STATUE.

THE FILF!? GET DAHN ERNIE!

I AIN'T GOIN' BACK INSIDE, D'YA HEAR ME COZZERS?!

...BUT VERN, I WAS REFERRING TO THE ARTIST JOHN CONSTABLE (1776-1837)!

TOO LATE, ERNIE!

BLAM!

SPOT THE CLUE WITH SIR ALAN SUGAR

HULLO CHUMS! WHEN I'M NOT POINTING MY FINGER AT PEOPLE, I LIKE TO TRY AND DISTRACT MYSELF FROM THE EMPTY, MEANINGLESS VOID INSIDE ME BY READING A JOLLY GOOD DETECTIVE YARN. HERE'S ONE CALLED **MURDER AT MARCHMOUNT MANOR**

INSPECTOR SHARPE'S OFFICE AT SCOTLAND YARD.

WE'VE JUST RECEIVED THIS EMAIL FROM MARCHMOUNT MANOR, SHARPE.

IT SAYS THAT LADY MARCHMOUNT HAS BEEN FOUND DEAD IN HER BEDROOM

I'LL GET OVER THERE RIGHT AWAY, CHIEF.

AT MARCHMOUNT MANOR, INSPECTOR SHARPE IS MET BY CONSTABLE HODGKISS.

HER LADYSHIP'S BODY IS THROUGH HERE, INSPECTOR. DEATH BY NATURAL CAUSES, BY THE LOOK OF IT....

IT APPEARS THAT LADY MARCHMOUNT WAS PREPARING TO GO TO BED WHEN SHE WAS SUDDENLY RUN OVER AND KILLED BY JEREMY CLARKSON IN A FERRARI

CLARKSON MUST'VE ACCIDENTALLY BLUNDERED IN THROUGH THAT OPEN WINDOW.

SHE WOULD INSIST ON LEAVING THAT WINDOW OPEN, INSPECTOR ~ I WARNED HER THAT CLARKSON COULD DRIVE IN AND RUN HER OVER, BUT SHE WOULDN'T LISTEN.

AND WHO MIGHT YOU BE?

I AM LORD MARCHMOUNT ~ LADY MARCHMOUNT WAS MY WIFE. AND THIS IS MISS SHAFTPLENTY, MY NEW FIANCEE

WELL LORD MARCHMOUNT, I DON'T BELIEVE THAT CLARKSON DID JUST HAPPEN TO STRAY IN THROUGH THE WINDOW...

LOOK HERE ~ THIS GIGANTIC GLASS TUMBLER AND POSTCARD HAVE GOT TRACES OF PAINT ON THEM ~ PAINT WHICH MATCHES THAT ON CLARKSON'S FERRARI.

SOMEONE HAS CLEARLY USED THEM TO SCOOP UP CLARKSON OFF THE ROAD OUTSIDE, CARRY HIM INTO THE HOUSE AND DELIBERATELY RELEASE HIM INTO LADY MARCHMOUNT'S ROOM

WHOEVER DID IT INTENDED LADY MARCHMOUNT TO GET RUN OVER AND KILLED...

...WHICH MEANS THIS IS A CASE OF **MURDER**

PERHAPS YOU CAN TELL ME PRECISELY WHAT HAPPENED THIS EVENING, LORD MARCHMOUNT?

CERTAINLY INSPECTOR. MY WIFE RETIRED TO BED EARLY, AFTER WE'D HAD A BLAZING ROW...

..I TOLD HER I WANTED A DIVORCE, SO THAT I COULD MARRY MISS SHAFTPLENTY. BUT THE BITCH JUST LAUGHED IN MY FACE, SAYING "THE ONLY WAY YOU'LL BE RID OF ME IS TO MURDER ME"

SHE THEN ANNOUNCED THAT SHE WAS GOING TO HER BOUDOIR.

SOME TIME LATER, WHILST I WAS MAKING SOME ADJUSTMENTS TO HER LADYSHIP'S WILL, A SCREECHING OF BRAKES FOLLOWED BY A THUD ISSUED FROM HER ROOM.

I QUICKLY SUMMONED OUR BUTLER, HIVES, AND WE RUSHED TO SEE WHAT HAD HAPPENED

WHEN I SAW THE OLD BAG WAS DEAD, I INSTRUCTED HIVES TO EMAIL THE POLICE, WHILST I OPENED A BOTTLE OF CHAMPAGNE

I SEE. SO IT WAS **YOU** WHO SENT THE EMAIL TO SCOTLAND YARD, HIVES.

THAT IS CORRECT SIR. LORD MARCHMOUNT WAS BUSY CELEBRATING HIS WIFE'S DEATH

WELL INSPECTOR IT SEEMS TO ME THAT LORD MARCHMOUNT IS OUR PRIME SUSPECT.

I WOULDN'T BE SO SURE!

CAN YOU SPOT THE CLUE?

THE MURDERER IS... HIVES THE BUTLER!

YOU RELEASED JEREMY CLARKSON INTO LADY MARCHMOUNT'S ROOM IN ORDER TO KILL HER.

I HAD TO KILL HER, INSPECTOR. ALL DAY LONG SHE'D HAD A VISIBLE BOGEY HANGING OFF ONE OF HER NOSTRIL HAIRS, AND I COULDN'T BEAR TO LOOK AT IT ANY LONGER.

SAVE IT FOR THE JUDGE, HIVES.

GOOD WORK, INSPECTOR. BUT HOW DID YOU KNOW THE BUTLER WAS GUILTY?

SIMPLE. HIVES WAS A CLEVER MAN: **BUT ONE THING ABOUT HIS STORY DIDN'T RING TRUE...**

DID YOU SPOT THE CLUE?

HIVES CLAIMED THAT HE SENT AN EMAIL TO SCOTLAND YARD ~ USING AN AMSTRAD EM@ILER SUPERPHONE

BUT A MATE OF MINE BOUGHT ONE OF THOSE, AND HE SAID IT WAS AN ABSOLUTE PILE OF SHIT WHICH NEVER WORKED PROPERLY. THEREFORE THE BUTLER COULDN'T HAVE SENT THAT EMAIL

OH, LORDY! IT'S THE FAT SLAGS

ONE DAY...

EEH, SAN... ANN SUMMERS'S GOT A SALE ON

Y' WANT T' GET YERSELF SOME KINKY UNDIES... GIVE BAZ A BIT OF A TREAT

WELL, HE NEEDS SUMMAT T' PERK 'IM UP... HE HAD THE DROOP LAST NIGHT

AGAIN!?

AYE!...BIN GOING ON WEEKS. CAN'T GET IT UP, HE CAN'T

'AVE Y' TRIED THESE CROTCHLESS KNICKS?

AYE, I'VE GOT SOME OF THEM...

CROTCHLESS BRIEFS

DEAD GOOD THEY ARE...THEY'RE NOT VERY EROTIC, BUT IF Y' PUT 'EM ON BACK T' FRONT, Y' DON'T 'AVE TO TAKE 'EM OFF TO 'AVE A SHIT.

WOT?...IT'S NO PROBLEM TAKIN' YER KNICKERS OFF TO 'AVE A SHIT, SAN

IT IS IF YER IN DIXON'S DOORWAY

TELL YOU WOT, THOUGH, HE'D GO FOR ME IN ONE OF THESE

DILDOS

GOT A THING ABOUT NURSES, HAS HE?

AYE! EVER SINCE HE SAW JOANNE WHALLEY PULL THAT BLOKE WHO PLAYS DUMBLEDOR OFF IN THE SINGIN' DETECTIVE, HE'S BEEN MAD ON 'EM

Y' SHOULD'VE SEEN HOW EXCITED HE GOT WHEN HE WAS GOIN' TO HOSPITAL TO 'AVE HIS PILES DONE...LIKE A LITTLE KID AT CHRISTMAS, HE WAS

I'LL GET ONE O' THESE... HE'LL BE HARD AS A ROLLIN' PIN WHEN HE SEES ME IN IT

AYE! AN' ABOUT A TENTH AS LONG

SHORTLY...

HEY, LOOK... THERE'S A FORTUNE TELLER IN THE MARKET... WHY DON'T YOU GO AN' ASK HER IF BAZ IS GOING TO GET A BONE ON TONIGHT?

GOOD IDEA

GYPSY CREAM
7TH DAUGHTER OF A 7TH HOOK-A-DUCK STALL OWNER
"I HAVE THE GIFT AND I WILL TELL YOUR FORTUNE!"

APPLES 50p/lb

SO...

AH, MY CHILD... I KNEW YOU WERE COMING...I SAW IT IN MY BALL, DEARIE.

OH?

YOU SEEK KNOWLEDGE FROM BEYOND THE VEIL

WELL, THAT KNOWLEDGE IS TEN POUNDS, MY LUVVIE

TEN?

CLUNK!

FUCKIN' 'ELL... 'OW MUCH IS IT FOR THIS SIDE OF THE VEIL?

'ERE'S A FIVER...NOW GET ON WI' IT...WOT'S ME FORTUNE?

THE MISTS ARE PARTING

I'M GETTING A MESSAGE FROM THE OTHER SIDE...BUT... IT'S... VERY FAINT...JUST ONE LETTER

...J... DOES THE LETTER J MEAN ANYTHING TO YOU?.. A NAME..?

J?... EEH, THAT'LL BE JIM! EEH, TRAY, THIS IS SPOOKY

IT CAN'T BE JIM... HE'S NOT DEAD

WELL, HE MIGHT BE DEAD

WELL HE WEREN'T THIS MORNIN'...

Y' BANGED 'IM JUST BEFORE WE COME OUT, REMEMBER?

WOT ABOUT JOE... HIM WHO USED TO WORK ON THE BINS?

WELL, HE IN'T DEAD, NEITHER YOU BANGED HIM THIS MORNIN' AN' ALL...RIGHT AFTER JIM...

JACK?.. WOT ABOUT JACK?

I DON'T THINK SO. Y' BANGED HIM LAST NIGHT

GYPSY CREAM

JOHN?...JERRY?...OH, GOD!... JIZZY FRANK!... I HAVEN'T BANGED HIM F' NEARLY A WEEK!

STOP LISTIN' EVERYBODY Y'VE FUCKED BEGINNIN' WI' J... THEY'VE GOT T' BE DEAD...D'Y' KNOW ANY- BODY BEGINNIN' WI' J, RIGHT...WHO'S DEAD?

YES! WE HAVE NO BANANAS

Looks like MI 2 star TOM CRUISE has been on a shopping mission- impossible. Our snapper caught the pint-sized scientologist coming out of the Beverley Hills Co-op. But Tom must have had his Eyes Wide Shut when he cruised down the fruit aisle, because the Top Gun actor has forgotten the bananas! Let's hope 'nana mad wife KATIE HOLMES doesn't give him days of thunder when he gets back!

JORDAN has made another boob - and we don't mean she's installed a third mammary gland on her already crowded chest! Our Katy was spotted recently out shopping with a mystery fella, but get this... she didn't have any bananas! Perhaps the stress of bringing up two kids whilst she and hubby PETER ANDRE are jobless has made her forget the potassium-flavoured fruits. It's understandable, but for Pete's sake, Katy, don't slip up again!

also snapped bananaless...

LIAM GALLAGHER coming out of the swanky Groucho club. But the Oasis loudmouth's musatoid fruits are conspicuous by their absence!

Every Which Way but Bananas!

He may have made a few spaghetti westerns, but it doesn't look like actor turned mayor of Carmel CLINT EASTWOOD will be making any banana ones. Because the good, the bad and the ugly truth of the matter is that the Hollywood veteran is the man with no 'nanas. Perhaps his gorilla chum CLYDE has eaten them all!

Bless me father for I have sinned. POPE BENEDICT XXI pops out to wave at his fans. But Mary, Mother of Jesus, where are his bananas?

Abba Banana!

It's the Swedish super group ABBA snapped thirty years ago recently, and not a nana between them. Mama Mia, what a gaff!

Spindly-pinned funnyman RUSSELL BRAND may have had sex with 2000 women, but when it comes to having bananas, he's a flop. Papped leaving the Radio 2 studios this weekend, the self-styled sex terrorist was clearly lacking in the 'nana department. Russell Brand may have issues, but he clearly hasn't got any bananas!

Hasta La Vista, Ba(nana)by!

He may be good at pumping iron, but hard man actor ARNOLD SCHWARTZENEGGAR must have muscles between his ears too. For the governor of California turned up at a glitzy night spot this week without any bananas! But don't worry, we're sure 'he'll be back' before long with some of the smile-shaped fruit!

I WILL never understand my wife. She recently threw out my favourite vest because it had been eaten by moths and was full of holes. The next day she replaced it with a brand new string vest! It had a whole lot more holes than the one she threw out!

T Turner
Galashiels

I'M A shop manager, and somebody recently asked for a refund because an item he had bought had a hole in it. Imagine his embarrassment when I pointed out that it was a doughnut shop.

T Barnton
Smethwick

I REALLY enjoyed the recent film *'Holes'* based on the book by Louis Sachar. Come on, Hollywood, make more films about holes for all us holes fans.

A holes fan
Wrexham

David Soul's WORLD OF HOLES

Hi. Remember me? I was the light-haired one out of Starsky and Hutch. Anyway, that's enough about me, let's get on to the hole talk. And my postbag has been full of holes this week. Letters about holes, that is! Here's a whole load of the best.

I CAN'T see the logic of buying lots of Swiss cheese. It contains holes, and the more of it you buy, the more holes, and therefore the less cheese you get. Surely if you buy less of the stuff, you get less holes and therefore more cheese.

Prof Roger Power
Dept of Holes
University of Essex

I'M A shop assistant, and a woman recently asked for a refund because an item she had bought had a hole in it. Imagine how embarrassed she was when I pointed out that it was a record shop.

T Smethwick
Barnton

IN general, I love holes. But there's one hole I can't stand. That's the one in the hull of the RMS Titanic that caused the ship to sink with the loss of 1500 lives.

Roger Whitaker
Surrey

FIVE years ago my doctor told me that I was in danger of becoming clinically obese and advised me to go on a 'hole-food' diet for the sake of my health. Since then I have eaten nothing but Hula-Hoops, doughnuts and bars of Aero. I now weigh 36 stone and have had four or five heart attacks. It just goes to show that doctors don't know everything.

Jack Palance
Bradford

I CAN'T understand you losers who are obsessed with holes. Holes suck. They're nothing more than big dents. Why don't you get a life and get interested in something good, like mounds and heaps?

Darcus Howe
Oxford

I WORK in a shop, and a customer recently brought several items back because they had holes in them. Her face turned red when I explained that it was a shop selling collanders, polo mints and those little sticky circles you use to reinforce punched paper before putting it into a ring binder.

T Smethton
Barnwick

BRITAIN'S LEADING ORIFICES AND APERTURES FORUM

DURING a recent row with my wife, she said that there were lots of holes in my argument. And she was certainly right. I was arguing about whether or not to throw out a chair that was riddled with woodworm.

R Brunswick, Hampshire

HOLES in the News

• • • • • • • •

▶ **CANCUN, MEXICO:** Chilli pepper farmer Boco Perez got the shock of his life when he fell into a hole which had suddenly opened up in his field. He fell right through the centre of the earth, finally emerging 10 hours later, feet first and travelling at a speed of 800 miles per hour through a pavement in Trinity Road, Aberystwyth.

• • • • • • • •

▶ HERTFORDSHIRE, ENGLAND: Police searching for the stolen Henry Moore statue 'Reclining Figure' have recovered it... minus its trademark hole. Big Chief Superintendant Frank Sitting Bull told reporters that he feared the hole, worth £3million, had been melted down and turned into holes in the bottoms of plant pots.

• • • • • • • •

▶ ARCHAEOLOGISTS excavating a Roman fort just outside Haltwhistle, Northumberland, have found the remains of a hole in the ground, thought to have been dug by Roman soldiers. The hole, made of soil and worms, is in a remarkable state of preservation and thought to be 1800 years old. "The hole's purpose is a bit of a mystery," said Newcastle University's Edward Canning. "It may have been dug for use in a religious ceremony, or perhaps for somewhere to put a post for a clothes line." Whatever its purpose, the hole is thought to be Britain's oldest complete hole in the ground and could be worth anything up to £30.

• • • • • • • •

▶ A WORMHOLE in the space-time continuum opened up outside Dolcis shoe shop on Peebles High Street last Saturday. Shoppers looked on in disbelief as several trainers, half a dozen Dr. Scholls and 3 brogues, all left feet, were sucked into a parallel universe. Manager Hamish McTavish said: "The annoying thing is, the missing shoes are still here, but I can't get at them as they exist as so-called 'dark energy' occupying a parallel dimension. So the right ones I've still got in the shop are no good to me."

THE FUNNY THINGS KIDS SAY... ABOUT HOLES

'OH, NO, Granny! You're curtains are full of holes," exclaimed my four-year-old grand daughter one day. She was talking about my net curtains. That was fifteen years ago and I still chuckle about it every half hour.

Edna Stuffing, Punto Arenas

I OPENED my Bible the other day so as I could check in Deuteronomy whether or not I am allowed to eat bats. Imagine my dismay when I discovered that bookworms had eaten large holes in many of the pages. "My Bible is ruined," I cried. "Don't worry, Gran," said my one-year old grand daughter. "It really is a Hole-y Bible now!" How we laughed.

Edna Parsnips, Adidas Abba

I WAS listening to a Radio 4 programme about space recently when the presenter mentioned Black Holes, saying one had been discovered which was over three million light years deep. "Gosh, Granny," said my two-week-old grandson. "I bet the spacemen needed a really big spade to dig that." How I laughed.

Edna Chipolatas, Punta Sabioni

MY DAUGHTER was giving birth last week and she asked my to be present at the birth. To calm my nerves, I started singing "There's a hole in my bucket." "No there isn't, granny. There are three. Two where the handle fits in and one in the top," said my new-born grandson as his head popped through my daughter's cervix. How we laughed.

Edna Sprouts, Brussels

Readers' Holes

ONCE again you've been sending me a whole lot of pictures of your favourite holes. Here are some of the best I have received this week. Each one wins a pound of Swiss cheese... which is full of holes, naturally!

THOUGHT FOR THE HOLE
with Anne Atkins

"We've all read in the papers recently of the tragic case of the little boy who was born with a hole in his heart. And it got me thinking, that in a sense, we all have a hole in our hearts, don't we? It's a God-shaped hole, and the Lord fills that hole with His love. It's just a shame that He was unable to fill the physical hole in that baby's heart. But I'm sure He had His reasons. More God-bothering bollocks next week, hole fans!"

YOU ASK, WE ANSWER
ABOUT HOLES

I'M writing a poem about holes, and for the life of me, I can't think of any animal that both lives in a hole, and rhymes with it. Could you please help, as I have to get the poem finished in time for the Queen's birthday?

Andrew Motion

Well, Andrew, that's a tricky one. I've thought about it very hard, and the only one I can think of is the mole. You might get away with the vole, but technically speaking, that lives in a burrow.

IT'S THE SOFTS

PATER... CEDRIC... MATER

GOSH, MATER... WHAT A WONDERFUL SPREAD YOU HAVE PREPARED FOR OUR PICNIC IN THE MEADOW

YES... THANK YOU. PLEASE MAY I HAVE A CUCUMBER SANDWICH? THEY LOOK COMPLETELY YUMMY

OF COURSE YOU MAY, CEDRIC

AND AFTER LUNCH, SHALL WE MAKE A REALLY, REALLY LONG DAISY CHAIN?

OH, NO, CEDRIC...

THE DAISIES ARE FAR TOO PRETTY TO GO PICKING THEM.

YES... AND REMEMBER, CEDRIC, THESE FLOWERS LIVE HERE... WE ARE ONLY GUESTS IN THEIR MEADOW

YES, MATER... FORGIVE ME

CRASH!!

HOO, BIFFA... YEE GAN SPREAD THE RUG OOT ON THE GROOND

REET, FATHA.

MUTHA... YEE GAN GET THE HAMPA OOT THE BOOT

AYE!

I CANNAT PUT IT ERE FATHA... THERE'S AALL NETTLES AN' COO SHIT AN' THAT

WELL THAT LOOKS A CANNY SPOT WHERE THEMS CUNTS IS SAT, SON... YUZ CAN PUT IT THERE

HOO, YEES LOT... THIS IS **WOR** PICNIC SPOT, THIS... AALL REET!?.. NOO FUCK OFF!

I'M TERRIBLY SORRY, BUT... I THINK... WE... WERE HERE FIRST

I SAID **FUCK OFF!**

COME ON, DEAR... WE'D BETTER DO AS HE SAYS... WE DON'T WANT ANY UNPLEASANTNESS

HEH! HEH!.. THAT'S THEMS LOT FUCKIN' TELT, SON

AYE!.. REET, LET'S SEE WOT WUZ'VE GOT FER W' PICNIC

BEER AN' TABS! FUCKIN' CHAMPION, THAT, MUTHA.

HAD ON A MINUTE

WHERE'S THE **SCRAN?** THEZ NEE FUCKIN' SCRAN IN 'ERE

THERE WAS NEE ROOM FORRIT IN THE HAMPA, SON...

GAN BORROR SOME GRUB OFF THEMS

HOO, CEDRIC... LEND US THEM SAMMIDGES, OR I'LL FUCKIN' KNACK YUZ

MATER!.. P.P.P. PATER!

ER...

WOT THE FUCK'S IN 'EM?

EH?

C..C..C..C CUCUMBER

THEZ NEE FUCKIN' **MEAT** OR OWT... THEY'RE AALL JUST FULL O' GREEN SHITE... AN THEZ NEE BASTAAD CRUST

I'M NOT EATIN' THESE. I'M ALLORGIC T' SAMMIDGES WI' OOT MEAT IN.

ARE YEE TRYIN' T' KILL US OR SUMMAT?

GOOD GRACIOUS... LIONEL... YOU MUST DO SOMETHIN'!

YES!

GURGLE!

YES, OF COURSE

CHOKE

ERM... ER... I SAY, YOU... YOU BIG BULLY... NOW YOU JUST LEAVE MY SON ALONE ... ...PLEASE

SMACK!

TAP!

144

D Y' SEE THAT, MUTHA?...HE WENT AN' AMPED WOR BIFFA... WI' HIS FINGA

LOOK...STOP!

AYE...LOOK, HE'S UST DONE IT AGAIN, FATHA...

EEH, HITTIN' A BAIRN....THAT'S THE -ORWEST O' THE LUR....COME ON.

HOO...BIG FELLA...WHERE D' YEE GEDDOFF?...PICKIN' ON A BAIRN, PER FUCK'S SAKE

WHY DIVVENT Y' PICK ON SOMEONE Y' AAN FRIGGIN' SIZE?...LIKE ME AN' FATHA.

KNUT!

HEH!

STOP IT!
STOP IT, YOU BRUTES...YOU ANIMALS

EEH, DID Y' HEAR THIS 'UN, FATHA...CAALLIN' US WORSE THAN SHITE...CAALLED US AALL THE FRIGGIN' NAMES UNDER THE SUN, SHE DID...LET'S KNACK 'ER.

MUTHA...YEE KNAA I'D NEVER HIT A LASS...Y'LL 'AVE T' KNACK 'ER YERSEL'

SMACK!

THUMP!

BOOT!

SHORTLY...

REET! THAT'S THEMS LOT TELT...AGAIN

AYE...LET'S GAN FINISH OFF THEIR FUCKIN' BAIT...

GROAN!
GASP!
CROAK!

...WE DESORVE IT AFTER AALL THE INCONVENIENCE THEY'VE CAUSED W'

SLURP! SCOFF!! MUNCH! GOBBLE!

THESE SAMMIDGES TASTE LIKE SHIT. IS THERE OWT FOR PUD?

AYE!...

...FANCY A FAIRY CAKE?

A FAIRY CAKE!?! ARE YEE CAALLIN' ME A FUCKIN' PUFF, BIFFA?

I THINK HE IS, FATHA...AN I'LL TELL Y' SUMMAT I' NOW, HE'S NOT FRIGGIN' WRANG!...

...SAT THERE EATIN' CUCUMBER SARNIES AN' DRINKIN' FUCKIN' TEA OOT OF A BURN CHINA CUP

EH!?
HEH! HEH!

ARE YEE CAALLIN' ME A PUFF AN' AALL?

NAH!..I'M CAALLIN' HIM A PUFF, FATHA...AN I'M CAALLIN' YEE A HEEMASEX

EH?..Y' FUCKIN' BASTAAD

AYE...Y' MOOTHY HOO-A

HOO! DIVVENT CAALL WOR LASS A HOO-A, YER LITTLE CUNT

HOO!. DIVVENT CAALL MY SON A CUNT, Y' FUCKIN' SHORTLIFTAH

BIFF!
OOF!
SOCK!
OOF!
OOYAH!
PUNT!

SHORTLY...

ACCIDENT & EMERGENCY

I'M SURE MY NOSE IS BROKEN, LIONEL...I'VE LOST SEVERAL TEETH... AND I'M SURE MY JAW IS DISLOCATED

NEVER MIND, PETUNIA. IT'S ALL OVER NOW... I'M SURE THE DOCTOR WILL SEE US SOON...

HOW ARE YOU, CEDRIC?

SOB!..MY PHYSICAL SCARS WILL HEAL, PATER, BUT THE MENTAL SCARS WILL STAY WITH ME ALL MY...

HOO!..YEEZ LOT...

...THEM'S IS WOR SEATS...

NOO FUCK OFF!

MILD MANNERED REPORTER BARRY BROWN HAS BEEN FIRED FROM THE FULCHESTER BUGEL FOR TURNING UP LATE FOR WORK WITH A HANGOVER AND SICK ALL DOWN HIS TROUSERS...

...AND DONT COME BACK, ELSE I'LL HAVE SECURITY PUNT ROU UP THE ARSE

BOSS

IF ONLY THEY KNEW OF MY SECRET IDENTITY, THEN THEY'D UNDERSTAND. BUT I CAN'T REVEAL IT TO THEM OTHERWISE I'D BE PLACING THEIR LIVES IN MORTAL DRUNK DANGER

BARRY, I JOST WANT TO SAY I THINK IT'S REALLY UNFAIR WHAT'S HAPPENED...

...I MEAN, CLEARLY YOU HAVE A PROBLEM AND YOU HAVE THE SAME RIGHTS TO WORKPLACE SUPPORT AS IF YOU HAD ANY OTHER MEDICAL OR PSYCHOLOGICAL CONDITION.

HOLD IT LOUISE... I THINK I HEAR SOMETHING..

WHAT? I DON'T HEAR ANYTHING...

I HAVE TO GO

USING HIS KESTREL SUPER STRENGTH, BARRY BROWN QUICKLY RUNS FROM THE BUILDING, FOLLOWING THE SOUND OF WHATEVER IS CALLING OUT TO HIM...

AH! MR BROWN, JUST IN TIME. I ONLY OPEN FOR BUSINESS THIS VERY SECOND.

YEAH. I HEARD YOUR KEYS JANGLING.

OFF LICEN

I

HELP! SOMEBODY! THIEF! HELP!

OH NO! THAT DEFENSELESS WOMAN IS BEING MUGGED RIGHT OUTSIDE MY SHOP. THAT'LL BE BAD FOR BUSINESS

MAYBE NOT. GIVE ME FOUR BOTTLES ...OF NEWCASTLE BROWN!

RIGHT AWAY, MR BARRY SIR

BARRY DRINKS ALL FOUR BOTTLES OF DUB IN QUICK SUCCESSION AND TRANSFORMS INTO THE BROWN BOTTLE!

THAT'LL BE £3.94.

AHHG. ME FUCKINN HEDD. AAH JUSS NEED A LITTLE NAPP.

JUSS A NAPP. I AANLY NEED A FUCKINN NAPP

SNORE!!

QUICKLY, MR BARRY SIR, THE MUGGER, HE IS GETTING AWAY!

HEH HEH!

BROWN BOTTLE QUICKLY PISSES HIS OWN PANTS IN HIS SLEEP, MAKING THE MUGGER SLIP UP

SLIP

FUCKINN' WASS GOIN' ONN? OH MY GOSH! BROWN BOTTLE! PLEASE DONT TOUCH ME ...I DONT WANT TB OR GOUT

CRACK

WHAA! OH, THANKYOU BROWN BOTTLE THAT WAS THE WORST EXPERIENCE OF MY LIFE. HOW CAN I EVER REPAY YOU?

HELP! SOMEBODY! PERVERT! HELP!

OVERPOWERED BY A WOMAN WITH A PURSE BROWN BOTTLE RETREATS TO THE SAFETY OF HIS FORTRESS OF SKOLITUDE AND ATTEMPTS TO ERASE HIS OWN MEMORY...

SKOL

OOH... THE FUCKINN' WORLD IS SPINNINN'

THAT WAS IT! BROWN BOTTLE SUDDENLY REALISED THAT IF HE DRANK ENOUGH THE WORLD WOULD SPIN SO FAST IT WOULD TURN BACK TIME TO A POINT WHEN HE WASNT FIRED! PROBABLY.

GLUG GLUG GLUG! ...OH, DANNY BO-O-OOYAH:...

GLUG GLUG GLUG! THE PIPES, THE FUCKINN PIPES ARE FUCKINN' CALLINN YUH BASTAAH!

GLUG GLUG GLUG... FROM GLEN TO GLENN... OOH, I THINK I'M GONNA FUCKINN VOMM... UGHHH...

OOH, IT'S FUCKINN WORKINN ... THE WORLD'S SPINNINN OUT OF FUCKINN CONTROL...

CRUNCH!

OOYAH, YAH BASSAAH!

THE NEXT DAY...

OOF. ME FUCKINN HEDD. NEVER AGAIN. JESUS, I'M DELICATE.

WAIT A MINUTE... THE DATE ON THIS PAPER... IT'S YESTERDAY!

MY PLAN WORKED - I'VE STILL GOT A JOB!

SUN PRINCE HARRY HAS A WANK

HOORAY!

HEY, DO YOU HAVE YESTERDAYS PAPER? I NEED A DUMP.

AYE. HERE IT IS.

AND...

GO ON BROWN, PISS OFF

PUNT

YAROO!

Letterbocks

viz Comic, PO Box 656
North Shields, NE30 4XX
e-mail letters@viz.co.uk

ST★R LETTER

How can police go around arresting people based on DNA evidence when we share 98% of our DNA with chimps? It might be chimps going around committing all the crimes.

H Montgomerie, Luton

I found this tip in a magazine at work. It could go straight into your *Top Tips* section.

Angie Rotherham

▼ Place an ice-cream tub in the basin to catch any excess water while washing hands. You'll quickly collect enough to flush the loo.
Alice Ridden, Wannock, E Sussex

HOLIDAY-MAKERS! When packing your case to come home, separate light and dark clothes. It

*Thanks, Angie. In it goes on this page

I was disgusted to see that in your *Arseholes and Twats of the British Isles* wallchart on the inside back cover, there was not one non-white face. By omitting arseholes like June Sarpong and twats like Richard Blackwood, you are guilty of blatant rac-

ism. I will not be buying your biggotted comic again, except to see if this letter is printed.

Jimmy Baker e-mail

As a doctor who works in an operating theatre, I would like to reassure my patients that I never look at their tits or fannies when they are unconscious. Especially if they are mingers.

Dr Johnny B e-mail

I think Sir Paul McCartney should try to put his current predicament into perspective. In olden days, if you were unfortunate enough to be robbed by an omniped, it would almost certainly be a pirate. At least he's going to come out of this alive.

Stella Matlock

I was recently having cyber-sex, at work, with a young medical student in India. After I had typed that I had taken off my pants, she typed "I stare at your cock with a half-smile." Has anyone else been so slighted by a typed remark from a woman 8000 miles away, 4 hours ahead, who they have never met?

Rico Suave Wolverhampton

The BBC is always telling us that we can "listen again" to our favourite bits of programmes by logging onto their website and using the Radio Player. However, when I logged onto their 6 Music page to replay my favourite bit of this Sunday lunchtime's *Music Week* programme, when the presenter Julie Cullen accidentally said "bollocks" after crashing a tape, then angrily told her co-host to "stop pulling that face at me. It was the first fucking take," it wasn't there.

S Pointon, York

Posh Spice recently revealed in an exclusive interview that she 'wishes she could be anonymous'. Don't we all?

M Hubbard e-mail

PS. The irony of saying such a thing during the course of an exclusive interview was clearly lost on her.

T★P TIPS

PREGNANT weatherwomen. When presenting the report, stand front on to the camera so as anybody living west of Stoke on Trent can see what the weather will be like in their area.

Heppy, West Yorks

PLACE an ice-cream tub in the basin to catch any excess water while washing hands. You'll quickly collect enough to flush the loo. *Alice Ridden, E Sussex*

SHOE shop staff. If I ask for a size 9, and all you have left are a size 7 or 12, then for future reference, I would rather not 'give them a try.' Call it intuition or whatever, I just don't think they'd fit.

Dan B, e-mail

WHEN cooking spaghetti, tie all the ends together. That way you can eat it in one long suck, eliminating the drudgery of washing up knives and forks.

Johnny Schott, Hackney

OBESE Radio 1 breakfast DJs. Why not discuss with your colleagues on air how you intend to spend your £600k salary? Your listener demographic of 16-25 year-old van drivers, warehouse workers and sixth-formers will really appreciate the insight.

Shifty, e-mail

BUS drivers. Increase the number of people who believe you when you cite traffic as an excuse for your late arrival by not stopping halfway through a route to exchange a racist joke with a passing colleague.

Dan B, e-mail

ELDERLY drivers. Pressing the pedal on your right will make your car go a little faster. Forget all that rubbish about suffocating at speeds above 15mph, it was all a myth.

Oliver Hardy, e-mail

Have Your Say...

SADDAM HUSSEIN has been found guilty of crimes against humanity and sentenced to death. Nobody denies that he is an evil tyrant who deserves punishment but, in a civilised society, is it still acceptable to hang someone? We went out on the street to find out what YOU think...

...HANGING is too good for Saddam who should be killed as slowly as possible. He should be put in a bacon slicer and have a wafer thin slice of him carved off every day, starting with the soles of his feet and ending with the top of his head. With slices an eighth of an inch thick, it would take a year and a half for him to die. That should give him time to reflect on his terrible crimes.

Frank Atkinson, troubadour

...I AGREE with Mr Atkinson. Hanging these days is like a bloody holiday camp. Killing Saddam bit by bit is a splendid idea, and I for one would pull the lever on the bacon slicer.

Arthur Twoshoes, butcher

...HANGING is too good for him. He should be made to go and see Des O'Connor in concert!

Roy Hudd, ageing funnyman

...SADDAM should be given the chance to escape the gallows by playing a real life game of Hangman. Each time he gets a letter wrong, a carpenter should add another strut to his gibbet. To reflect the enormity of his crimes, the authorities should choose a really difficult word, like QUIXOTIC, MINUSCULE or BRASHNESS.

June Wind, lexicographer

...HANGING is far too good a way for Saddam Hussein to die. I think he should be cryogenically frozen, then, hundreds of years in the future, when scientists have invented a nastier means of execution, he should be thawed out and killed in that way.

T Barnaby, blacksmith

...THE sentencing of Saddam Hussein to death in a trial hastily founded and financed by an occupying force in flagrant contravention of the Geneva Convention has left a bad taste in my mouth. Mind you, I just drank some milk that had been left out of the fridge four days, so it might have been that.

Dr Pigot, doctor

...HANGING is too good for him. He should be give a season ticket to watch Bolton Wanderers!

Roy Hudd, not funnyman

...HE should be hung but then drawn and quartered like Guy Fawkes. Before they put him to death the Iraqi people could first drag him round the street in an old pram, asking for 'A penny for Saddam Hussein'. Any money raised could be given to charity, such as a donkey sanctuary or the North Yorkshire Air Ambulance.

R Turpin, fletcher

...HAS anybody thought that Saddam Hussein may be a sexual pervert who, like late INXS star Mick Hutchence, derives some sort of twisted sexual pleasure from asphyxiation? In those circumstances, hanging him would just be playing into his hands. He should be hanged, but there should be a school nurse standing by to rap him sharply on the bell-end with a cold spoon at the first sign of arousal.

Edna Carstairs, retired nun

...HANGING is too good for him. He should be made to go and see Des O'Connor in concert! Oh, no, I've already done that one, haven't I?

Roy Hudd, senile funnyman

What is it with diabetics? One minute they're on the floor with a loved one standing by screaming *"Give him some chocolate! Give him some chocolate!"* The next day someone offers them a piece of chocolate and quick as a flash they say "No thanks, I'm diabetic." I wish they'd get their story straight.

T Potter
e-mail

Whilst on a cruise this summer, on the back of my cabin door was a notice reading 'Please think of the environment. Recycle where possible and switch off all appliances when not in use'. All this on a ship travelling at 17 inches to the gallon.

King of Macclesfield
e-mail

Why is it that all parrots are taught to say 'who's a pretty boy, then?', when the fact that they are named Polly suggests that they are all female?

anon
e-mail

I wonder if any of your readers could help.

I start work in a bakery in less than 2 hours and I'm far too fucked to even consider turning in. Any ideas for an excuse? Please bear in mind I've already told them that my grandad suddenly passed away, 2 months ago.

Paddy Radford
Liverpool

MFI's new tag line is 'You dream it, we make it'. They are obviously relying on my dreams being mostly about cheap cupboards.

Peter Marwood
e-mail

what DO they look like?

IS it just me or do all koala bears look like Michael Winner?

Paulo, e-mail

HAS anyone else noticed that Phil Mitchell out of *EastEnders* looks like an uncooked sausage in a shirt?

Dr James Feelgood, e-mail

Vicars in a Twist

IN HIS recent book, *The God Delusion*, Oxford egghead *Richard Dawkins* asserts that there is no more reason to believe in God than there is to believe in fairies at the bottom of the garden. It is a controversial view, and it has got our ecclesiastical readers hot under their dog collars...

...DARWINIAN atheist Richard Dawkins tells us how we are all descended from monkeys. How fascinating. But what he fails to explain is where the monkeys came from. The answer, of course, is that God made them. And He also put the bananas, nuts and the PG Tips in the trees.

Rev T Worms, Hull

...ACCORDING to Dawkins, my ancestors were monkeys. Well I've got news for him. I've been tracing my family tree, and I'm descended from a family of coal miners who lived in and around the Leeds area in the 1930s. Not a monkey in sight. Put that in your pipe and smoke it, 'Professor' Dawkins.

Fr. Frank Cheese, Goole

...IF we are all descended from monkeys as Professor Dawkins suggests, then why haven't we all got blue bottoms? Or

perhaps he has. If he'd care to take his trousers down in public and show us a blue bot, then perhaps people would give his rantings more credence.

Rev. J Spiteful, London

...GOD gives us a sense of morality which is completely lacking in atheists like Richard Dawkins. Without God in my life telling me what to do, what would there be to stop me going out, raping and murdering women like the Yorkshire Ripper did?

Rev. J Foucault, Pendogget

...CLIFF Richard believes in God, and has had more than a dozen No.1 hits in a pop career that has lasted nearly half a century. Professor Dawkins does not believe in God, and has yet to have a single that makes it into the Top 40. What more evidence does Dawkins need that his atheistic approach is wrong?

Father T Vitriol, Surrey

RICHARD DAWKINS THE GOD DELUSION

It's Friday. It's five-to-five. It's...
Iraq-a-Jack!

WE WERE promised a short war and a swift return to democracy. But three years on, every night's news is filled with terrible events in Iraq. The situation seems to be spiralling into all-out civil war and the politicians have lost the plot. As the Middle East threatens to erupt into chaos, we asked the former *Crackerjack* presenters what they would do to solve this seemingly intractable problem.

Stu Francis laid the blame squarely at the Pentagon's door. *"Every time I turn on the TV and see the terrible news from Baghdad, I could crush a grape, I really could. And when I hear the Washington Hawks making excuses for their ill-thought out policies, ooooh, I could rip a tissue,"* he said.

Former slapstick stalwart **Peter Glaze** was furious that the situation had been allowed to degenerate into what he saw as another Vietnam. *"I...I...splllbb..I..I...lllblth.. splllbbql.......I...splllbqb..I...I...lllblth..spllqlbb... spll!,"* he told us, stamping his little feet and shrugging his shoulders in frustration. *"Doh!"* he added.

Former *Junior Choice* kiddie's favourite **Ed Stewpot-Stewart** knew exactly what should happen next. *"The politicians need to get together and decide a date for troop withdrawal. In the same way that the first World War was brought to an end on the 11th hour of the 11th day of the 11th month, I think the Gulf war should finish on Friday at five-to-five. And all the troops on returning home should be given a Crackerjack Pencil,"* he told us.

Hollywood Legend Palance Dies Again

HOLLYWOOD star *Jack Palance*, the actor who first died ten years ago, has died for a second time at the age of 87.

Palance, who was a familiar face in westerns, such as *Shane* and *The Magnificent 7*, passed away for the second time at his California ranch after a second long illness. His family who were once again at his bedside are believed to be arranging a simple service at the Beverley Hills church where he was first buried in 1996.

friend

Close friend James Coburn said: "It's terrible

Hollywood Great Laid to Rest for Second Time

news. We were all really cut up when he first died, and it isn't any easier second time around."

Palance's double widow, Edna was last night being comforted by her two sons, Jack Jr and Jack Jr II

BOB HOLNESS PLAYED THE SAXOPHONE ON 'BAKER STREET.' — YOU'RE TALKING RUBBISH.
* Rude Kid
LET'S GO COLLECTING CONKERS, DEAR. — FUCK THAT AND FUCK YOU!

OKAY, AUNTIE ADA. WE'LL PICK YOU UP AT TEN O'CLOCK TOMORROW, THEN. TEN O'CLOCK.

TEN O'CLOCK, YES.

WE'LL GO TO THE MUSEUM, OKAY? YOU'LL LIKE THE MUSEUM.

OOH, THE MUSEUM...YES, I LOVE THE MUSEUM, ME.

TEN O'CLOCK TOMORROW.

I'LL BE READY.

11 O'CLOCK NEXT MORNING...

..AUNTIE ADA! AUNTIE ADA! IT'S ME! DEREK!.. ARE YOU ALRIGHT..!?

BANG! BANG! ...BANG!

BANG!

EEH! WHO THE RUDDY HELL'S THAT..?

...BANGING ON ME DOOR FOR AN HOUR.

BUGGER OFF! ME 'USBAND'S A POLICEMAN!

AUNTIE ADA! ME-DEREK! YOUR NE...

WHAT DO YOU WANT?

THE MUSEUM, ADA. WE'RE TAKING YOU TO THE MUSEUM...! WE ARRANGED IT YESTERDAY, REMEMBER?

WE RUDDY WELL DID NOT. I WOULDN'T OF ARRANGED TO GO TO NO MUSEUM... I CAN'T ABIDE BY THEM PLACES, ME.

MUSEUMS... ₹TCHOH!₹... ALL FULL OF DUSTY OLD JUNK.

I'VE NEVER HEARD OF OWT SO DAFT.

WELL, WOULD YOU LIKE TO COME ALONG ANYWAY..? THE TWINS HAVE BEEN LOOKING FORWARD TO SEEING YOU...

₹SIGH₹ GO ON THEN. I'LL BE DOWN IN A MINUTE.

SHUFFLE SHUFFLE

SHUFFLE SHUFFLE

CLAMBER

TRICKLE TRICKLE

...WASH WASH...

PLOIK!... GURGLE GURGLE

2 HOURS LATER...

VVV VV V...

AUNTIE ADA! AT LAST..!

WHERE HAVE YOU BEEN? YOU WAS SUPPOSED TO BE HERE AT TEN..!

BUT....

I WERE RIGHT LOOKING FORWARD TO ME TRIP TO THE MUSEUM...

...BUT YOU'VE SPOILT IT FOR ME NOW.

...AND LOOK AT THIS WEATHER YOU'VE BROUGHT WITH YOU... IT'S FILTHY.

FILTHY WEATHER.

OH, I DON'T KNOW, AUNTIE ADA. IT JUST LOOKS LIKE A SH...

NEVER USED TO BE LIKE THIS WHEN I WERE A GIRL, DEREK. MUST BE ALL THEM MOON ROCKETS THEY'RE SENDING UP.

...ALLUS USED TO BE GLORIOUS, IT DID, IN MY DAY.

MIND YOU, ME DAD WOULD NEVER LEAVE THE HOUSE WITHOUT HIS HAT AND COAT ON, YOU KNOW.

NEVER TOOK HIS HAT OFF, ME DAD. HE WERE A PROPER GENTLEMAN.

I NEVER SAW 'IM WITHOUT HIS HAT ON, YOU KNOW, ME DAD. HE EVEN KEPT IT ON WHEN THEY HANGED HIM FOR THEM RAPES.

Continued over..

...THEY HAVE AN EMISSION, YOU KNOW, MEN... WHEN THEY HANG 'EM...

OH, ER... WE'RE HERE, LOOK CHILDREN.

WELL YOU'LL HAVE TO GO BACK. I NEED THE TOILET.

DON'T WORRY. THERE'S BOUND TO BE A LADIES' IN THE MUSEUM, AUNTIE ADA.

OOH, NO. I COULDN'T.

I CAN'T GO ON A STRANGE LAV. IT'S GOT TO BE ME OWN.

BUT...

NO. I CAN'T. NEVER HAVE DONE. YOU DON'T KNOW WHO'S BEEN SAT THERE BEFORE YOU, DO YOU..?

COULD HAVE BEEN A BLACK MAN OR ANYBODY.

HURRY UP, DEREK. I'VE GOT THE MONKEY'S TAIL.

½ AN HOUR LATER...

SHAN'T BE TWO TICKS.

10 MINUTES LATER...

½ AN HOUR LATER...

...ERM... I THINK I'D BETTER GO AND SEE IF SHE'S OKAY. SHE MIGHT HAVE HAD A FALL OR SOMETHING.

...AUNTIE ADA..!? AUNTIE ADA..! HELLO?!

AUNTIE ADA..! ARE YOU ALRIGHT?

DEREK..? IS THAT YOU..?

AUNTIE..?

I'M IN HERE.

...ADA! WHAT ARE YOU DOING?

I'M TRYING TO GET THROUGH TO 'SPIN THE WHEEL' ON DES & MEL. IT'S ONLY A POUND A TRY, YOU KNOW, AND THEY LET YOU PHONE IN THIRTY TIMES.

...BUT WE'VE BEEN WAITING FOR YOU OUTSIDE FOR THE BEST PART OF AN HOUR! WE'RE GOING TO THE MUSEUM, REMEMBER?

OOH, YES, THE MUSEUM. THAT'D BE NICE. I LIKE THE MUSEUM, ME. I'LL COME WITH YOU.

...LOVELY TOILETS THEY'VE GOT THERE. VERY CLEAN.

OUR DEREK WERE SUPPOSED TO BE TAKING ME BUT HE NEVER TURNED UP.

...MIND, HE'S ALLUS BEEN A BIT OF A TURK, THAT DEREK. I'VE NEVER LIKED HIM — NEVER. AND THAT WIFE OF HIS, SHE'S NO BETTER NEITHER. SHE'S NOBBUT A COMMON SLUT. THEY NEVER COME TO SEE ME, YOU KNOW.

NOT LIKE YOU.

THEY'RE ONLY AFTER ME MONEY.

WELL, THEY'RE GETTING NOWT.

½ AN HOUR LATER...

...THERE YOU GO. TWO ADULTS, TWO CHILDREN AND A SENIOR CITIZEN...

THAT'LL BE THIRTY-TWO POUNDS EIGHTY FIVE.

YOU'LL HAVE TO BE QUICK, THOUGH. WE SHUT IN TWENTY MINUTES.

OOH, LOOK AT THIS, AUNTIE. I BET THIS BRINGS BACK A FEW MEMRIES!

EEH, YES. WE HAD ONE OF THESE! WIND UP IT WAS, NOT ELECTRIC, WITH A BAMBOO NEEDLE.

SIDNEY USED TO PLAY HIS 78s ON IT, YOU KNOW, DURING THE WAR... AL BOWLLY DOING MY MELANCHOLY BABY... YOU MADE ME LOVE YOU BY DICK HAYMES...

...AND HIS FAVOURITE, GRACIE FIELDS SINGING THE HORST WESSEL SONG.

...EEH, ME MAM HAD ONE OF THEM... AND THEM... OOH, YOU DON'T GET THEM ANY MORE... EEEH, WE HAD ONE OF THEM AN' ALL'... THERE WAS NO WASHING MACHINES, YOU KNOW, IN THEM DAYS... YOU HAD TO HAVE ONE OF THEM INSTEAD...

EEH, THAT TAKES ME BACK.

...WE HAD ONE OF THEM TOO... AND THEM... I REMEMBER THEM... WE HAD TWO OF THEM.

...AND I USED TO WEAR ONE OF THEM WHEN I WENT DANCING AT THE PALAIS.

151

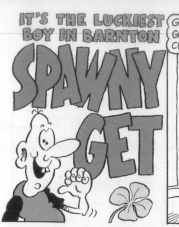
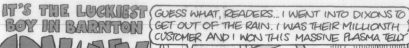

...GER! I'D BEST TAKE IT DOWN TO THE ...DERS...IT'S GOING TO COST A **MINT** ...GET THAT FIXED

FZZZT! FZZZT.

SO...

LESLEY REID TV REPAIR SOLUTIONS

WELL, SPAWNSWORTH...THIS ISN'T GOING TO COST A PENNY TO REPAIR...

EH? REALLY?

YES, REALLY...

NOT A SINGLE **PENNY**

BECAUSE IT'S COMPLETELY **FUCKED**...HERE'S 50p FOR IT FOR SCRAP

BAH!

! HEH! ...ORP!

BAH!

NEWSPAPERS · SWEETS

OH, WELL, I'D BETTER GET STARTED

ECHO WORLD CUP TODAY ENGLAND v GERMANY

HEY, THIS ISN'T LITTER...IT'S A FRONT ROW TICKET TO THE WORLD CUP FINAL!...SOMEONE MUST OF DROPPED IT...

...AND LOOK...SOMEONE ELSE HAS DROPPED A RETURN PLANE TICKET TO BERLIN

HA!

YOU SPAWNY GET

TEN MINUTES LATER...

Welcome to BARNTON INTERNATIONAL A...

SHORTLY...

WOULD YOU RUB MORE SOAP INTO MY KNOCKERS, SPAWNSWORTH?

WAHAY!

THEN MINE

THEN MINE

THEN MINE

UGH!..UGH!..UGH!..UGH!..UGH!..

WAHAY!

BOING! BOING! BOING!

SUDDENLY...

ER...I'M AFRAID YOUR ENERGETIC 10-IN-A-BATH GANG BANG HAS LOOSENED SOME OF THE BOLTS HOLDING THE ENGINE ON...I'M AFRAID WE'RE GOING TO CRASH...

...AND WE'VE ONLY GOT ONE PARACHUTE!

...OT A MATCH...10-10 ...EXTRA TIME UND NOW ...S GONE DOWN TO ZE PENALTIESLICHT

BAH! THE BEST GAME EVER IN THE HISTORY OF FOOTBALL, AND I WENT AND MISSED IT...

FUCK MY LUCK!

PUNT!

HEY, KID...I'M IMPRESSED BY THE WAY YOU KICKED THAT TIN

HEY, WOW!

TO THE PITCH

...IT'S SVEN URINE ERIKSSON!

ALL MY ENGLAND PLAYERS ARE COMPLETELY KNACKERED FROM ALL THE GAMES...I'M GOING TO TAKE THE BIGGEST GAMBLE OF MY FOOTBALLING LIFE...

TO THE PITCH

...I WANT **YOU** TO TAKE OUR FINAL PENALTY

...NNGH!

IT'S IN!

TRUNDLE! TRUNDLE!

GOAL!

YOU SPAWNY GET

WELL DONE, SPAWNSWORTH! HERE'S THE WORLD CUP, A £5 MILLION WIN BONUS, AND A SEXY GIRLFRIEND WHO WOULDN'T GIVE YOU THE TIME OF DAY IF YOU WEREN'T A MILLIONAIRE FOOTBALLER

LET ME GIVE YOU A BLOW JOB RIGHT NOW, SPAWNSWORTH

FAB 21

EXCUSE ME...I'M FROM LIONS I VAID 1055...WE WANT YOU TO ENDORSE FAB 21 ICE LOLLIES. HERE'S A LIFETIME'S SUPPLY.

WHO'S A SPAWNY GET...WHO'S A SPAWNY GET, YOU'RE A SPAWNY, **YOU'RE** A SPAWNY, YOU'RE A SPAWNY GET!

* ENGLAND STILL IN WORLD CUP AT TIME OF DRAWING

155

MINISTER FOR SEX

HE'S the most fanciable man in the House of Commons. Lady MPs go weak at the knees every time he strolls up to the dispatch box, and his saucy sexploits put every other red-blooded politician to shame. He's John Prescott, part-time MP for Hull, part-time Deputy Prime Minister and full-time sex machine.

Recent tabloid accounts of his X-rated raunchy adventures with blonde secretary Tracey Temple have set tongues wagging across the country, yet this office fling is thought to be just the tip of the iceberg. If the rumours are true, Tracey is just the latest in a long line of conquests stretching back more than 20 years. This news has come as no surprise to women, as there can be few ladies in the country who are immune to the Cabinet Casanova's heavyweight charms.

EXCLUSIVE

DPM WAS HOT STUFF IN PIE SHOP

One woman who has experienced Prescott's sexiness at first hand is the assistant manageress at the pie shop where he goes for breakfast, elevenses and lunch every day when he is in his constituency. Maude Scratter, 52, has worked at Hull's North Bank Pies for 30 years, and knows only too well the effect that the Deputy Prime Minister has on women. Because he once had the same effect on her pies.

"I remember one day he came in for his usual 3 meat sqaures and 2 steak bakes," she explains. "Unfortunately, my microwave had broken that morning and I explained that I wouldn't be able to warm them up for him. "Leave it to me, Maude," he laughed. Then he shot the pies the sexiest look I have ever seen. Within a few seconds, steam started to come out of the top of them, and after a couple of minutes they were sizzling hot. If his lovers' fannies get as hot as those pies, he'd better be careful he doesn't burn his manhood when he sticks it up them," she added.

DREAMBOAT PRESCOTT PUT FERRY IN A SPIN

Another person who has witnessed the MP's incredible sexual charisma at close quarters is ferry worker Albert Featherstone. In the late 60s, Albert was a lavatory cleaner on the Hull-Ostend ferry where the young Prescott worked as a waiter.

"I remember one time when John was given a tray of tea and biscuits to take up to the captain on the bridge," he recalls. "He knocked on the door and walked in with the tray and immediately the needle on the ship's compass began to spin out of control. Prescott's sexual magnetism was so strong that the navigation equipment was going haywire! Before long, the ship began to list and tilt so much it was in danger of turning over and sinking. Prescott was ushered out of the bridge and taken below decks whilst the crew regained control. After that, he was told that for safety reasons he must remain at the back of the ship at all times."

JOHN'S JUMP START GOT DOT GOING

When he's not driving women wild, the dreamy DPM is most likely to be found driving around in one of his famous Jaguar cars. And it was while he was behind the wheel of one of them that he met Dot Herpes. The attractive 45-year old Grimsby divorcee had broken down in a country lane when Prescott pulled up in his plush XJ6

"He looked under the bonnet of my car and told me that I had a flat battery," she remembers. "He said he would get me started again, and got a pair of jump leads out of his boot. He connected one set to my battery, but I couldn't believe what he did with the other end. Instead of fastening the clips onto the battery in his Jag, he shoved them down the front of his trousers.

"I don't know what he did with them, but my car started immediately! I didn't have to turn ther key or anything. He had started my car using sex power alone. In fact, there was so much electricity coming down those wires that the horn on my car started sounding, the electric aerial went up and down and my headlights exploded. It was the sexiest thing I have ever seen."

"If his lovers' fannies get as hot as those pies, he'd better be careful he doesn't burn his manhood when he sticks it up them!"

THE WORKINGS OF A SEX MACHINE

FORGET Omar Shariff, Robert Redford and George Clooney, It's 68-year-old deputy PM John Prescott who gets Britain's women frothing at the ballot box. To the female of the species, the 20-stone bruiser's appeal is obvious, but to men it's a little harder to understand. But if Prezza's way with the ladies is a mystery, one thing's for certain - every red-blooded fella would like to know the secret of his appeal in the hope of recreating his success with the fairer sex!

We asked *Dr Frances Batter,* Professor of Sexology at the University of Wisconsin to explain exactly what makes the Deputy Prime Minister irresistible to women.

86% of Women Gagging for Taste of Prescott's Right Honourable Member

MINISTER'S PELVIC THRUST WORKED ANIMAL MAGIC ON ELEPHANT

egent's Park Zoo keeper Terry Morris saw up close the amazing effect that Humberside hunk has over members he opposite sex. And such is the power Prescott's erotic punch that it can even ss the species barrier.

remember one day he and Tony Blair were filming a party political broad- at the zoo when Lulu the elephant out of her cage," Terry recalls. "People screaming in all directions. Tony Blair icked and climbed up a tree, but John scott just stood right in Lulu's path.

As she thundered towards him, trumpet-, with rage, Prescott remained cool as a cumber. He put one hand on his hip and other behind his head and thrust his pel- forwards once, like Mae West. I don't ow how he did it, but it made the noise a kettle drum being struck. I couldn't ieve what happened next; Lulu the el- hant was knocked flat on her back!

"It was like she'd been shot. If Prescott s enough va-va-voom to stop an 8-ton arging elephant with a single hip thrust, en the women of Britain must be putty in s hands," added Terry.

HAIR

Despite what bald men claim, women love a good head of hair on a man, and at 68, Prescott sports a healthy thatch of surprisingly brown hair. In addition, his barnet is styled to look as though it has been cut by his mam, Phyllis, with the kitchen scissors on a Sunday tea-time. This 'basin cut' accentuates his air of vulnerability and brings out the mothering instinct in women. Whether or not this is a deliberate ploy by the deputy premier only he knows. But judging by the profusion of notches on his bedpost, it is certainly one that works.

EYES

The eyes are the first point of contact between prospective lovers, and when Prescott fixes a woman with his watery 'come to bed' gaze, resistance is futile. And the huge, dark bags underneath his eyes confirm that once he gets her between the sheets, there'll not be a lot of sleeping going on! The promise of an all-night sex session with the author of 'Alternative Regional Strategy: A Framework for Discussion, (1982)' is one that few ladies could resist.

VOICE

Traditionally, the language of love has been French. Charles Aznavour, Sacha Distel and Maurice Chevalier regularly turned women's knees to jelly with words such as 'l'amour', 'ma cherie' and 'ho-honh, ho honh, he-honh', all uttered with a romantic Gallic lilt. Prescott may not be French, but his Warrington accent, fine tuned at Elmesmere Port Secondary School has an emotional honesty that can charm the underwear off any lady.

CHINS

It's a scene familiar from many nature documentaries; the male frogs in a pond inflating their chins to impress a prospective mate. In nature, it's a case of the bigger the chin, the more attractive is the male to the female. Today we may not live in ponds eating flies, but that primeval amphibious instinct remains as strong as ever deep within a woman's psyche. Prescott's chin air bags are a signal to women, unleashing their primitive desires and leaving them like putty in his fingers.

HANDS

Salty seadog Prescott's hands have been toughened by his early life in the merchant navy. Twelve years as a waiter on a North Sea ferry, operating a tea urn and collecting tips has left them strong and powerful enough to punch someone in the chin when they throw an egg at him. But these same hands are gentle enough to caress a woman's breast to orgasm, an ability that ensures he is constantly in demand as a lover.

GUT

Since the dawn of creation, women have looked for mates who could provide security and sustenance for themselves and their offspring. Back in cave-man times, a well filled stomach on a Neanderthal man was a sure sign that a prospective mate had got it took to hunt successfully. Today we may buy our food from shops, but the primeval instinct remains as strong as ever deep within a woman's psyche. Prescott's pendulous bilge tanks are a signal to women, unleashing their primitive desires and leaving them putty in his fingers.

SWEATY ARSE CRACK

Weighing in at 20+ stone, wearing a nylon suit and sitting squashed between John Reid and Gordon Brown on the cramped Commons front bench, Prescott's buttock cleft is an erotic factory pumping out clouds of the sort of sexy pheromones that drive women wild. It has been calculated that one whiff of his intoxicating arse vinegar after a hard day in the chamber would contain sufficient chemical attractants to arouse all the women in a town the size of Peterborough.

Arseholes and Twats

of the British Isles

Jim 'Nick Nick' Davidson

Germaine Greer

Morrissey

Tony Parsehole

HRH Prince Edward

Dame Ellen MacArthur

Oh-Oh Seven!

BRITAIN'S security services were put on **RED ALERT** last night after a **LICENCE TO KILL** went missing from the set of the latest James Bond film. The document, which gives the bearer unlimited powers to assassinate at will, vanished from the dressing room of Daniel Craig, the latest actor to star as the suave superspy.

Casino Royale, the 21st film in the series, was being shot at Pincwood Studios when the theft took place. During a break between scenes Craig, 24, put the document on his make-up table whilst he went to the toilet. When he got back, he found someone' had sneaked in and pinched it, along with a Rolex watch and a wallet containing £18 and a Nectar card. MI5 chiefs are said to be furious, as the double-0 licence had been loaned to the filmmakers with the proviso that it was kept securely under lock and key when not needed on set.

Pincwood Studio police sealed the studios within minutes, but it is believed that the thief had already made his escape. And now it is feared that the permit may end up in the wrong hands, perhaps those of a lorry driver, a serial killer, or worse.

Police superintendent Will Hay told reporters: "We cannot emphasise enough what a serious situation this is. Whoever has this licence can kill as many people as they want, and they will be immune from prosecution. And what's more, it doesn't expire until 2016."

By our Secret Intelligence Staff
PAN'S PEOPLE
(oxcept Babe)

Authorities already fear a worst case scenario in which the licence is sold to Al Q'aeda boss Osama Bin Laden. "It's a nightmare waiting to happen," a senior Scotland Yard source told reporters. "A mad fundamentalist with carte blanche to wander around systematically murdering everyone in Britain whilst the police have to stand by, powerless to stop him."

Actor Craig was last night said to be at an undisclosed location, being comforted by close sources. One told us: "Daniel is absolutely devasted. He realises that his little slip-up in not locking his dressing room could lead to a decade of legalised massacres throughout the country. He could have the blood of millions on his hands. By any measure, it's not the best of starts to his career as James Bond. Though arguably not as bad as George Lazenby's."

Her Majesty's Government — Licence to Kill

In the name of Her Majesty Queen Elizabeth II of the United Kingdom, the bearer of this licence is hereby entitled to kill any person or persons at their discretion without hindrance, and with full freedom from arrest, trial and prosecution under the law of the United Kingdom, the Commonwealth and its dominions.

Valid from 21st March 2006 Valid until 20th March 2016

647632 88 12 - 00%

SPECIMEN

00 DANNY BOY: Licence *(left)* left unattended by Bond star Craig *(above)* could fall into hands of evil Osama *(top)*.

Who Would YOU Do?

EVERYONE has *someone* they would **LOVE** to murder if there was no danger of prosecution - whether it's a beligerent boss, a noisy neighbour or Jimmy Carr, we've all got at least one name on our hit list.

We asked as many famous Bonds as we could think of who they would take out if they had a *Licence to Kill*.

Jennie Bond
Former BBC Royal Correspondent

"I am a pacifist, and I believe all killing is wrong. However, if I had to chose someone to do away with, I think I would kill everyone in the world who thought the Queen was anything less than absolutely wonderful. I'd shoot them in the head like pigs. With dum-dum bullets."

Nicholas Bond-Owen
38 year-old Child Actor

"When I played Tristram Fourmile in George and Mildred, Mr Roper from next door used to make life a misery for me and my on-screen parents. I think I'd use my licence to kill him. Perhaps I'd cut the brake cable on his motorcycle/sidecar combination, or pour petrol through his letter-box when he and his ugly wife Mildred were fast asleep."

Garry US Bonds
Veteran R'n'B vocalist

"Killing somebody is a serious thing to do, and I don't think I could do it unless I felt the person really deserved to die, like Nasty Nick Bateman off Big Brother One. He knew the rule about not taking a pencil into the house, but he smuggled one in nonetheless. What he did to his fellow housemates Craig, Nicola, Mel, Darren, Thomas and Anna was unforgiveable"

Jon Bond Jovi
Toy Poodle Rock God

"I don't have to think twice about who I'd murder if I was allow-ed to. It's the goddam milkman who comos up my path every morning at 4.30, clinking bottles and whistling. And he wears shoes with freakin' Blakies in. I'd put a line of cheesewire across my gate at throat level. That would sort the goddam son of a bitch out."

VIZ VALUE

BEST BEFORE 24 DEC 2008

WEIGHT
0.68 kg
1lb 8oz

The Last Turkey in the Shop

A Flaccid Cock Containing Fowl Giblets Plucked from Issues 152-161

Genuine Battery-farmed Book
Produced in accordance with welfare standards approved by the Royal Society for the Prevention of Cruelty to Annuals

Golden drummers: Graham Dury, Wayne Gamble, Stevie Glover, Davey Jones & Simon Thorp

Twizzlers: Tony Coffey, Alex Collier, Andy Dawson, Simon Ecob, John Fardell, Barney Farmer, Robin Halstead, Jason Hazeley, Lee Healey, James MacDougall, Christina Martin, Alex Morris, Joel Morris, Paul Palmer, Lew Stringer, Cat Sullivan, Nick Tolson & Brian Walker

Parson's nose: Richard Downey

Raised in a windowless shed by **Dennis Factory Farms Ltd.,**
The Old Slaughterhouse, 30 Cleveland Street, London WT 4JD
ISBN 1906372403 • First printing Autumn 2008

You can subscribe **VIZ** online at www.viz.co.uk